Soil Clay Mineralogy

Soil Clay Mineralogy

A Symposium

Edited by

C. I. Rich
G. W. Kunze

The University of North Carolina Press
Chapel Hill

Copyright © 1964 by
The University of North Carolina Press

Manufactured in the United States of America

Library of Congress Catalog Card Number 64-13558

Printed by the Seeman Printery, Durham, North Carolina

Preface

In recent years considerable interest in clay mineralogy has developed in several fields including geochemistry, sedimentary petrology, soils, crystallography, petroleum research, and paper chemistry. Soils is one of these fields in which great interest in clay mineralogy has been expressed. Within the United States, and especially within land–grant universities of the South, there has been a marked upsurge in soil clay mineralogy research in the past ten years. The most active stimulus for soil clay mineralogy research within the South has been the Regional Cooperative Research Project S–14 on Soil Properties.

To develop this interest in clay mineralogy, the S–14 Technical Committee conceived the idea of organizing a seminar of four–week duration in which outstanding clay mineralogists would be invited to present lectures and give laboratory guidance to those faculty and advanced graduate students who were actively engaged in research or in teaching and research in soil clay mineralogy in the universities represented by this committee.

The S–14 committee sought and subsequently received endorsement of the proposal from the Southern Agricultural Experiment Station Directors. The Southern Regional Education Board formally co-operated with the thirteen Southern land–grant institutions in the sponsorship of the seminar to be conducted by the Virginia Polytechnic Institute in 1962.

The National Science Foundation made a financial grant under their Advanced Science Seminar Program to enable Virginia Polytechnic Institute to engage outstanding lecturers to conduct the seminar. Nine prominent research workers and teachers in clay mineralogy were invited to give lectures and conduct laboratories in the area of their particular specialties. Seven were from the United States and two from other countries.

During the period July 21–28, 1962, forty–one participants came to Virginia Polytechnic Institute for the seminar. Of the group, twenty–seven were staff members of universities or research establishments and fourteen were graduate students. The participants came from thirteen Southern states and one from the U.S.D.A. Salinity Laboratory staff.

The lectures were presented from a fundamental point of view and are applicable to clay mineralogy research and teaching in general. Thus, the principal objective of this volume is to present a somewhat condensed version of these lectures to the scientific community at large, particularly to all those working with clay mineralogy, regardless of their ultimate interest in this subject.

It was generally agreed that the seminar was a success, and thanks are due the lecturers for their learned and enthusiastic contributions and to the participants for their genuine interest and hard work. Thanks are also due the National Science Foundation for its generous support and for suggestions during the planning of the seminar. The Southern Regional Education Board, the Southern Agricultural Experiment Station Directors, and the administrative staff of Virginia Polytechnic Institute are also thanked for their assistance and support. In particular, thanks are extended to Dr. Alice P. Withrow, of the National Science Foundation; to Dr. William L. Bowden, Associate Director for Regional Programs of the Southern Regional Education Board; to Dr. Eric Winters, Administrative Advisor to S–14; to Dr. Wilson B. Bell, Dean of the College of Agriculture, Virginia Polytechnic Institute; and to Dr. L. A. Pardue, formerly Vice–President of Virginia Polytechnic Institute.

Seminar Organizing Committee
G. W. Kunze
R. J. McCracken
H. F. Perkins
L. F. Seatz
C. I. Rich, Chairman

Seminar Participants

Auburn University

Fred Adams   James A. Gibbs
*Joe B. Dixon

University of Arkansas

*Don A. Brown   Bob E. Fulton
Merlin E. Horn

Clemson Agricultural College

*T. C. Peele   Albert Norman Plant
John T. Gillingham

University of Florida

*John G. A. Fiskell   R. E. Caldwell
Luther C. Hammond   Ray B. Diamond

University of Georgia

*H. F. Perkins   Fred C. Boswell

University of Kentucky

*Thomas B. Hutcheson, Jr.   Harry Hudson Bailey

Louisiana State University

*A. G. Caldwell   William H. Patrick, Jr.

Mississippi State University

Rollin C. Glenn   Joe V. Pettiet
*Victor E. Nash

North Carolina State of The University of North Carolina at Raleigh

*Ralph J. McCracken   Ralph A. Leonard
Maurice G. Cook

Oklahoma State University

*Lester W. Reed   Arthur Blake Onken
Joe R. Gingrich

University of Tennessee

*Russell Jay Lewis   Robert G. Gast

Agricultural and Mechanical College of Texas

Morris E. Bloodworth   Curtis L. Godfrey
*George W. Kunze   John A. Kovar

Virginia Polytechnic Institute

Grant W. Thomas   Stuart B. Cotton
Richard I. Barnhisel   Dwayne H. Fink
William R. Black   *Charles I. Rich

U. S. D. A.—Agricultural Research Service

Earl H. Grissinger   Brian L. McNeal

---

* S-14 representative

Contents

Tables

Figures

Chapter III

Chapter IV

Chapter V

Chapter VI

Chapter VII

Chapter IX

Soil Clay
Mineralogy

I... Processes of Origin and Alteration of Clay Minerals

W. D. Keller

Introduction

This paper is a revision of five one-hour lectures given at the Soil Clay Mineralogy Seminar in 1962. As is well known, the cadence and emphasis of an oral presentation differs from the approach that is optimum for a paper to be read. To revise a lecture completely from oral to optimum written presentation amounts essentially to rewriting it, which may take considerable time. On the other hand, if some compromise is made in each approach, the paper may be intelligently readable although it still retains some characteristics of the spoken presentation. It is with this objective that the following paper has been revised from the original lectures.[*]

When I was asked to discuss the origin and alteration of clay minerals, I pondered the question of which approach to take: (1) actual case histories leading to a conclusion, doubtless the best scientific approach, or (2) a statement of principle and/or process involved and this process supported with actual field illustrations. In the economy of time, and for pedagogical stimulation of thought, I have decided to take the

[*] Numerous lantern slides were shown at the lectures to illustrate details of points presented. Although the pictures are not reproduced in this paper, literature references have been cited to substitute for them.

latter. So, let us place ourselves in the geologic rock cycle, and then try to answer the question: "By what processes are clay minerals formed?" The processes that come to mind after one scheme of organization are listed in the following table (Table 1).

Table 1. Processes of origin of clay minerals

1. Crystallization from solution
2. Replacement by clay minerals
3. Weathering of silicate minerals and rocks, not clay minerals (characterized by chemical energy [activity] of H^+, hydrolysis and hydration)
   a. Cold "fresh" water, usually somewhat carbonated
   b. H^+ and chelating compounds from micro- and macro-flora, and organic residues
   c. Lake and ocean water (various Me^{n+} ions)*
4. Weathering of clay minerals
   (H^+ by Donnan effect; desilication)
   a. Fresh water
   b. Action of plants and their residues
5. Diagenesis, reconstitution, and ion exchange
   (characterized by chemical energy [activities] and addition of K^+, Mg^{2+}, $Fe^{2,3+}$, Al^{3+}, Ca^{2+}, Na^+, sol. SiO_2; bonding energy of clay minerals; increasing temperature and pressure)
   a. Replacement and sorption of ions from ambient solutions
   b. Fixation of ions
   c. Reconstituted crystal structure
   d. Modified crystal structure
6. Hydrothermal alteration of minerals and rocks
7. Laboratory synthesis
   a. Elevated temperature and pressure
   b. Ordinary surface temperature and pressure
* Me^{n+} indicates metallic cations.

Crystallization from solution

Clay minerals can be deposited or crystallized directly from solution, i.e., simple solution — if dissolution is ever simple. This is illustrated by small, clay–filled geodes occurring in the Warsaw shale (Mississippian in age) of Missouri–Illinois. These are relatively impervious, quartz–walled geodes set in another relatively impervious rock, the Warsaw shale, which contains illite as the main clay mineral. The white fluffy clay mineral is kaolinite, which I interpret was precipitated from solution in the geodes (Tarr and Keller, 1937).

Dickite occurs in small cavities or geodes inside chert nodules from the Burlington limestone at or near the unconformity which exists between it and the Pennsylvanian–age rocks above (Tarr and Keller,

1936). The dickite crystals are euhedral, unattached, and fluffy in the cavities; I see no explanation for their origin except crystallization from solution. Dickite has commonly been reported in the literature as a hydrothermal variety of kaolinite. The unconformity occurring here is anything but hydrothermal. I think long, intensive leaching substituted chemical energy for thermal energy. You may say that these rocks were buried deeply enough to be hot enough to form dickite. Then I ask why fire clay at the same stratigraphic horizon is disordered kaolinite, not dickite. The question unanswered as to the origin of kaolinite–dickite deposited from solution is: was $H_4Al_2Si_2O_9$, or $Al_2O_3 \cdot 2SiO_2 \cdot 2H_2O$, or $(OH)_4Al_2Si_2O_5$, deposited in those ratios, or was Al^{3+} carried into the cavities in solution where it picked up SiO_2, perhaps from the quartz, to form the kaolin minerals? I know no criteria by which to determine what mechanism operated. Synthetic kaolinite, although in very scant yield but sufficient to be identifiable, was precipitated at room temperatures from aqueous solution into which silica and alumina were introduced separately (silica as "Ludox," from the Pyrex flask, and in ethyl silicate; alumina from $AlCl_3 \cdot 6H_2O$ and Al metal plate) at pH 4.5 to 5.5 by De Kimpe, Gastuche, and Brindley (1961). This would suggest that alumina was carried in solution into the geodes, but whether silica was dissolved from the walls or introduced from outside is still unknown. More is known about the solubility of silica than of alumina.

Silica is certainly sufficiently soluble to provide for large quantities of dickite or kaolinite; Krauskopf (1959) reviewed the fine work that he and others have done on the solubility of silica (about 140 ppm. of amorphous silica) in distilled water. In surface waters of the earth, however, part of the story may be different; Lovering (1959), for example, found the solubility of silica in water to be more than doubled in the presence of extract from *Equisetum,* and the solubility of silica is increased by rise in temperature and pH, especially above 9 (Siever, 1962; Walker, 1962). Because the solubility of silica is notably decreased when alumina is also in solution (Okamoto, Okura, and Goto, 1957), a difficulty arises with transporting much kaolinite, *per se,* very readily in solution. The form in which silica is held in solution is generally considered to be mostly monomeric, but some polymerization is indicated.

The solubility of alumina has been reported by Correns (1949) to be highly dependent on pH. Its solubility in complex geologic systems is known probably no better than that of silica. Among petrologists, alumina has been traditionally regarded as the most immobile of the common rock–forming oxides, but there is ample evidence that under proper conditions it moves extensively in solution. Alumina is mobile in acid soil (Coleman, 1961; Rich, 1960; Shen and Rich, 1962). Sherman and Ikawa (1959) found gibbsite in amygdules in weathered Hawaiian basalt and described unequivocal geologic evidence to support their contention that: "The aluminum is transported in percolating waters to the cavity as aluminum hydroxide and is precipitated as the hydroxide on exposure to air in the cavity. It then is converted to trihydrate of aluminum oxide on aging in a drier atmosphere." Abbott (1958) also found on Kauai Island, Hawaii, "little question that the fractures and cavities were filled by lateral or downward migrating, alumina–bearing solutions."

Based on these observations, one might favor the mechanism of kaolinite formation by the migration of dissolved alumina and subsequent reaction with either local or introduced silica. Simultaneously with the transport of Al to form kaolinite, we have recognized that gibbsite, a high–alumina mineral closely associated with clay minerals, may be deposited also from solution.

Replacement

Because replacement mechanisms may, but not necessarily, introduce additional complications, the preceding examples have been chosen by severely restricting them to avoid citing illustrations in which mineral replacement was clearly part of the depositional process. An example of crystallization of a clay mineral from solutions and involving replacement is a vanadiferous clay—mica replacing an otherwise fairly pure and clean quartz sandstone (usually referred to as Navajo sandstone) a few miles north of Rifle, Colorado (Botinelly and Fischer, 1959). Clay–mica flakes fringe the quartz grains like whiskers and invade, caries–like, the quartz. One can logically ask if (1) all the Al, V, and Si came in by solution and replaced quartz in the same manner that silica replaces cellulose in petrified wood, or if (2) only Al and V were introduced by solution, and that they then reacted with silica in the quartz to form the clay mineral. I do not know the answer and am uncertain as to how to find out which mechanism operated. The mechanism of replacement must be compatible with the formation of pseudomorphs—i.e., pseudomorphic replacements—and these limit speculation about it. Correns has faced the challenge and has offered an explanation for pseudomorphic replacement of feldspar by kaolinite, which I will bring up when we discuss clay mineral formation by weathering, but it probably does not apply here.

Other examples of replacement of quartz by kaolinite have been reported many times by geologists and mineralogists, and need not be repeated here. Instead, I point out the replacement of wood (i.e., cellulose) by a mixture of diaspore and kaolinite. Although this is an example of replacement, we do not know if clay moved in by solution or by bulk movement, filling a cavity vacated as the wood was removed (Keller, 1938). Allen (1952) has described the migration of clay minerals and especially high alumina minerals, such as boehmite, diaspore, and gibbsite replacing several different minerals, including chlorite in chromite. Bardossy (1959) has observed movement of alumina in the Hungarian bauxites. Glauconite, a clay mineral, replaces even igneous rock, as well as pelletal silt (Ojakangas and Keller, 1964). Apart from the problems of origin of clay minerals by replacement, the ways by which replacement, *per se,* can operate are in great need of investigation. Nevertheless, I hope to have shown you that clay minerals may originate by crystallization from solution. This process may help us explain occasional other anomalies confronting us later.

The weathering of solid rocks

Ultimately the formation of clay minerals, or the derivation of ions which combine to form clay minerals, stems from the weathering of the so–called primary rocks, which are mainly silicates—particularly aluminum silicates. Argillation by weathering is a complex process, or perhaps better, a group of multiple, interrelated processes

Table 2. Argillation processes and agents

1. Inorganic-organic (energies)
2. Solid state conversion-solution transition
3. *In situ*-remote precipitation
4. Reaction with ground water
   a. Hydrolysis
   b. Hydration
   c. Oxidation
   d. Carbonation
   e. Mineral acids
   f. Salt solutions
   g. Organic acids and fluids
   h. Chelation
   i. Ion exchange

that can be discussed most easily by taking them up individually (Table 2).

Argillation processes may be inorganic or organic in category. That is, the energy which drives the argillation reactions may be expended independently and inorganically, or alternatively, by the intermediary contribution of living organisms (commonly plants) or fluids derived from them. Argillation processes may be further categorized in terms of the principal reactions by which they are effected, such as hydrolysis or ion exchange, or by the dominant reactant, such as H_2O, O_2, CO_2, mineral acids, alkalis, salt solutions, organic acids and fluids, chelators, and others. Furthermore, the course of argillation may be traced by way of solid state (or almost so) reactions, or by solution chemistry. In terms of location, argillation may take place *in situ* with respect to parent rock, or at the end of a 5000–mile transport.

For convenience, let us begin with argillation that accompanies the reaction of a typical primary aluminum silicate mineral, such as a feldspar, with water. The reaction includes simultaneously (and un-avoidably because of the composition and properties of water) hy-drolysis, dissolution, hydration, and oxidation. The oxidation potential of the water is conditioned further by the partial pressure of O_2 in the atmosphere (including the soil atmosphere in the soil) where argillation occurs, and likewise carbonic acid is developed in the solution in con-centration related to the pressure of CO_2 to which it is exposed. There-fore, oxidation and carbonation accompany hydrolysis. Since all the complexities inherent in the reaction with water cannot be simplified by individualizing them, and since they are present at all aqueous reac-tions, the reactions of different minerals with water can be described in relative degrees only.

The reaction of an aluminum silicate with water under ordinary geologic conditions may be illustrated by grinding nepheline ($NaSiAlO_4$; $KNa_3Si_4Al_4O_{16}$) under water.

Hydrolysis occurs and may be summarized in a schematic reaction as follows (see Yaalon, 1959, for formal weathering reactions):

MeAl silicates $+ HOH \rightleftharpoons Me^{n+} + OH^- + Al^{3+} + Al(OH)_x^{y+}$
$+ Al(OH)_3 + AlO_2^- + Fe^{2+, 3+} + Fe(OH)_3 + H_4SiO_4$
$+ SiO_a^{b-} + MeSi^+$ complex $+ H(Me)Al$ silicates (clay minerals and zeolites).

The presence of both positively and negatively charged ions, or com-plexes, of both Al and Si was demonstrated by movement of those elements into both anode and cathode chambers during electrodialysis of leucite (Correns, 1961). Hydrolysis is indicated because when pH indicator paper is pulled through the slurry a pH of 10 to 11 is registered. This is the abrasion pH of the mineral, as described by Stevens and Carron (1948). The abrasion pH of the feldspars ranges from 8 to 9 in the K-feldspars, to 10 in albite, and from 8 to 11 in the amphiboles and pyroxenes. The pH of the supernatant liquid is ordinarily not as high as that recorded within the slurry, probably for two reasons: (1) CO_2 dissolved in the water reduces the pH of the solution, and (2) the maximum pH is generated at the broken fresh surfaces of the mineral particles where ions of the metals (Na and K in nepheline) are exposed at the broken surfaces and react with the dissociated water, and such surfaces are not a part of the clear liquid. It is interpreted that the pH of the slurry, rather than the pH of the liquid, represents the pH, or nearly so, of the reaction system of the mineral with the water—i.e., of the interface when the reaction is occurring —and that inferences drawn on the effect of pH on the hydrolysis reaction should be based on the pH of the reaction interface, which is that registered by the slurry (Keller, 1957).

The interface (silicate–water), which is a crucial location in the course of events leading to argillation, will be discussed, with pertinent references, from the following viewpoints: (1) formation of an amorphous layer, (2) formation of hydrated alumina minerals or primary bauxite, (3) formation of kaolinite, (4) formation of endellite, (5) formation of zeolites, (6) a zone of transitional destruction of the primary silicate, (7) a locus of pseudomorphic replacement, and (8) formation of muscovite mica (or interzone) and thence to kaolinite (Table 3). Although the interface (or interzone) of the surface of a crystal with water may be a critical locus of activity, it is not all–important in the argillation process because alteration of silicates within their interior to

Table 3. At the silicate-water interface

1. Amorphous zone
2. Hydrated alumina minerals
3. Kaolinite
4. Endellite
5. Zeolites
6. Transitional zone of destruction
7. Pseudomorphous replacement
8. Mica (muscovite), thence kaolinite

clay minerals has been commonly observed in megascopic and micro-scopic occurrences (Bates, 1960; Keller, 1961).

Recent studies of the properties and products at the surfaces of silicates reacting with water include those of Correns (1963), Morey and Fournier (1961), De Vore (1959), Garrels and Howard (1959), Hemley (1959), Nash and Marshall (1956), Morey and Chen (1955), and Frederickson and Cox (1954a, 1954b). Garrels and Howard, and Nash and Marshall have discussed the physical chemistry of silicate mineral surfaces, and De Vore, the crystal chemistry of feldspar surfaces. Correns and students conducted experiments leading to calculations of the thicknesses and composition of the transitional zones between the unaltered mineral and the hot or cold water with which it reacted.

Correns and his students ground silicate minerals in ball mills and then weathered the fine particles (size ranged from a few microns to less than 1 micron in diameter) by shaking, electrodialysis, and refluxing in hot water. The liquid was separated from the solid fraction and both were analyzed. Since I will quote only part of Correns' summary of the results of many experiments in his laboratory, the interested reader should go back to the original detailed reports of each experiment. Correns found that the highest rate of solubility of a mineral in water occurred in the first stage of grinding. This conclusion is valid and applicable also in the field, as was observed independently by Keller (1961a) in a study of the hydrothermal kaolinization of a volcanic glassy rock in Mexico. The most pronounced and abrupt change occurred in the stage of alteration next to the fresh rock. The activities of the ions in the broken crystal surfaces are high.

Correns found that adularia alters in water to a thin decomposition layer of SiO_2 and Al_2O_3 around the K–feldspar grain, and that film so reduces the diffusion of the K–ions in this K–spar that their rate of mi-gration roughly equals the decomposition rate of the SiO_2–Al_2O_3 layer. In experiments with particles of K–feldspar with less than 1 micron radius at pH 3, the thickness of the residue layer, calculated from the amount of dissolved K, Al_2O_3, and SiO_2, was about 300 A, or about the thickness of 30 elementary or unit cells. This thickness shows no *further* increase as solution continues. The dissolution of K was higher in the first stages of the reaction. This observation was corroborated by Keller, Balgord, and Reesman (1962), who pulverized feldspars and other sili-cates under water at room temperature. However, the reaction of Cor-rens' adularia at pH 3 during slow filtration (71 ml. per day) continued for some time and reached "a kind of equilibrium which . . . bears roughly the relationship 1 K_2O : 1 Al_2O_3 : 6 SiO_2" in the solute. "These experiments show that, under the given conditions, potassium feldspar breaks up into ions and that these ions are moved" (Correns, 1963). He concluded further, after assuming that all the potassium had been removed from the layer (although he stated, "this assumption is, strictly speaking, not valid"), "that there occurred no new formation of kaolinite or montmorillonite or similar minerals in these layers, as the relationship SiO_2 : Al_2O_3 does not bear the faintest relationship to that of such minerals." Thus under the conditions of the experiment a transitional zone of mineral decomposition, but not a clay mineral, is developed. Using hot water, the mineral weathering of K–spar appeared to be equivalent to mineral dissolution.

Albite (Na–feldspar) responded somewhat differently. Correns credits unpublished work by Bieger (1952), in which albite at pH 6 and low rate of filtration developed a residue layer of constant 20 A thickness. Regarding its composition (p. 447), "it seems quite possible that in a closed system the ratio SiO_2 : Al_2O_3 of 2 would be reached." This ratio is the same as that present in kaolinite.

A somewhat different trend in the composition of the residue layer occurred in leucite, KSi_2AlO_6, reacting with water (Correns, 1963). At pH 3 the SiO_2 : Al_2O_3 ratio was relatively high (4.68 to 11.68, depending upon temperatures and grain size), whereas at pH 5.8 to 11, the SiO_2 : Al_2O_3 ratio was 2.66 to 3.91. More specifically, at pH 3 and 22°C., particles 3 to 10 microns in radius yielded a SiO_2 : Al_2O_3 ratio of 10.5:1, whereas at pH 6.8, and the same temperature, particles less than 1 micron in radius yielded a SiO_2 : Al_2O_3 ratio of 3.68, which is within the clay mineral range. Thus, a higher ratio of SiO_2 to Al_2O_3 was present in the immobolized zone, or film, at low pH. Correns reported that the residue layers gave no X–ray diffraction or electron diffraction lines.

In summary, the rate and products of the reaction between silicate minerals and water were affected by the temperature, the size of particles, and the concentration of ions in solution. The last was modified by changing the pH and the rate at which the filtrate was removed from the reacting system, and by addition of certain ions in solution. With respect to the SiO_2 : Al_2O_3 ratio of the residue layer on feldspar and leucite, Correns reported a wide range from about 2:1 (that in kaolinite) upward through the same ratio as was present in the parent mineral, to as high as 11.68:1 when the pH was relatively low (pH 3). He found the residue layers to be amorphous. On the other hand,

Morey and Chen (1955) reacted orthoclase with water at 350°C., 5000 psi., for 38 days, and found boehmite. Albite, at the same temperature and pressure, yielded analcime ($NaSi_2AlO_6 \cdot H_2O$), paragonite, muscovite (1–M polymorph), and boehmite in the residue. Albite at 200°C. and 2000 psi., and at 100°C. and about 40 psi. yielded boehmite and kaolinite. Nepheline that was refluxed in water at 295°C., 2500 psi., by Morey and Fournier (1961) yielded boehmite, muscovite, and analcime. Therefore, crystalline minerals composed of hydrated alumina and aluminum silicates can be formed on the surfaces of tectosilicates reacting with water, a situation radically different from the observations of Correns, who found an amorphous residue and film.

Correns (1963) attributed the formation of crystalline products, rather than amorphous layers, in Morey and Chen's experiments to "less alkali ions entering into solution" and "at high temperatures a thicker residue layer forms more quickly." He assumed that the experimental conditions of Morey and Chen were such that pseudomorphs, such as kaolinite after feldspar, might begin to form. Correns tackled the problem of pseudomorph formation by using a model of pseudomorphous AgCl after rock salt, which forms pseudomorphously from highly concentrated solutions. Correns (1963) stated: "It is obvious that a necessary prerequisite for the formation of pseudomorphs is that at first a precipitate forms on the crystal and that the reaction then proceeds through this precipitate into the crystal. Therefore, the concentration of the reacting ions in the outer solution must be so great that they are able to penetrate through the initially formed precipitate–skin into the crystal." Correns' experiments were conducted with very dilute solutions, a condition which, according to him, precluded formation of pseudomorphs.

Let us now take stock of what the undissolved products are when a silicate reacts with water under laboratory conditions. At 100°C., and above, the mineral products may be clay mineral, zeolite, or hydrated alumina (boehmite). At room temperature, the residue is a gel in which the $SiO_2 : Al_2O_3$ ratio varies widely—at pH 3, the $SiO_2 : Al_2O_3$ ratio is very high (about 11), and at neutrality and pH above 7 it declines toward 2. Gels of this type in nature are progenitors of allophane, the amorphous member of, or allied to, the kaolin group (Ross and Kerr, 1934). That gels of this type become allophane and then pass through the sequence metahalloysite to kaolinite has been reported by Fieldes (1955) in New Zealand from work on soil clays derived from the weathering of rhyolitic or andesitic ash. Fieldes adapted a mechanism suggested by Tamura and Jackson (1953) for the transition of alumina and silica through allophane to kaolin as follows:

(1) Precipitated hydrous alumina crystallizes to a gibbsite structure in which aluminum is contained within octahedral sheets of hydroxyls and adjacent sheets are linked by hydrogen bonds.

(2) Partial dehydration removes from the gibbsite some hydroxyls which are replaced by the oxygen atoms of silica tetrahedra from solution. Silica is taken on at random, in this way cross-linking between octahedral sheets of alumina and forming a random structure full of channels but relatively rigid. This form of silicated alumina corresponds to allophane A [allophane A of Fieldes].

(3) When sufficient silica is available, under the influence of wetting and drying, silica reorients unidirectionally to form a hexagonal silicate sheet coordinated with the sheet structure of gibbsite resulting in a kaolin type mineral.

This concept of a mechanism for formation of halloysite is logical and permissive, and probably describes how kaolin minerals develop from a gel. Regardless of its accuracy as to detail, numerous other field occurrences of allophane, halloysite, and gibbsite have been reported, so there is no doubt that the transformation occurs. Noteworthy among such reported occurrences are those of Bates (1960), who stressed the direct alteration in Hawaii of plagioclase to halloysite, and pseudomorphs of both halloysite and gibbsite after feldspar; of Sudo (1954), and Sudo and Ossaka (1952), who described kaolin and hydrated halloysite, in addition to montomorillonite, as alteration products of volcanic ash in Japan; and of Hay (1959) who reported the alteration of plagioclase to halloysite$\cdot 4H_2O$ on St. Vincent, B.W.I.

Parenthetically, you may have noticed that alteration of feldspar directly to kaolinite, i.e., the well–crystallized or highly ordered variety of kaolinite, has not been mentioned. I will consider this transformation via mica in a section to follow.

So far, however, the evidence from field occurrences may be integrated with that from the laboratory and summarized to state that aluminous silicates react with water to give rise, via a gel phase, to either (1) hydrated alumina, such as boehmite and/or gibbsite, or (2) a hydrated aluminum silicate — that is, a clay mineral. Field occurrences show that the clay mineral formed is commonly either allophane or halloysite, which then *perhaps* goes to kaolinite, or it is montmorillonite which is the predominant (in terms of volume) argillation product of volcanic ash (glass and accompanying silicate mineral particles). Logically, the next question is what factors influence or determine which of these minerals is formed. Since field evidence is more abundant than laboratory evidence on this point, I will present it, and then move to a generalization.

Evidence from bauxite

Bauxite (gibbsite, boehmite, and diaspore, but diaspore less commonly than boehmite) may originate from the direct alteration of a primary silicate rock (Gordon, Tracey, and Ellis, 1958, p. 140; Harrison, 1934), and via kaolinization from primary silicate rocks (Mead, 1915; Gordon, Tracey, and Ellis, 1958, p. 138). Parenthetically, bauxite may originate from practically any aluminous rock (Harder, 1952), but at this point we wish to consider and contrast the processes of (1) direct bauxitization, and (2) bauxitization via kaolinization.

Direct bauxitization has been reported by Gordon, Tracey, and Ellis (1958) from nepheline syenite, and from basic igneous rock by Harrison, who wrote under the heading, "Primary lateritisation" that "the microscopic observations in each case I have studied indicate that *the mineral at first and direct formation from the plagioclase feldspars is gibbsite*" (italics by Harrison, 1934, p. 37). The "basic igneous rocks" were dolerite (presumably what is termed diabase in American nomenclature) at Tumatumari and Hope quarry localities, hornblende schist at Yarikita Hill, and amphibolite at Issorora Hill and Atobani. Quartz diorite (termed an intermediate rock by Harrison) containing plagioclase, hornblende, quartz, and accessory minerals, occurring at the Blue Mountain quarry, altered to primary quartz–laterite. It is significant that nepheline in nepheline syenite; pyroxene in diabase; and amphibole in hornblende schist, amphibolite, and quartz diorite (the rocks cited from Harrison's paper) yield primary bauxite and abrasion pH's of 10 to 11, and calcic plagioclase yields pH 8 to 9.

Acidic igneous rocks, as Harrison termed alkali–feldspar and muscovite pegmatites at Mazaruni quarry, and granite at Kalacoon and Mazaruni quarries, are specific examples illustrating his following statement, "Under tropical conditions, *acidic rocks,* such as aplites, pegmatites, or granites and granitic gneisses, do *not* undergo primary lateritisation, but gradually change through katamorphism into pipe or pot-clays, or more or less quartziferous and impure kaolins" (Harrison, 1934, p. 10). The abrasion pH of K–feldspars, albite, and quartz are 8, 9, and 6 to 7 respectively, notably and critically lower with respect to solubility of Al_2O_3 in water than the abrasion pH of nepheline, pyroxenes, and amphiboles.

Above pH 10.5 both SiO_2 and Al_2O_3 are relatively highly soluble, and I interpret from their abrasion pH (10 to 11) that the reaction at the interface of nepheline, pyroxene, amphibole, and calcic plagioclase with relatively fresh rain water yields the result that these minerals can dissolve soluble Al_2O_3 and SiO_2 in low concentrations. For Al_2O_3 and SiO_2 to remain in solution it would be necessary for rain water to be present in great abundance, so that saturation of Al_2O_3 and SiO_2 would never occur in the ground water. Such a condition would be met in a climate where (1) rain fell practically every day, and perhaps several times in 24 hours, (2) drainage was so good that the low–concentration solutions were carried away without reaching saturation in Al_2O_3 or SiO_2, and (3) the temperature was warm, increasing the solubility of silica. Such conditions are commonly met in the climates of the so–called tropical rain forest when there is a slight increase in solubility of Al_2O_3 and SiO_2 due to high temperature of the tropics.

I infer that under these conditions Al_2O_3 and SiO_2 might be carried away in solution from the parent rock and redeposited elsewhere, either separately as deposits of gibbsite and chalcedony or quartz, or in combination as a hydrous aluminum silicate, such as a member of the kaolin group. If the Al_2O_3 were deposited separately, bauxite might be formed. If the pH at the reaction or dissolving interface of the silicate mineral is about 9 to 9.5, and rain is abundant, the SiO_2 may be dissolved and carried away, leaving the Al_2O_3 behind, i.e., *in situ* on the weathering rock, because of its low solubility and relative immobility in the pH range. Under the conditions primary laterite, or direct bauxitization could occur.

Next, consider a mineral–water system in which (1) the pH is 8 or below, (2) the drainage is poor, or (3) the rainfall is not excessively profuse. If the pH is 8 or below, the solutions from the interface of an aluminum silicate mineral and water may be supersaturated with both Al_2O_3 and SiO_2, resulting in a clay mineral. If the pH is 4.5 (permissibly somewhat higher), Al tends to coordinate octahedrally and kaolinite may develop, for it is recalled that De Kimpe, Gastuche, and Brindley (1961) synthesized kaolinite from solutions of aluminum ions and silica in low concentration at pH 4.5. Evidence of retention of silica in alumina gel, or silica in the gel with alumina (i.e., which probably leads to argillation), or the formation of a hydrous silicate of aluminum at pH 9 to 4, is found in the experiments of Correns (1963), and especially in those of Okamoto, Okura, and Goto (1957). Correns, it will be recalled, found the Si:Al ratio in decomposed leucite to be 10.5:1 at pH 3, notably higher than 3.68:1, which was developed at pH 6.8. Hence, argillation is compatible with lower pH, as is direct bauxitization with higher pH. Okamoto, *et al.,* found that molecularly dispersed silica originally at concentration of 35 mg/L (or approximately 0.6 mmol/L) was reduced by precipitation to 15 mg/L (0.25 mmol/L) at pH 8.5 by the addition of 20 mg/L of Al (0.37 mmol of Al_2O_3) as aluminum sulphate, and to approximately 2 mg/L (0.035 mmol/L) by the addition of 100 mg/L of Al (1.85 mmol/L of Al_2O_3) as aluminum sulphate. Thus, at pH 8 to 9 the presence of Al (sulphate) in solution reduces strongly the solubility of SiO_2. Such precipitation of silica by Al did not occur at SiO_2:Al ratios as high as 90:1 (Okamoto, *et al.,* 1957, p. 131). The possible influence of the sulphate anion on precipitation of dissolved silica was not discussed.

To return to the geologic field conditions, if the drainage or the rainfall is poor, evaporation rate is low enough that saturation of the solutions with respect to Al_2O_3 and SiO_2 ensues, clay minerals (i.e., hydrated *silicate* of alumina), rather than the hydroxide of alumina, may form. This process is suggested as an explanation for argillation of the aluminum silicate rock rather than direct bauxitization. Whether the kaolinite is further altered to bauxite is another step in a process which will be discussed later.

Granites, or other rocks dominated in composition by feldspars, hydrolyze inherently at a lower abrasion pH than those containing nepheline and the mafic inosilicates; this would predispose them toward kaolinization rather than direct bauxitization. Another factor which may be highly significant is the common presence of K in the feldspars of granite. Apparently the presence of K in reacting alumina–silica gels facilitates the formation of muscovite mica, and muscovite mica appears to weather preferentially to kaolinite (Harrison, 1934, p. 59; Sand, 1956).

The foregoing illustrations have been offered in an effort to show that the solid products formed during the hydrolysis of an aluminum silicate, whether they be bauxite or clay minerals, may be dependent on (1) the pH of the reacting system (that of the micro–environment of the reacting interface), which in turn is modified by the parent mineral as indicated by its abrasion pH; (2) the proximity to saturation of the hydrolyzing solution with respect to Al_2O_3 and SiO_2, as modified by the profusion and regularity of rain fall, evaporation, and effluent drainage; and (3) possibly the presence of potassium in the hydrolyzate. When conditions are such that the solid formed is a clay mineral, it has been observed that the same parent material may give rise, under variations of the conditions, to two (or possibly more) different clay minerals; for example, volcanic ash may alter either to montmorillonite or kaolinite. Now, what are the conditions that lead to the genesis of each of these kinds of clay minerals? The formation of clay minerals, as of all other mineral phases, represents a response of some particular materials to certain energies. Pertinent and distinguishing compositions and properties of the kaolinite and montmorillonite groups of clay minerals are tabulated in Table 4.

Table 4. Distinguishing compositions and properties of the kaolinite and montmorillonite groups of minerals

Al/Si is 1:1	Al/Si (approx.)* 1:2.4
H/Si is 2:1	H/Si is .5:1
(M)+: H is 0:1	(Fe,Ca,Mg,Na)+: H is 3–.5:1
Abrasion pH 5.6-6.6 (13 samples)	Abrasion pH 6.2-9.8 (9 samples)
7.2 (1 sample)	5.2 (1 sample)
Synthesis pH 4.5	

* From the suggested montmorillonite formula of Ross and Hendricks (1945, p. 45). Beidellite has a higher Al:Si ratio.

Formation of kaolinite

Kaolinite signifies, relatively, a high ratio of Al to Si; high H, but *no* Na, K, Ca, Mg, Fe; an acid abrasion pH; and synthesis restricted to low pH of 4.5 (De Kimpe, *et al.,* 1961) or 2.5 (De Kimpe, *et al.,* 1964). In terms of geologic environment these factors may be met by the alteration of aluminum silicate parent material, under extensive leaching conditions, where pH of 7 or below is optimum. In essence, this means a terrain and climate where Ca, Mg, Fe, Na, and K are removed freely, and H ions are supplied abundantly by acid or from dissociation of water.

The importance of efficient, effluent drainage is shown by the observation of Mohr and Van Baren (1954) that laterite and montmorillonite were formed a short distance from each other from the same parent volcanic material and in the same climate, except that the laterite site was well drained, while the montmorillonite site was water–logged and silica and metal ions were not removed. Good drainage may mean high relief of the land, steep slope, and high permeability of soil.

Iron may be removed from the chemical or reacting system either by oxidation to relatively insoluble Fe_2O_3, which is seen abundantly in red kaolinite soils, or by "reduction" (from the geologic viewpoint) to relatively insoluble iron sulfide, which occurs commonly in kaolinite fire clays. Thus, although an oxidizing environment is commonly associated with kaolinization — and indeed this is most common — the important effect in the kaolinization process is removal of Fe from the reacting system, which can also be effected under geologic reducing conditions.

A relatively high ratio of Al with respect to Si, which is indicated by the composition of kaolinite and its synthesis (De Kimpe, Gastuche, and Brindley, 1961), may arise from either a highly aluminous parent rock, addition of Al ions, or differential removal of silica. In pure water, silica is appreciably more soluble below pH 8 than is alumina, and extensive leaching of an aluminum silicate will effect enrichment of alumina. For the effect of K and Na on silica removal, it may be recalled that silica is prepared in soluble form industrially as K and Na "water glass," and in colloidal solution ("Ludox," e.g.) stabilized by low concentrations of alkali metals, indicating that the presence of alkali metals may aid its remaining in solution. Therefore, Al enrichment with respect to Si is likely to occur from rocks high in Na and K, but low in Ca and Mg. On the other hand, concentrated solutions of water glass are gelled, flocculated, or precipitated by the addition of strong Ca and Mg solutions. These effects are interpreted geologically as indicating that K and Na feldspars (and feldspathoids) would probably lose silica (and be enriched in Al) by solution more readily than would Ca and Mg silicates, and that, therefore, granitic rocks would be more likely to kaolinize than would mafic or Ca–Mg rocks. This is an inference which actually accords with field observation.

The presence of acids during argillation, whether they be carbonic, organic, plant root, or mineral, will provide sources of H ions in higher concentration than in water, and will accelerate the processes of hydrolysis and expulsion of M ions (other than Al and Si) for which H is substituted, thereby effecting kaolinization. However, acids, an environment lower than 7 in pH, are not absolutely necessary for the formation of kaolinite, provided M ions are removed and H ions introduced. For example, Noll (1936) showed in hydrothermal laboratory experiments that with very low concentration of K, kaolinite formed under mildly alkaline conditions, although it was accompanied by montmorillonite. I would guess that montmorillonite would be scanty if the concentration of alkaline earths was also very low. Zen reported a possible kaolinitic phase resulting from the devitrification of volcanic glass in modern bottom oceanic sediments off the coasts of Chile and Peru, although the identification of kaolinite and other minerals was made "with varying degrees of confidence" (Zen, 1959a, p. 31).

The kaolinization process which has been considered so far is characterized by an amorphous gel phase, intermediate in stage of alteration between the parent silicate and the daughter product, a member of the kaolin group. This is the probable mechanism by which feldspar weathers directly to endellite, the hydrated halloysite from the southern Appalachian region described by Sand (1956). Alumina–silica gel is thought by Fieldes (1955) to go through the stages allophane, halloysite, and then kaolinite. This sequence was not observed by Sand (1956) in his work on the genesis of kaolins in the southern Appalachians. On the contrary, he found no evidence of transition between halloysite and kaolinite (p. 28). Halloysite was formed directly from feldspar, but kaolinite (specific mineral) was formed directly from potash feldspar through the intermediate stage of mica. Bates (1960b) observed a similar mechanism (K–feldspar–mica–kaolinite) in Hawaii. Sand found that "The kaolinite is pseudomorphous after the mica, and the basal planes of the kaolinite orient, in general, parallel to those of the mica" (p. 37). Ross and Kerr (1930, p. 172) described as an intermediate weathering product between feldspar and kaolinite from Franklin, N. C., a "muscovite–like kaolin mineral," but after analyzing it chemically and optically, state (p. 173): "It is therefore evident that the muscovite–like mineral that has been called secondary muscovite is not a mica at all but a clay mineral. Chemical analyses of partly purified material suggest that it is similar to kaolinite in composition but contains less water."

In our present stage of knowledge, it may be stated that K–feldspar alters to kaolinite via intermediary mica under certain conditions, but directly to kaolinite under others, and that it alters to halloysite (endellite) via a gel phase, possibly including transitory allophane.

De Vore (1959) has suggested an interesting mechanism by which rearrangement of the atoms exposed on a broken surface of feldspar might give rise to mica or clay minerals. This is a transformation essentially from solid, crystalline feldspar to solid, crystalline mica or clay without going through an intermediary gel stage. The rearrangement is most easily visualized by manipulating a three–dimensional model of feldspar. Briefly described, single chains of O–Al–Si forming the (100)—(010) surface of ordered feldspar (whose charges are neu-tralized by H) might be polymerized into O–Al–Si ordered mica sheets, and by simple transformation be converted into the kaolinite sheet structure. Perhaps this solid–solid transition is the route by which at least some feldspar alters directly to kaolinite, but definitive evidence on the mechanisms which actually occur is lacking.

Mechanisms of argillation

Definitive evidence of the mechanism by which argillation proceeds is rarely easy to discover in field studies. Lest we get too far from actual field occurrences I will draw on a few field examples of argilla-tion. First, the alternation of a glassy rock, perlite, to halloysite–endel-lite will be considered. Near the village of Etzatlán, 75 miles west of Guadalajara, Mexico, is an occurrence of glassy igneous rock, a perlite, which has been altered to halloysite by hot spring waters (Keller, 1961a). A roadway has been cut through fresh rock to the center of the clay deposit, exposing the complete transition from glass to clay over a distance of about 100 feet. Sequential samples were analyzed chemically, microscopically, and by X–ray diffraction. No. 1 was col-lected from the best clay, halloysite (originally it was endellite); No. 3, 40 feet from No. 1; No. 4, 70 feet from No. 1; and No. 6, fresh perlite, 100 feet from No. 1.

Desilication occurred during argillation (SiO_2 decreased from 71.37 per cent to 47.75 per cent), alkali metals were lost, and H^+ was added. A typical diffractogram of No. 6 (silicate glass) shows a broad rise in reflections from about 4.4 A to 3.3 A, which has been interpreted to originate from silica tetrahedra. As argillation progresses a broad peak at about 7.1 A, characteristic of the kaolin group, and the band from about 4.4 A tapering downward begin to develop. Thus, a random distribution of O, Si, and Al in the glass begins to mobilize and articu-late into tetrahedra and octahedra, and then arrange into a sheet struc-ture.

Endellitization of feldspar in Appalachian occurrences was described by Sand (1956, p. 38) in a way that seems logical, and which might well apply here: "Effective leaching from the feldspar of all its bases probably destroys its structure and the colloidal silica and alumina are arranged into the random structure of hydrated halloysite. It is signifi-cant that hydrated halloysite, not its dehydrated product, always was present except where samples were obtained from dried exposures."

Direct endellitization of the Etzatlán glass without intermediary mica formation is indicated by direct invasion of the glass by very fine–grained, low–birefringent clay without any suggestion of mica between the clay and the glass. Curiously, and contrary to Correns' laboratory observations, the argillation of the perlite did not begin as a continuous wave spreading from microscopic cracks within the rock, in the manner that ordinary surface oxidation or massive hydrothermal alteration spreads from a joint pattern in rocks. Instead, alteration began in the interior of certain apparently more vulnerable (to attack) "pearls" in the perlitic structure. On a macroscopic scale, however, a zone comprised of many individual, selective alteration centers advanced into the fresh rock. The advancing zone was followed by a zone in which alteration became complete.

The clay in the completely argillized portion is exceedingly fine–grained and randomly oriented, as is indicated by extremely weak interference colors and lack of an organized pattern of preferred orientation of interference color (crystal orientation). This random distribution of the tiny clay crystals (crystalline to X–ray) is interpreted as arising from, and being influenced by, the random organization of Si–O–Al–Me ions in the glass. It is logical that leaching of the "Me" ions and hydration of the Si–O–Al would leave poorly organized endellite. Leaching was sufficiently efficient, and perhaps at a low enough pH, that a member of the kaolin group of clays was formed.

In several field occurrences of argillized crystalline — not glassy — rock, the megascopic and external structures of the rock were maintained (pseudomorphism retained on a grand scale). One is kaolinization, at depth, of Cornwall granite near St. Austell, England. Because of the convincing evidence of occurrence beneath relatively unaltered sills, the kaolinization is thought to have been done by rising solutions (Howe, 1914; Ussher, Barrow, MacAlister, and Flett, 1909; summarized by Holmes, 1950). The rock is so soft and clayey that the pick point of a hammer penetrates it easily. If this rock had been softened by supergene leaching (weathering) on the outcrop it would probably have been called saprolite. Other kaolinite occurs in the Colettes–Echassieres area in central France, but presumably has an origin similar to that in the Cornwall district of England (Holmes, 1950; de Launay, 1901; Rosler, 1902). Part of the kaolinite in Bavaria is derived by alteration of granite, but the deposit east of nearby Hirschau represents kaolinized, Triassic (Keuper) arkose. Whether the kaolinization at Hirschau was due to hydrothermal rising solutions, or to supergene (a) acid spring waters, or (b) water percolating through brown coal, is controversial (Holmes, 1950; Kohler, 1903; Stahl, 1912; Lilley, 1932). In our own country, the Georgia kaolin deposits have originated, according to Kesler (1952, pp. 167-68) as follows:

Weathered rocks of the Piedmont furnished the sand and kaolin of the Tuscaloosa formation. The debris evidently was deposited in coalescing deltas and alluvial fans along the Cretaceous shoreline, and in part redistributed by stream and ocean currents, as shown by no abundance of minor unconformities. The lenses of kaolin were deposited in pools and lakes of fresh or salt water, nearly isolated from the currents.

Lest it be thought that all softened, desilicated rocks and saprolitic material is kaolinitic, there occurs a montmorillonitized (poorly crystallized) volcanic rock that was softened by surface leaching of a boulder deposit some 15 or more feet thick, eroded by a stream at a locality west of Oyamel, in the state of Michoacan, west of Mexico City. Similarly, montmorillonitic clay was produced by surface leaching of a boulder deposit high on the bluffs of the Columbia River near Rainier, west of Portland, Oregon (Wilson and Treasher, 1938, p. 27).

Formation of montmorillonite

Conditions leading to the formation of montmorillonite contrast with those under which kaolinite is developed. It is expected that the chemical system in which montmorillonite is formed will be characterized by a high Si:Al ratio, and a relative abundance of Mg, Fe, Ca, Na, and K, with correspondingly lower concentration of H ions. In terms of parent material, mafic rocks and volcanic ash of intermediate composition, which are relatively rich in Mg, Fe, and Ca, supply the cations which occur between the O–Si–Al sheets of montmorillonite clay minerals, and therefore are more likely to alter to montmorillonite than to kaolinite. Furthermore, the divalent cations tend to flocculate silica (they flocculate the silica in concentrated water glass solutions) and thus tend to retain the high Si:Al ratio in montmorillonite.

The climate (both macro and micro) of the weathering environment and the efficiency of drainage are just as important as parent material in the following ways. If the climate is semi–arid (i.e., precipitation less than potential evaporation) hydrolysis of the silicate occurs while it is wet, but as drying ensues, the solution of cations originally dilute becomes saturated with respect to Mg, Ca, Fe, Na, etc., and their combination with O–Si–Al during drying can develop montmorillonite.

Thus, by utilization of the divalent ions in the ground water even granitic rocks (rich in K and Na, but typically in Ca) can alter to montmorillonite in a semi–arid climate, whereas if rainfall on them had exceeded evaporation they would have given rise to kaolinite. At the other extreme in climate, excess of rainfall over evaporation, if the drainage is poor so that the concentration of Mg, Ca, etc., builds up, the chemical system again produces montmorillonite. Hence, the interplay of materials and energy governs the precise product formed, and climate and material are descriptive of the process and product only to the degree of precision with which they describe the chemical system.

Field evidence in support of the preceding clay systems has been cited in the observation of Mohr and Van Baren (1954) that volcanic ash alters to either montmorillonite or laterite in the same region if the terrain is, respectively, water–logged or well drained. In Oregon localities I have seen where volcanic ash weathers through a sequence of montmorillonite next to the ash and thence upward and outward, where leaching was more efficient, to kaolinite (*b*–axis disordered). I have seen andesite in Guanajuato, Mexico, alter hydrothermally via montmorillonite to kaolinite.* The large deposits of bentonite which are mined commercially in the United States (Knechtel and Patterson, 1962) and elsewhere, originated commonly from volcanic ash and were deposited and hydrolyzed in relatively permanent (non–refluxed) bodies of water, such as lakes or marine embayments, in which monovalent and divalent cations could build up high concentrations.

Roles of plants and other sources of acidity in weathering and argillation

The hydrolysis of primary silicate minerals produces a relatively soluble, highly dissociated $Me^+ OH^-$ "compound" yielding an alkaline solution, and a scantily soluble H^+ aluminum silicate (plus aluminum hydroxides under appropriate conditions). In an ordinary humid or semi–arid climate, but excluding a tropical rain forest, the aluminum silicate is typically a clay mineral. Schematically, on a world-wide scale, the ocean's alkalinity represents perhaps the OH^- from hydrolysis and the H^+ in the Al silicate clay, the H^+ counterpart to the OH^- from the water.

As the concentration of OH^- builds up during hydrolysis, the activity

* See Altschuler, Z. S. Dwornik, E. J., and Kramer, H. (1963) Transformation of montmorillonite to kaolinite during weathering: *Science,* v. 141, pp. 148-52.

of H^+ from water declines and thus the rate of hydrolysis is retarded. Alternatively, if additional H ions are contributed by carbonic acid, sulphuric acid (from oxidizing pyrite), humic and other organic acids, and others, they drive the hydrolysis reaction further in the argillation direction. Carbonic acid enhances the solubility of Mg especially (Keller, Balgord, and Reesman, 1962), and because of complexing of CO_2, the solubility of both Ca and Mg is increased beyond that represented by dissociated Ca and Mg bicarbonates (Garrels, Thompson, and Siever, 1961).

High acidity motivates the decomposition of clays by mobilization of Al into positions of exchangeable cations, and further spontaneous reaction may continue the decomposition. Coleman (1961, p. 30A) discussed this point as follows:

Aluminosilicate clay minerals found in acid soils have major proportions of the cation–exchange sites countered by aluminum ions; in most instances from 90 to 98 per cent of the exchange acidity can be attributed to aluminum, apparently present as Al^{3+}.

Hydrogen-saturated clays prepared by treatment with mineral acids or H-exchange resins are not stable but change spontaneously toward exchange saturation with Al^{3+} (and other lattice cations such as Mg^{2+}). The alteration rate varies with the nature of the clay and is greatly accelerated by a rise in temperature. Such clay decomposition, with the movement of lattice ions to exchange sites, proceeds so long as exchangeable hydrogen is present in appreciable amounts. In soil layers where biological activity is a factor, CO_2 production by higher plants and micro-organisms, along with nitrate and sulfate production, yields H ions which displace metal cations such as Ca and Mg, resulting in further clay decomposition.

Aluminum-saturated clays themselves are not stable: Al^{3+} ions on exchange sites may hydrolyze to produce interlayer polymers, and Al^{3+} ions displaced into a soil solution through ion exchange hydrolyze to form gibbsite-like substances. Such hydrolysis reactions are accelerated in the presence of absorbents and produce H ions that promote further clay decomposition or are removed from a weathering zone by leaching or volatilization. Because of the hydrolysis and/or adsorption of Al ions, it appears that significant amounts of Al can be transported through weathering zones only as complex ions or perhaps as protected sols.

Humic and other organic acids and compounds implement weathering and by their H^+ simultaneously implement argillation by chelating some of the metal cations released during hydrolysis. Common chelators include chlorophyll and other porphyrins, certain enzymes, certain amino acids, citric, lactic, tartaric, and malic acids (Weinstein, Robbins, and Perkins, 1954; Schatz, 1955). Wallace (1961) states that Fe–

chelating agents may be secreted by Fe–deficient bacteria and certain plants.

Schatz, Cheronis, Schatz, and Trelawny (1954) demonstrated that rocks, such as basalt, granite, volcanic ash, wyomingite, and glauconite, were weathered under alkaline conditions, pH 8.0, more intensely in the presence of 17 chelating organic substances, such as acetate, lactate, tartrate, citrate, salicylate, etc., than in distilled water. They state that "A particular compound may be a strong acid and a weak chelator, or vice versa; acid strength is not a reliable index to chelating ability." About the role of lichens, symbionts (fungi and bacteria), they say: "The ability of lichens to thrive on bare rock above timberline is unique. . . . But lichens contain unusually large amounts of a wide variety of complex organic compounds not found elsewhere in nature" (Vartia, 1950, as quoted by Schatz, *et al.,* 1954). Many of these are powerful chelators by which lichens weather rock material and extract essential trace elements (Schatz, *et al.,* 1954, p. 48). In a later abstract, Schatz, *et al.* (1957), stated that "lichen acids are polyhydroxy poly-carboxylates which complex metals."

That lichens and mosses are the first megascopic plants to grow on the surface of bare rock is well known to earth scientists. Within four years, or less time, after a lava flow has stopped moving they can move onto andesite–basalt, as is shown by the occurrence at Parícutin, taken about four years after the lava had congealed. The primitive forms of plants, including bacteria, "soften up" the notably strong bonds between elements in silicate crystals, and provide a substrate on which argillation can proceed. Because they—especially bacteria—coat and cover very intimately the rock and mineral particles, they aid increasingly the process of argillation of the silicates. Although I doubt that any bacteria are specific clay formers (and thereby I do not endorse Logan's hypothesis for the formation of indianaite, actually endellite–allophane; Logan, 1919), I regard bacteria as one of the most important and essential adjuncts to the processes which result in argillation. I think they merit much more study.

After some clay has been formed so that it becames a significant part of the soil and is present as a coating (the "argillans" of Dr. Brewer, Chapter II) of particles of undecomposed silicate minerals, that clay acts as an agent of weathering to produce more clay from silicate parent mineral and rock. The contact exchange sequence need not be two–stage clay transfer; instead, clay coating a silicate mineral particle may serve as a single–stage bridge between rootlet and mineral particle. Furthermore, acid clay (which has been made acidic by either leaching or by extraction of Me cations from it as nutrient ions by, and for, plants) is a potent source of H^+ and an agent of weathering of silicate minerals that are decomposed by hydrolysis. As the acid clay weathers the silicate mineral, it becomes stocked with Me ions, and then as these are removed by plant roots, the clay goes back for more Me cations from the silicate mineral. The plant is the ultimate agency of weathering, and the sun, as it furnishes energy for photosynthesis, ultimately energizes the weathering reaction. The amount of weathering necessary if the plant nutrients are kept in balance in the soil is no small item.

In comparison to the time spent on inorganic processes, only a short time has been spent on weathering by plants. This I deem disproportionate to the relative importance of the two processes in terms of the volume of weathered products and clay produced. Modern agriculture is pulling vast amounts of Me ions from the soil, and this effect is undoubtedly promoting much argillation. Before modern time as well as in the present, bacteria and other micro–plants, in my opinion, have done far more work toward silicate decomposition than documentation indicates. Basically, micro–plants are able to do this work because they possess the energy to do it—energy transmitted to them by the sun— whereas inorganic reactions must be driven by built–in chemical energy and have fewer direct contributions from solar energy than those available to plants. This is an important factor because a requisite for any reaction is energy.

The origin of illite and some related problems

The approach to the origin of clay minerals heretofore has been centered about the process as the focal point, but in discussing the origin of illite it will be more efficient to begin with the material itself. To define illite, reference is made to the paper naming it: illite "is not proposed as a specific mineral name, but a general term for the clay mineral constituents of argillaceous sediments belonging to the mica group" (Grim, Bray, and Bradley, 1937; Bradley and Grim, 1961). Most of the illite clay minerals are dioctahedral, but some are known that are trioctahedral (Grim, 1953, p. 67). Levinson (1955) identified four which are mica polymorphs in specimens called illite: 3–layer trigonal (3T), 2–layer monoclinic (2M), 1–layer monoclinic (1M), and 1–layer monoclinic disordered (1Md). Illites commonly contain more H_2O and less K_2O than do muscovites, and commonly yield a 10 A basal spacing that is a band tailing toward higher spacings, which may arise from randomly mixed, or interspersed, water layers.

From the foregoing documented properties of illite (some of which are essentially mutually exclusive), and in accord with the original proposal of constituents (plural) of argillaceous sediments, I think we must conclude that illite may vary somewhat—but not too widely— from sediment to sediment, and encompass in totality the following possible variations in composition and origin: (a) It may be essentially monomineralic (one phase and/or one polymorph of mica) out of at least four possible polymorphs, (b) it may be a mechanical mixture of more than one polymorph of mica, (c) it may be composed of randomly mixed mica polymorphs with relatively small amounts of possibly water, montmorillonite, or chlorite, (d) it may originate from a variety of parent materials, either from katamorphically degraded mica, or by anamorphic construction from constituent ions, and (e) it probably represents a close approach of the constituent material by either kata-morphic or anamorphic processes to equilibrium with an environment of subaqueous sedimentation and the subsequent regimen of sedimentary rocks. In accord with the foregoing concepts of illite, I regard it almost as a rock name parallel with, for example, limonite and bauxite. It is very useful, especially to sedimentary petrologists.

Now, if my concept of illite is acceptable, we may inquire further how illite may originate—that is, what materials and what processes will give rise to "constituents of argillaceous sediments belonging to the mica group" (Grim, Bray, and Bradley, 1937). I have attempted to summarize them in Table 5.

Mica of igneous and metamorphic derivation, including especially that fine, shred–like and filamentous sericite seen so abundantly in thin

Table 5. Materials and processes in the genesis of illite

1. Mica (both dioctahedral and trioctahedral) of primary crystallization from the fluid phase of magna,
2. Mica, especially sericite, originating by both deuteric alteration and solid–state transformation in igneous rocks (as muscovite at temperatures below the melt-ing curve of "granite"*),
3. Mica of metamorphism,
4. Partly "degraded, stripped, or open" mica resulting during weathering,
5. Authigenic mica,
6. Diagenetic mica,
   a. Single–stage reconstitution (as during K–fixation),
   b. Multi–stage transformation.

* (Yoder and Eugster, 1955).

sections, may be reduced in size and more or less degraded in crystallinity and composition via the sedimentary rock processes of weathering, transportation, and reposition as argillaceous sediment. It may pause in its course in that temporary stopover, soil. Trioctahedral types in soil are near the source in northeast Scotland (Walker, 1950), and distantly widespread in much of the glacial drift in North America.

Another source of micaceous material which is potentially illite is the hydrous mica resulting from the weathering of feldspar as observed by Sand (1956) and others before him, as noted in the discussion on kaolinite. That much of this mica is probably partly degraded is indicated by a band at the 10 A spacing rather than a sharp peak indicative of primary mica.

Authigenesis of both muscovite and phlogopite has been discussed and endorsed by Yoder and Eugster (muscovite discussion, 1955, p. 274; phlogopite discussion, 1954, p. 182). Some of the examples they cite from the literature were later challenged, especially the semantics of authigenesis, diagenesis, and cation adsorption in discussions by Weaver (1958, 1959). Uncertainty of recognition of authigenic mica (or kaolinite) has been pointed out by Norin (1953), but little doubt expressed as to the development of the crystals *in situ*. Easy synthesis of mica lends support to the almost certain concept that it forms authigenically and would thereby be a process by which illite might originate.

For at least five years, diagenetic illite has been a topic of controversy for at least two reasons: (1) confusion, or lack of agreement, about the definition of diagenesis, and (2) differences in opinion as to whether cation exchange alone in a sediment constitutes diagenesis. I am not going to take a strong position on either side of the arguments for two reasons: (1) at a symposium on diagenesis held by the A.A.P.G. in which I happened to participate, the first conclusion reached was that no rigorous definition of diagenesis that had been proposed was acceptable to most geologists, and that the term "diagenesis" should be abandoned, and (2) most can be learned about the diagenetic process by simply discussing changes undergone by clay minerals during last stages of transportation, deposition, and after deposition, without attempting to tie them to a definition. I will take a firm position later, however, using a field example that illite has been formed from pre–existing montmorillonite within a sedimentary formation of nonmarine origin, and I will cite other evidence of formation of illite called diagenetic.

Before going on to this example I will comment briefly about the place of K–fixation in diagenesis from the viewpoint of many geologists. Although geologists have, for many years, observed that K was sorbed by clay minerals, it was agronomists who really carefully studied the effect. Thus, our geologic literature recorded that the content of Na and K was nearly the same in the average igneous (primitive) rock (3.84 per cent Na_2O and 3.13 per cent K_2O; Clarke and Washington, 1927), but that after weathering of the rocks the resulting average shale contained more than twice as much K_2O (3.24 per cent) as Na_2O (1.30 per cent). The Na goes in solution to the ocean where about 48 times (molar basis) more Na than K is dissolved in the water. Thus, the K is held by the clay (soil) on the land and in the marine clay sediment. The active process of K–fixation was early described by Volk (1934), a soils man. Mortland and Gieseking (1951) observed that K was fixed more completely from a silicate, K_2SiO_3, than from any other K salt; this effect of silica on K–fixation I feel intuitively has important geologic implications meriting much more investigation. The paper of Wear and White (1951) relating K–fixation to crystal structure is important from the viewpoint of crystallography, and Van der Marel's papers (1954, 1955, 1959) discuss comprehensively K–fixation from the soils viewpoint. Many others (too numerous to cite here) have written on K–fixation in soils. Specific fixation of K by vermiculite was reported by Barshad (1954) and later by De Mumbrum (1959). Mortland, Lawton, and Vehara (1957) studied fixation of K by clay minerals and found little change in the X–ray diffraction patterns of vermiculite and illite after fixation or release of "fixed" K; however, those of Wyoming bentonite showed a general decrease in the intensity of (001) and indications of random interstratification.

The preceding documentation and the experiences of many hundreds of farmers that K is fixed by soil leave no doubt that K–fixation occurs. Is this fixation diagenesis? Does it form mica? The answers to these questions are dependent mainly upon semantics, the definitions of diagenesis and mica.

If any change, such as cation exchange, in a mineral is a diagenetic change, then obviously it is diagenesis. Many geologists want to restrict diagenesis to a more fundamental, and relatively more permanent, change in the crystal structure than cation exchange, and under this definition K–fixation would not be diagenesis unless mica is formed.

Is mica formed? Again the viewpoint is divided. If the clay to which the K is fixed represents a degraded, or K–deficient and K–de-

pleted mica, as a degraded illite or degraded vermiculite, and the K–
fixation is merely a restoration or reconstitution of the pre–degraded
mineral, some geochemists would prefer not to place this change in the
category of diagenesis. To satisfy these purists, it must be shown that
the seat of deficiency of charge is located in the tetrahedral layer, that
K is held in the interlayer largely by it, and that the crystal structure is
that of a monoclinic 1M, 2M, $2M_2$, 3T mica. Merely collapsing a mineral
to 10 A in (001) spacing is not deemed sufficient to make the mineral
a mica, or to put the process into diagenesis. I have no particularly
strong or unchangeable feeling about this controversy and do not want
to sell you one side or the other; I merely want to point out the natural
history of what is going on and indicate the artificial categories in
which it does not fit well.

While on the subject of fixation of K, I think we may well recognize
that a somewhat similar problem exists for Mg, and to a less advanced
stage in controversy for Al. Certainly Al is fixed by vermiculite and
montmorillonite (Rich, 1960; Shen and Rich, 1962; and Coleman,
1961).

Examples of diagenesis

The field example of diagenetic illite to which I alluded previously
occurs in the Brushy Basin member, the upper member of the Morrison
formation on the Colorado Plateau (Keller, 1958, 1962). Over hundreds of square miles the Brushy Basin member is composed dominantly
of montmorillonite, the noncollapsible variety (with KOH, as treated
by Weaver, 1958b), derived by alteration of volcanic ash, which is a
network, not a phyllosilicate, structure. Relics of shards and some mica
and feldspar remaining in the clay provide the evidence for the ash.
The montmorillonite weathers on the outcrop to a typical frothy "pop-
corn'" surface. Over most of the Colorado Plateau region the Brushy
Basin is off-white, gray, pink, yellowish–red, red, or purple in color.
Its composition from a typical occurrence is characterized by 3.07 per
cent Fe_2O_3, 0.35 per cent FeO, 4.51 per cent MgO, and 0.39 per cent
K_2O.

At one locality, however (Blue, or Lone Tree, Mesa, 11 miles
north of Uravan, Colorado, and extending several miles in each direction), anomalous illite occurs in the Brushy Basin. Here the Brushy
Basin clays are blue in color instead of pink to red; they yield a 10 A
basal spacing. A typical composition is presented in Table 6 (sample

Table 6. Analysis of mudstones from the Morrison formation

	Sample 55–180	Sample 55–177	Sample 55–223
SiO_2	49.03	56.64	58.40
Al_2O_3	17.93	20.99	24.16
Fe_2O_3	13.11	3.90	3.07
FeO	1.31	0.66	0.35
MgO	2.79	2.95	4.51
CaO	0.39	0.65	0.69
Na_2O	0.10	0.45	0.51
K_2O	7.84	7.11	0.39
TiO_2	1.06	0.61	0.44
P_2O_5	0.37	0.22	0.13
H_2O+	6.00	5.77	7.29
Total	99.93	99.95	99.94

Sample 55–180: Glauconitic mica. Blue Mesa, Uravan, Colorado.

$$(Si_{3.49} Al_{0.51}^{-0.51}) (\underset{2.07}{Al_{0.99} Fe^{3+}_{0.70} Fe^{2+}_{0.08}}^{-0.27} Mg_{0.30}) (K_{0.71} Na_{0.01} Ca_{0.03})^{0.78} O_{10} (OH)_2$$

Sample 55–177: Blue mudstone. Hydrous mica, analcime, chlorite (slight). Blue Mesa.

Sample 55–223: Pink bentonite. Montmorillonite with small amount of quartz and hematite. Near Thompson (Floy), Utah.

Approximate only:

$$(Si_{3.79} Al_{0.21}^{-0.21}) (\underset{2.26}{Al_{1.63} Fe^{3+}_{0.15} Fe^{2+}_{0.04}}^{0.30} Mg_{0.44}) (Ca/2NaK) O_{10}(OH)_2$$

Excess plus charge due to free SiO_2 and to Fe_2O_3.

* This is Table 1 from Keller (1958).

55–177). This clay is an illite (1M polymorph in a green phase), or perhaps in part a mixed–layer illite–montmorillonite. Potassium has been added and incorporated throughout approximately 400 feet of Brushy Basin clay to convert the montmorillonite to a 10 A mica. The source of the potassium is postulated to be solutions from evaporites of the Paradox formation which have risen through salt–cored anticlines in the vicinity.

The blue color is interpreted to arise from resonance between iron atoms (ions) occurring in the clay structure in two states of valence, the 2–valence representatives being separated by not more than 10 ionic radii (Weyl, 1951; Shively and Weyl, 1951). The significant points about the blueness are, first, that it was an anomalous color and therefore drew special attention, the extra work on this clay resulting in the discovery of the 10 A phase, illite; and second, that in the development of a new 10 A phase from montmorillonite the $Fe^{3+}-Fe^{2+}$ iron was left in appropriate reorganized association from which blue arose. Thus, I interpret the change in basal spacing from that of montmorillonite to that of illite to have been accompanied by other intracrystalline arrangement which included the blue–producing $Fe^{2+}-Fe^{3+}$ adjustment. Has this intracrystalline arrangement included also a shift in the site of the change? Presumably it has, but this could not be proved by formula calculation because of impurities (quartz) in the clay which was analyzed.

That the Brushy Basin clay at Blue Mesa was originally montmorillonite and subsequently changed by diagenesis to illite is indicated not only by its stratigraphic equivalence to montmorillonite in the Brushy Basin beds surrounding Blue Mesa, but also by the presence of poorly developed (diffuse diffractogram) montmorillonite in partially altered, coarse, sand–size material washed out of the blue clay. Therefore, I interpret this occurrence to be a valid demonstration of diagenesis of illite from montmorillonite derived from a non-phyllosilicate.

Diagenesis of illite brings foremost to the minds of sedimentary petrologists the formation of illite diagenetically in shales of marine origin. This discussion will move in that direction, but will approach the process by detouring through the diagenesis of glauconite, an iron-rich variety of illite, because evidence of diagenetic glauconite is better substantiated than that of aluminous illite. I intend to review documented work to show, for example, that (1) illite can be diagenetically transformed to glauconitic mica, which is support for Burst's (1958b) concept of diagenetic relationships of micas, to which Hower (1961) has contributed, and (2) that age determinations substantiate the formation of glauconite in sediments during a long interval after deposition of sedimentary rocks. We may then draw a parallel between its origin and that of typical, or aluminous, illite.

That illite has been transformed to glauconitic mica is shown by the occurrence of a green platy matrix and pellets in a zone about 15 feet thick at the top of the Brushy Basin member of the Morrison formation on Blue Mesa near Uravan, Colorado. This is the locality where the illite present was interpreted as having resulted from the diagenetic alteration of montmorillonite. The X–ray diffractogram of the glauconitic mica almost duplicated that of well–ordered glauconite (Burst, 1958a) from the Bonneterre formation, but refractive indices and birefringence of the glauconitic mica were lower than those of the Bonneterre glauconite. Chemical analyses show the change from illite to glauconitic mica was accompanied by an increase of Fe_2O_3 from 3.90 to 13.11 per cent, and FeO from 0.66 to 1.31 per cent. The Al_2O_3 decreased from 20.99 to 17.93 per cent, MgO decreased slightly, and K_2O increased insignificantly from 7.11 to 7.84 per cent (see Table 6).

This alteration process would be represented graphically on Burst's diagram (Burst, 1958b, p. 493) by a horizontal line drawn from illite toward glauconite. I think there is no doubt about this being an example of diagenesis and that the glauconitic mica is but one step (merely lacking addition of more iron) from typical glauconite.

That glauconite is formed extensively in association with, and probably by the intermediary action of, organisms is abundantly documented, as summarized by Burst (1958a). Burst believes glauconitization occurs in two steps: collection of argillaceous material or a phyllosilicate such as biotite, as Galliher reported (in 1935), and ionic fixation and adjustment to environment. Implicit in these conditions is that degraded (crystal structure) material adjusts more readily to fixation of K and Fe than do well–crystallized minerals, and that a local environment of low oxidation potential within a generally strongly oxidizing system is most effective for glauconitization. Burst emphasized the role of organisms (fecal pellets, test fillings, mucous, etc.) in glauconitization, as did Bradley and Grim (1961, p. 221), who stated that glauconite "is not parallel in concept to illite, but carries in addition some organic connotation."

It should be pointed out, however, that the formation of glauconite can be independent of organisms. Galliher (1935) described the transformation of biotite to glauconite, and we have observed in our laboratory at Missouri the replacement by glauconite of rhyolite sand grains in the transitional beds of the Upper Cambrian La Motte–Bonneterre formations (Ojakangas and Keller, 1964). These occurrences, and replacements of volcanic glass, pyroxene, and feldspar cited by Takahashi (1939), are independent of organic work.

Most convincing evidence of diagenesis, and of diagenesis of glauconite continuing in a sedimentary formation during a geologic interval of time, was reported by Hurley, Cormier, Hower, Fairbairn, and Pinson in 1960. They found that measurements of geologic age on glauconite were never definitely higher than expected limits in the time scale, and were 10 to 20 per cent lower than the ages determined on micas associated with dated igneous rocks. Furthermore, the content of K_2O increases, and the percentage of expanded layers is greater in younger glauconites than in older ones. "This," they state (p. 1793), "suggests that the glauconite pellets continue to develop into purer mineral grains over long periods of time, with a decrease from 30 per cent or more of expandable layers in young glauconite to about 10 per cent in glauconite of early Paleozoic age. Almost without exception Lower Paleozoic glauconite was found to contain more than 5 per cent K. . . . If the glauconite undergoes a slow purification with time, in which the expandable layers gradually become well ordered glauconite, up to about 20 per cent of the mineral in lower Paleozoic samples may not be truly authigenic. It is believed that this is the cause of the apparently lower ages in the Paleozoic."

For our purposes of consideration of the formation of glauconite and diagenesis, I consider very highly significant the following points from the work of Hurley, *et al.*: (1) expandable clay is transformed to non-expandable micaceous clay, (2) simultaneously with this crystal transformation, K is fixed, and (3) the process has been continuing over a long time (geologic time). Does not this same mechanism operate to transform expandable clay (montmorillonite) to illite, the aluminous analog of glauconite, as Burst's diagram indicates? I think so, and although evidence of illite, especially that in shales of marine origin, is not so clearly demonstrable and overwhelmingly convincing as it is for glauconite, I will present what I have found available. Along with illite, and in retrospect, chlorite may have passed unnoticed in earlier work in X–ray identification of clay minerals, and some chlorite may have been misidentified as kaolinite. It is therefore reasonable to believe that chlorite is more abundant in mudstones than documentation before the early 1950's would indicate. After discussing possible mechanisms for diagenesis of illite I will survey the evidence for diagenesis of corrensite, one of the chloritic clays.

Diagenesis of illite in shales of marine deposition

The question of whether or not illite is formed diagenetically in marine shales reaches further in significance than merely validating or invalidating the reality of that process. Diagenetic marine illitization, if it does occur, can account for the origin of vast quantities of this micaceous clay mineral. It disposes of an equally large amount of another pre–existing clay mineral; it fixes great amounts of K whose source must be accounted for; it adds a paragraph to the documentation of geologic history; and it enlarges the scope of sedimentary petrology.

Therefore, the question merits a fairly thorough review of the evidence upon which inferences of diagenesis were based.

Evidence of diagenesis of clay minerals (e.g., illite) in marine shales is based obviously on the observed predominance of clay minerals in the shales (or mudstones). Such good evidence of occurrence of clay minerals is not necessarily evidence of their origin, either diagenic, authigenic, or otherwise, because a clay mineral *found here,* does *not necessarily* mean it was *formed* (originated) *here* (Keller, 1956, p. 2690). This fact is well recognized by experienced workers. I find, however, that some students even now, and probably some geologists 5 or 10 years ago, reading about the responses of clay minerals to the conditions under which the clays were formed, assumed casually or naïvely and incorrectly that clay minerals necessarily responded to conditions prevailing where the clays were deposited as they did to conditions under which they were formed. By thus taking otherwise sound statements out of context, unwarranted conclusions were sometimes drawn in respect to the power and effects of diagenetic processes.

To illustrate the disparity that may occur between environments of origin and deposition of clay minerals, take an example of a clay mineral which, after being formed under hypersaline, hot, arid conditions in Death Valley, is then blown via a dust storm to snow and glaciers in Colorado or Wyoming. After mixing with glacial rock–flows, the clay mineral may be deposited in fresh–water, outwash, or river sediments, and is then in an environment and association quite incompatible with that of its origin. Alternatively, it may be deposited in the Gulf of Mexico and build shale quite different from its source rock. Thus, caution must be used in drawing conclusions of genesis or diagenesis from clay mineral sediments.

Observations that have been interpreted as evidence of diagenesis are best considered in two categories: (1) from ancient sediments in which the record and reactions might be a product of geologic time, and (2) from recent sediments in which diagenetic reactions might be observed. Studies of clay minerals in ancient rocks were reviewed by Grim (1953), who noted that illite dominated the clays in ancient sediments and that kaolinite was scantily present, particularly in the older ones. Grim suggested that illite may have been formed at the expense of other clay minerals. Weaver (1959) reviewed the pertinent literature (14 papers) and added observations of his own to conclude that (1959, p. 154) "illite is the dominant clay mineral of the pre–Upper Mississippian sediments. Post–Lower Mississippian clay suites are more

variable in composition; illite becomes less abundant and montmorillonite and kaolinite more abundant." Weaver favors the same type of
origin for all Paleozoic illite, but that of the post–Lower Mississippian,
he states, "is best related to a change in regional tectonics." In Pennsylvanian–age rocks, the clay mineral varieties are diverse: kaolinite,
chlorite, montmorillonite, mixed–layer illite–montmorillonite, and illite,
paralleling the diverse environments of sedimentation during the Pennsylvanian period. In Mesozoic and Tertiary–age sediments montmorillonite, along with illite, becomes relatively more abundant (as does
evidence of volcanic ash) and kaolinite increases, especially in coal–
bearing rocks and others of continental origin.

To summarize the gross evidence of the ancient rocks on clay minerals, illite persists through sedimentary rocks of all ages and becomes
relatively more abundant in the older ones (pre–Upper Mississippian).
This increase may possibly be due to tectonic and sedimentational conditions favoring the concentration and preservation of illite, as suggested
by Weaver (1959, p. 170), or alternatively, to diagenetic reactions.

In contrast to buried ancient sediments, recent sedimentation affords
the possibility of making direct and immediate observation of the materials and changes (which may be diagenetic) occurring in their distribution. Furthermore, opportunity to use the present to interpret the past
has attracted the attention of numerous investigators, whose documented
work bears on diagenesis. One of the earliest studies was by Grim,
Dietz, and Bradley (1949), who concluded that in the Gulf of California
and off the California coast kaolinite was lost during diagenesis—that
is, altered probably to illite or a chloritic mineral as a product. Montmorillonite occurred widely spread, and (p. 1786) "In general very little
montmorillonite seems to be lost during marine diagenesis." Millot
(1949) published a book relating the distribution of clay minerals to
the environments of their origin–occurrence. Grim and Johns (1954)
observed that in Mississippi River delta sedimentation montmorillonite
being carried in the river water decreases where it comes in contact
with saline water, and there is a commensurate increase in chlorite–
kaolinite and illite. This change might be due to diagenesis. On the
other hand, Murray and Harrison (1956) found no difference in clay
mineralogy between that on a sea knoll and the abyssal plain, and
montmorillonite was identified from the Sigsbee Deep. The crystallinity
of the clay minerals increased below a depth of a few centimeters in
the cores. Powers (1954, 1957) reported that in the James Estuary,
the Patuxent River, and Chesapeake Bay, weathered illite was altered

to "a better illite by K$^+$ fixation," or to a chlorite–like clay "through a mixed–layer illite–vermiculite–chlorite stage." Griffin and Ingram (1955) reported that in the Neuse River Estuary kaolinite became less abundant downstream, whereas chlorite and illite increased relatively. Similarly, Nelson (1960) observed in the Rappahannock River proportionately less kaolinite in the saline zone, but chlorite occurred exclusively and illite showed progressive increase in quality of crystallization in the saline zone. Off the North Carolina coast, however, Murray and Sayyab (1955) found no significant relation between the type of clay mineral and distance from shore or depth of water.

Van Andel and Postma (1954) observed illite to be the dominant clay mineral in the Gulf of Paria. They also noted that kaolinite was distributed fairly uniformly, but montmorillonite was more abundant in the open gulf than in the delta portion (delta and estuarine environment). They suggested that illite and kaolinite are flocculated earlier than montmorillonite when river water carrying them is mixed with saline water, and that this accounts for the observed clay mineral distribution. Pryor and Glass (1961) studied the clay minerals in 9 (or more) formations in the upper Cretaceous and Tertiary–age sediments in the Upper Mississippi embayment and found kaolinite, illite, and montmorillonite in all of them. They interpreted the distribution by concluding that kaolinite was deposited dominantly in the fluviatile environment, that nearly equal amounts of kaolinite, illite, and montmorillonite were deposited in the inner neritic environment, and that montmorillonite was dominant in the outer neritic environment. They attributed segregation of clay minerals in the depositional environments to size sorting of clay particles and floccules.

Milne and Earley (1958) concluded that distributional patterns of clay minerals in the recent sediments in the part of the Gulf of Mexico which they investigated were due primarily to differences in clay minerals traceable to source areas and environments. This left diagenesis out of the picture.

Griffin (1960) comprehensively reviewed the river–borne sediments deposited in the Gulf of Mexico and found the clay mineral types to be distributed in the Gulf in accord with the river sources. A slight increase in the ratio of kaolinite to montmorillonite occurs where the Mississippi and Apalachicola Rivers enter saline water (see Griffin, 1962, published after preparation of this paper).

The foregoing publications have been cited not so much for their own sake as to indicate the observations upon which a case for diagenesis of recent clay minerals has been made. Looking at them objectively, there is presented in them no consistent sequence, or pattern of distribution, of clay minerals going from nonmarine to marine environment, nor an exclusively definitive type of clay mineral in any individual part of the marine environment; that is, no environment of deposition contains a monomineralic mudstone. Weaver (1959, p. 158) is correct in stating that the major reasons offered for inferring alterations in certain recent clay minerals "cannot be considered as proving exclusively any of the alterations suggested." Indeed, Weaver's (1959) paper treats more fully, and with better documentation than has this review, the weaknesses of arguments for quick–acting diagenesis of clay minerals in recent sediments, and if I were not going to add support in another way to the concept of a long–time diagenetic reaction I would not be repeating this documentation because I cannot improve upon Weaver's excellent report.

Processes and agents other than diagenesis that could possibly effect fractionation and segregation of clay, hitherto interpreted as diagenetic changes of one clay (Weaver, 1959), are as follows: sorting of clay minerals according to size of particles by the effect of streams, waves, and longshore currents (the last emphasized by Griffin, 1960); variable and differential contribution of clay minerals by multiple streams entering a depositional basin; variable and differential contribution of clay minerals by tributaries to a single large stream, as montmorillonite from the Missouri River and illite from the Ohio to the Mississippi River; low–water and high–water stages on rivers, and nonuniform flooding from different portions of the drainage basins; and fractionation of clay minerals by nonuniform flocculation where fresh–water streams deliver clays to the ocean. In other words, clay minerals separated in type might be interpreted incorrectly as representing changed clay minerals. Flocculation of colloids yields results observable in sediments through the parameter of size, and transportation–settling effects due to sizes of floccules entirely independent of the original colloids (Keller, 1936). Settling is relatively simple, *per se,* but under real marine conditions it is complex (Whitehouse and Jeffrey, 1955). That clay minerals mixed artificially can be separated from one another in suspension under special laboratory conditions was demonstrated by Beavers (1950) and Beavers and Marshall (1951). They first studied the cataphoresis of clay minerals in the presence of polyvalent chlorides ($LaCl_3$, $ThCl_4$, and six–valent "hexol," $Co[(OH)^2 Co(NH_3)_4]_3Cl_6$). Relative amounts of these flocculating chlorides in a solution which induces first visible coagulation were, relatively, 1 for kaolinite, 4 to 10 for illite, and 10 to 35 for montmorillonite. The charges on kaolinite, halloysite, illite, Putnam soil colloid (beidellite), and quartz were reversed (negative to positive) by treatment with hexol, but trivalent $LaCl_3$ reversed the charge on only kaolinite and quartz. Curiously, starch (such as potato starch) coagulates montmorillonite although the mixture remains negative in charge. "This action," according to Beavers and Marshall (1951), "is not well understood. It may be a property of a particular fraction of the starch." Whitehouse, Jeffrey, and Delbrecht (1960, p. 73) report that "Complex carbohydrates, in general, increase the settling rates of montmorillonitic clay minerals and phosphoproteins tend to decrease the settling rates of kaolinitic minerals." It appears to me that the possible effect on the coagulation, or, alternatively, on the prolonged dispersion, of clay minerals by various organic substances occurring in environments of transportation and deposition of sediments is a fertile field for further investigations. Long–recognized factors affecting the sensitivity of clay colloids to flocculation include the size of colloidal particles, charge on the particles, concentration of the sol, charge and concentration of the electrolyte, presence of a protective colloid (organic), presence of a flocculating organic substance (such as starch), and perhaps turbulence of the suspension (Keller, 1936). At any rate, selective or preferential flocculation of clay minerals in the laboratory supports a hypothesis of similar effect in the field.

The suggestion of Van Andel and Postma (1954), attributed to Whitehouse (1951/52), that higher sensitivity of kaolinite and illite than of montmorillonite to flocculation when transported by river water into the ocean might explain the distribution of clay minerals in the Gulf of Paria has support from laboratory and theoretical work, and opposes the idea that kaolinite alters to illite farther from shore. Also the sequence kaolinite, then mixed types of clay minerals, and finally dominant montmorillonite, moving outward from shore in the Mississippi Embayment, as reported by Pryor and Glass (1961), accords directly with the flocculation sequence observed by Beavers and Marshall (1951). It seems probable to me that kaolinite–montmorillonite sequences in other recent and ancient sediments may have originated similarly by differential flocculation.

The preceding possible methods, alternatives to diagenesis, by which changes may occur in clay mineral occurrences do not negate quick diagenesis as a factor. We must be careful not to swing the pendulum so far as to lose open mindedness. The sorption by degraded 3–layer minerals of K to form reconstituted illite, and of Mg to form chlorite, or chlorite–like minerals, is well documented. Perhaps this process of reconstitution should not be called diagenesis, or alternatively beyond quick cation exchange it is a halfway step to diagenesis.

We have now reviewed a rather considerable number of observations and diverse groups of interpretations (with alternative interpretations of them) which appear to leave the issue in a beautifully diffuse state of confusion. With respect to recent clay minerals in a marine environment, a good case has been made for cation exchange and reconstitution of illite and chlorite from degraded 3–layer minerals. However, mineral segregation due to variations in source and to size sorting of particles and floccules is more probable than diagenesis in accounting for most of the observed mineral distribution that has been interpreted as mineral change. As to the origin of ancient aluminous illites of marine deposition, although I think that diagenesis is not proved unequivocally, the dominance of illite in the older Paleozoic shales is so pronounced that many experienced geologists lean toward diagenesis as being their most probable origin and will look for further evidence and a possible mechanism by which they can originate.

Even Weaver, who has argued strongly and soundly against the diagenetic origin of clay minerals, and who suggested that illite in the pre–Upper Mississippian shales is compatible with the probably non-diagenetic illite in associated carbonate rocks (Weaver, 1959, p. 170), wrote in 1961, regarding clay minerals in the Late Cretaceous rocks of the Washakie Basin of Wyoming (Weaver, 1961), "Montmorillonite, when buried to depths of several thousand feet, starts to be converted to a mixed–layer illite–montmorillonite as a portion of the montmorillonite layers contract to form illite–like layers. At a depth of approximately 10,000 feet no discrete montmorillonite remains (Burst, 1959; Powers, 1959; Weaver, 1959, 1960). This can be seen in the Lewis of the Washakie Basin." Whether or not it is illitization, this change is diagenesis.

Burst (1959) studied the clay mineral relationships in the subsurface of the Wilcox (Eocene) formation which extends continuously from outcrop in southern Illinois and Missouri to a depth in excess of 13,000 feet in Louisiana, and found "progressive diagenetic conversions with depth. Montmorillonite, a common constituent of Wilcox outcrop material, becomes less evident below 3000 ft. and is not normally found in an unmixed state below the 9000–10,000 ft. overburden level. At depths between 3000 and 14,000 ft., montmorillonite lattices are commonly interspersed with illite components, the frequency of which increases with depth to a virtual elimination of montmorillonite swelling characteristics below 14,000 ft."

Powers (1959, p. 318) observed "from several deep wells in Gulf Coast Tertiary sediments . . . [that] clay minerals in the shallow sediments at depths of burial less than about 5000 ft. consist predominantly of montmorillonite with only small amounts of illite, chlorite, and mixed-layer clay. . . . With increasing depth there is a slight increase in the amount of 10 A illite and a pronounced increase in mixed–layer illite. There is no discrete 17 A montmorillonite below 9000–12,000 ft. The mixed–layer illite occurs principally with montmorillonite, but vermiculite and chlorite are also observed in mixed–layer form with illite. Probably all the kaolinite and montmorillonite and most of the 10 A illite have a detrital origin, whereas the remaining clays are diagenetic, forming either in the depositional environment or post depositionally."

Of paramount interest to the present inquiry into diagenesis of illite (the ferriferous variety as glauconite) is a paper by Hurley, Cormier, Hower, Fairbairn, and Pinson (1960) on the reliability of glauconite for age measurement by K–Ar and Rb–Sr methods. They concluded from this entirely different and independent approach that glauconite was being formed in sediments during geological time (since the Lower Paleozoic)—a straightforward criterion of diagenesis—and that K was being incorporated, timewise, into the crystals of glauconite. A pertinent paragraph of the paper (Hurley, *et al.*, 1960, p. 1793) is cited:

Glauconites have interlayered structures. The interlayering involves mainly non-expandable 10 A layers and expandable (montmorillonitic) layers. The potassium content of glauconites is inversely proportional to the per cent expandable layers. Furthermore, the percentage of expandable layers is greater in younger glauconites than in older. This suggests that the glauconite pellets continue to develop into purer mineral grains over long periods of time, with a decrease from 30 per cent or more of expandable layers in young glauconite to about 10 per cent in glauconite of early Paleozoic age. Almost without exception Lower Paleozoic glauconite was found to contain more than 5 per cent potassium.

The significant observation in regard to the present problem is that the formation (crystallization) of glauconite and incorporation of K was time dependent over a long period of time. Burst (1959, p. 328), however, in his paper on diagenetic conversion of montmorillonite to illite in the Wilcox formation, believed that "Geologic age, however, does not seem to be the controlling feature in the reduction of clay swelling capacity. . . . This paper shows that anomalies of this type may

be related to differences in burial depth and geothermal gradient." I
wish to suggest that all of the factors such as time, burial depth, and
geothermal gradient contribute significantly to the diagenetic formation
of a 10 A clay mineral.

Mechanism of clay mineral collapse to 10 A and incorporation of potassium

Observations have gone unchallenged that 3–layer clay minerals
transported from fresh–water rivers to the ocean sorb the common
metal cations, including K, and that part, if not all, of the montmorillonite collapses upon deep burial to a 10 A mineral that is presumably

*Table 7. Modified from table 3 of Carroll and Starkey (1960),
"Exchangeable* Ca^{2+}, Mg^{2+}, *and* Na^+, *total cation exchange capacity and per cent of exchange capacity completed with cations other than* H^+ *of the experimental clay minerals under various conditions in sea water"*

Mineral	Exchangeable cations meq./100 g.					CEC determ'd	Percentage Exchange Positions Filled
	Ca^{2+}	Mg^{2+}	Na^+	K^+	Sum		
Montmorillonite							
Natural	11	15	54	—	80	89	90
Sea–Water 150 days	8	32	21	—	61	76	80
Mixed–layer							
Natural	26	7	—	—	33	33	100
Sea–Water 150 days	5	7	5	—	17	28	61
Illite							
Natural	17	3	—	—	20	20	100
Sea–Water 150 days	8	8	—	—	16	28	57
Halloysite							
Natural	1.8	1.7	0.6	—	4.1	11	37
Sea–Water 10 days	4.1	5.4	0.6	—	10.1	31	32
Kaolinite							
Natural	0.5	0.4	—	—	0.9	5	18
Sea–Water 10 days	1.4	1.7	—	—	3.1	16	19

illite (but not proved conclusively). Sorbed Mg may promote the formation of chlorite, or chlorite–like mineral. The mechanism of these reactions will next be considered by following the observations in the laboratory of responses of clay minerals treated with sea water.

Powers (1959) measured the uptake of elements from sea water during 1.5 hours treatment by Georgia kaolinite, Polkville (Miss.) bentonite, Patuxent River clay, and Chesapeake Bay clay, and found that Na^+, Mg^{2+}, and K^+ were taken up in that order. The amounts of uptake of the three elements relative to each other showed no variation in those clays.

Carroll and Starkey (1960) immersed montmorillonite (Osage, Wyo.), mixed–layer illite–montmorillonite (Highbridge, Ky.), illite (Fithian, Ill.), kaolinite (Bath, N.C.), and halloysite (Tintic, Utah) in sea water for 10 days, and additional samples of the first three for 150 days. They found that Mg^{2+} ions from sea water moved into the exchange positions in the minerals in preference to Ca^{2+} and Na^+ ions. Part of their data are tabulated below in Table 7.

Potts (1959), in a small number of experiments, immersed clays ($<5\mu$) collected from suspension in the Missouri River (Easley, central Missouri) in ocean water 36 and 86 hours. The original river clay contained dominantly montmorillonite (expanding clay) and lesser amounts of 14 A, 10 A, and 7 A clay. Data on the exchangeable cations in the clay before and after treatment as indicated are given in Table 8.

The observations and data of Carroll and Starkey, and of Potts, similar in that treatment of land–derived clay in ocean water, resulted in (1) a marked increase in exchangeable Mg, (2) decrease in total exchangeable ions and exchange capacity in the 3–layer clays, but (3) an increase in exchangeable ions and exchange capacity in the 2–layer

Table 8. Exchangeable cations, Missouri River clay treated in ocean water

Meq in 100g dry clay

Cations	Untreated Clay	36 hr. in ocean water	86 hr. in ocean water	HCl treated*, 86 hr. in ocean water
Ca^{2+}	60.7	38.3	17.3	12.9
Mg^{2+}	20.1	29.7	39.3	36.2
Na^+	1.7	1.8	3.4	3.8
K^+	1.4	1.4	2.0	1.9

* Treated with 5N HCl for 3 min. to remove $CaCO_3$

halloysite and kaolinite. Carroll and Starkey (1960, p. 99) attribute the increased sorption of Mg to the fact that "there is more magnesium than calcium in sea water and, in addition, calcium is tied up in the buffer mechanisms of sea water." Powers (1959, p. 314) noted that "the ratio of Mg^{2+} to K^+ in sea water, in numbers of atoms, is about 5:1, assuming complete ionization."

The exchange and sorption of cations from seawater by river–borne clays may be examined in terms of energies that drive the process in two different ways: (1) energies of the solutions involved, and (2) energies of binding of cations by the clays. Consideration of the solution energies is approached as follows. It is assumed that the clay carried in the rivers is in equilibrium with the ions dissolved in the river water. The James River, of which an analysis is recorded in *Clark's Data of Geochemistry* (Clark, 1924, analysis L, p. 77), will be taken as a typical example of river water carrying clay to the ocean. The composition of the river solution, recalculated in mols per liter is as follows:

Ca^{2+}	0.000506 mols/L
Mg^{2+}	0.0001957 "
Na^+	0.0001113 "
K^+	0.00003438 "

It is assumed that ionization is approximately 100 per cent at these low concentrations, and that these also represent activities.

When clay carried by that solution is poured into the ocean, it comes into equilibrium with ocean water. Molal activities of the free ions in the ocean water may be calculated using the data from Garrels and Thompson (1962), as follows:

Ion	Molality	Per Cent Free Ion	Activities Free Ions	Molal Activity Free Ions
Ca^{2+}	.0104	91	.00264	0.00002498
Mg^{2+}	.0540	78	.0169	0.000794
Na^+	.4752	99	.356	0.1675
K^+	.0100	99	.0036	0.00006237

The solutions may be used as measuring instruments. If one modifies Woodruff's method, they may also be used to study ionic equilibria between soil clay and dilute salt solutions (Woodruff, 1955a, 1955b), to measure the free energy per chemical equivalent that would accompany the transfer of the river solution (ionic activities) to the ion activities in sea water. The following equations are applicable, where "a" refers to the activity of a given ion in the solution.

$$\Delta F = RT \ln \frac{a_{river}}{a_{ocean}}, \text{ or}$$

$$\Delta F = 1364 \ (\log a_{river} - \log a_{ocean}) \ cal.$$

Since the clay minerals are in equilibrium with their suspending solution (a reasonable assumption), there will be zero difference of free energy between clay and solution; and the ΔF for the hypothetical solution transfer will be similar for the clay, i.e., per equivalent of cation exchanged, as follows:

		ΔF	
Ca^{2+}	James River to ocean	891	cal.
Mg^{2+}		−415	
Na^+		−4332	
K^+		−353	

A minus value indicates that the spontaneous change will tend to be in the direction of increase in sorption of that ion from ocean water; a plus value indicates a tendency to decrease the sorption of that ion. Potts found that the clay transferred from river water to sea water for 86 hours exchanged ions percentagewise in relation to those held in river water as follows:

Ca^{2+}	decreased to	34%	of original
Mg^{2+}	increased	195%	" "
Na^+	increased	200%	" "
K^+	increased	140%	" "

This direction and order of change is qualitatively in accord with the solution chemistry; it is another way of expressing what Powers and Carroll and Starkey reported as differences in concentration.

The actual ions held by the clay, and the strength by which they are held, includes also the binding energy of the clay for the several ions. Marshall (1954, pp. 376–77) and students have investigated over 40 different clay–ionic systems, homionic and polyionic, part of which are applicable to the question at hand. Marshall pointed out immediately, however, that "Evidently it is not possible to predict cationic activities in polyionic clays from data obtained only on homionic systems." Instead, Jarusov's rule (Jarusov, 1937) that "the cation with the higher mean free bonding energy preempts those surface positions which manifest greater mean free bonding energy" (Marshall, 1954, p. 383), applies best to polyionic clay systems.

Fortunately some of the work in Marshall's laboratory is applicable to clay such as is carried by the Missouri River. For example, the clay from the Putnam soil, an expanding, beidellitic clay which is presently being eroded by tributary streams of the Missouri River, was studied by McLean (1950) in K–Na systems. In K–Na mixed systems the bonding energy of potassium to Putnam clay is about 30 per cent higher than in single systems, and the reduction of the bonding energy of sodium is even greater (Marshall, 1954, p. 377). On Wyoming benton-ite, the effect of Ca is to reduce the bonding energy of K; thus, in the ocean water where Ca is lower in concentration than in river water, the binding of K will increase. Arizona bentonite showed stronger bonding energy for K than did Wyoming bentonite.

Of highest importance to the question of K sorption and fixation in regard to the problem at hand was the discovery by Barber and Marshall (1951, 1952): (1) that in K–H systems, K–Ca, K–H and Ca, the bond-ing energy for K was higher when present at less than 10 per cent saturation than when present in larger amounts in two illites, Putnam clay, attapulgite, and impure halloysite, (2) that the bonding energy for K appears to rise almost asymptotically for very small fractions of saturation, and (3) that it is indeed quite high (Marshall, 1954, Fig. 10, p. 382).

It is most significant and important that in these polyionic systems as the saturation of the clay becomes lower with potassium, the higher the bonding energy between the two! When this concept is extrapolated to 3–layer clays carried by a river into the ocean it is understandable why K moves into a position of fixation. Marshall wrote of this, although he was not discussing diagenesis, "These are fixation effects" (p. 381).

Powers (1957, 1959) attacked this problem of K sorption and sug-gested that at an increased depth of burial the sorption of K^+ would increase until it equalled that of Mg^{2+}, which he called an "equivalence level." However, as is being proposed in this paper the sorption of K is a function of both availability from solution and also from bonding energy between K and the clay; the fixation of K by a 3–layer clay does not call for a high concentration of K—indeed the opposite is desired —and the relatively low saturation of exchangeable K on clay minerals in the ocean makes for tightest holding and fixation.

Attention has been directed in a preceding paragraph to the de-crease in cation exchange capacity of river–borne montmorillonite and mixed–layer illite–montmorillonite after being treated with ocean water, as observed both by Potts and by Carroll and Starkey. This decrease is interpreted as being due to conversion of easily exchangeable cation sites to fixed cation sites or to some on which tightly bonded ions, such as K, are being held too tightly to be displaced by ordinary cation exchange reactions.

The source of adequate amounts of available K to produce illite from montmorillonite or degraded illite was considered by Powers (1959, p. 322). He found inadequately low the amount of K available on exchange positions and in interstitial water, but analyses of bulk samples of clay yielded more than enough, and he suggested sources in bacteria or ligno–proteins. Can it be that more K resided in tightly bonded positions on the clay than was detected by Powers using ordinary cation exchange reactions?

In summary, the following model is suggested for the reactions undergone by river–borne 3–layer, Ca–rich clays when poured into the ocean. The change in ionic concentrations in solutions pulls Ca from the exchange positions and tends to substitute Na, Mg, and K in that order of abundance. Because of the bonding energies of clays, reacting in the polyionic systems as described by Jarusov's rule, Mg is sorbed in a maximum of exchange positions. The retention of Mg within the clay complex may be enhanced further in the alkaline environment of ocean water because $Mg(OH)_2$ can exist as brucite, a stable, relatively insoluble mineral, whereas $Ca(OH)_2$, NaOH, and KOH are highly soluble at the concentrations in which they are present. Mg may return to the clay minerals to give rise to reconstituted chlorite, and conceivably it could form chlorite anew, or perhaps corrensite. Simultaneously with the incorporation of Mg, an acid–forming reaction occurs which tends to reverse and inhibit Mg fixation, and protons are set free as each Mg^{2+} combines with $2OH^-$ from $2H_2O$.

Although potassium hydroxide cannot precipitate interlayer to the clay sandwiches like $Mg(OH)_2$ does, nevertheless, because K is bonded with notably high energy at low saturation of exchangeable bases, it is available to become fixed and to cause the collapse of the clay to 10 A. That this can and does occur is shown by the development of glauconitic mica at Blue (Lone Tree) Mesa (Keller, 1958), and under deep burial (Burst, 1959; Powers, 1957; Weaver, 1961). One important requirement must be met: there must be present enough K, though apparently not necessarily in high concentration at any one time, as is shown by the continued addition of K to glauconite that has been developing since early Paleozoic time (Hurley, *et al.,* 1960). The development of illite and glauconitic mica was apparently localized at Blue (Lone Tree) Mesa (Keller, 1958) because of the localized source of K coming from evaporite minerals in rising, salt–cored anticlines.

Another requirement, less obvious but possibly equally important, is the presence of appropriate charge suitably located in the lattice. I am not prepared to go further than to speculate as to how this may come about. One possibility is that Mg, which is abundantly available in solution, may move into the octahedral layer and neutralize the charge on that layer, leaving any deficit in charge in the tetrahedral layers to be satisfied by potassium fixed in the interlayer position. Another possibility, suggested previously, is that Mg moves into the octahedral layer substituting for Al which, in turn, moves into the tetrahedral layer displacing Si, and the deficit in charge (double) is neutralized by K. The silica might remain, thereby silicifying the shale, or it might move out in solution, as suggested by Towe (1962).

The purpose of the long preceding discussion was to argue that possible illitization, or formation of mixed–layer illite–montmorillonite at least might be a two–stage process: (1) quick, cation exchange, and (2) longer–time fixation of potassium, aided probably by deep burial and perhaps rising geothermal gradient. However, clay mineral diagenesis is not restricted to illitization. The formation of Mg–rich clays, such as chlorite, vermiculite, and corrensite, by the addition of Mg^{2+} to degraded chlorites, degraded illites, and montmorillonite is another possibility.

Bailey, *et al.* (1962), separated the illite from several cyclothemic shales and clays of Pennsylvanian age into $2M_1$ and 1Md polytypes on a basis of particle size. K–Ar dates showed the $2M_1$ component to be considerably older than Pennsylvanian, indicating it was detrital. The K–Ar age of the 1Md component is less than half the age of Pennsylvanian sedimentation. The low age may be due to preferential Ar loss because of the small particle sizes involved, or to the reorganization and K–fixation in montmorillonite and degraded micas in post–Pennsylvanian time. These occurrences illustrate the derivations summarized in Table 5.

Corrensite

Corrensite was named by Lippman (1954) for a regularly interstratified, 1:1, chlorite—swelling chlorite clay mineral, but later was applied (1956) to a regular interstratification of chlorite–vermiculite. Bradley and Weaver (1956) described a regularly interstratified chlorite–vermiculite mineral from the Brazer limestone (upper Mississippian in age) from Juniper Canyon, Moffat County, Colorado, which they referred to as corrensite. It yielded a regular series of basal spacings extending from a fundamental periodicity of 29 A in untreated clay, to 31 A in clay treated with ethylene glycol, and 23 A when the clay was heated to 550°C. MacEwan, Amil, and Brown (in Brown, 1961, p. 427) recognized the diversity, or "confusion" (as they termed it), in the description of corrensite but commented further on what may be highly significant to the origin, not only of corrensite, but also to other clay minerals allied to the chlorite clan as follows: "If the swelling chlorite contains extra magnesium in the form of brucite layers (possibly imperfect) then there may exist a series of minerals intermediate between Lippmann's original corrensite from Zaisersweiher (and the similar material described by Martín–Vivaldi and MacEwan, 1957) and Bradley and Weaver's 'Corrensite' from Juniper Canyon, and the apparently similar material described by Earley, Brindley, McVeagh and Vanden Heuvel (1956) as a regularly interstratified montmorillonite–chlorite from Ward County, Texas."

Compatible with the possibility of a series of minerals in the chlorite–vermiculite group is the synthesis of chlorite–like minerals from montmorillonite by Slaughter and Milne (1960). Brucite, developed in interlayer position as $Mg(OH)_2$, was precipitated in the clay suspension up to the calculated maximum of 6 $Mg(OH)_2$ per structural unit of clay. Slaughter and Milne also synthesized a chlorite–like mineral containing precipitated $Al(OH)_3$, i.e., an aluminum–chlorite–like mineral.

Grim, Droste, and Bradley (1961) reported a range of mixed–layer clay mineral sequences of the corrensite type from clay partings in the ore beds in a New Mexico evaporite section. Pertinent to the origin of the minerals in the partings, they state: "They clearly represent material that accumulated in, and has remained in, an environment of high Na, K, and Mg activity from Permian time to the present" (p. 228). Furthermore (p. 234),

It seems highly unlikely that so nearly monomineralic detrital chlorite could ever have been introduced into an evaporite environment to serve as parent for these specimens, but intermittent influxes of montmorillonite minerals and similarly constituted degradation products are easily conceived. Such sedimented solid would presumably then be constrained to come to heterogeneous equilibrium with the highly saline basin solution. Under such equilibrium conditions, activity ratios of each pair of ion species in solution demand an activity ratio in any given solid phase that probably has some relation to relative population in the solid. . . . Among the layer silicates it has long been apparent that convenience of fit and arrangement in interlayer space bears on the activities of interlayer ions. The Mg^{2+} "ion" activity is a much smaller fraction of the population of Mg^{2+} in chlorite and a smaller fraction in vermiculite than in montmorillonites. The same is true of the active fraction of K^+ in montmorillonite.

The development of corrensite, i.e., a 1:1 alternation, is explained in terms of the chemical system in which it originates as follows (p. 235):

Observed subaerial alteration of chlorite to vermiculite indicates the relatively more acid (or less basic) character of vermiculite with respect to chlorite.

Heterogeneous equilibrium at moderate pH in the liquid phase apparently requires the presence of both chlorite and vermiculite in the solid. In view of the success of the important Pauling principle that a complex solid structure tends to become electrostatically neutral in the smallest practical volume, it seems only natural that its extension to neutrality in the acid-base sense is equally valid. For the articulated layer structures, best economy of space is achieved by regularly alternating intergrowth of the two species of layers.

Peterson investigated the mineralogy and petrology of upper Mississippian carbonate rocks of the Cumberland Plateau in Tennessee (Peterson, 1962) (a paper to be highly recommended) and found corrensite in association with both calcite and dolomite, and chlorite–vermiculite and montmorillonite containing mixed 10 A layers in association with calcite. Mixed–layer ordering, like that found in corrensite, occurs only in chlorite–vermiculite mixtures that have a composition near a 1:1 ratio of chloritic to vermiculitic layers (Peterson, 1961). The mineral assemblages of the rocks, with only minor exception, obey the Gibbs Phase Rule within the choice of chemical components that was made. The six–component system chosen was MgO–CaO–Al_2O_3, which could be plotted on a tenary diagram, plus CO_2 and H_2O being perfectly mobile and SiO_2 in excess.

Peterson has written with notable perception of the geochemical problems (and their probable solutions) of the genesis and diagenesis of argillaceous dolomite. Particularly significant are the following quotations:

Electronmicrographs of well-ordered corrensite show that it is crystallized in flat plates that have distinct crystal outlines, some of which suggest the pseudohexagonal outline common to macroscopic crystals of micaceous minerals. In addition, corrensite is a mineral that is not found in sediment loads of modern streams. This fact alone suggests that it was formed either in the depositional environment or during diagenesis. . . . Diagenetic chemical reactions take place in response to a trend toward chemical equilibrium, not away from it. Evidence has been presented (Pray, 1960) demonstrating that the interstitial solutions are not extensively extended from carbonate sediments by composition, thus allowing the bulk chemical composition of the sediments to remain essentially unchanged and also representative of its depositional environment (Peterson, 1962, p. 28). . . .

. . . the compositional variations of the complex chloritic minerals are the result of adjustment to the original bulk chemical composition of the sediment, including the solutions trapped in the pores of the sediment. These mineral assemblages may be the true equilibrium products or they may be metastable assemblages resulting from a temporary adjustment to the conditions necessary to nucleate dolomite either in the depositional environment or very shortly after deposition (1962, p. 30).

In relation to diagenesis, Peterson wrote (1961, p. 1265):

The demonstration that minerals have formed or altered during deposition, or that they have been in some form of reactive equilibrium, does not prove that the rock in which they are found constitutes an equilibrium assemblage. Such a demonstration, however, does illustrate the importance of chemical processes in producing the properties of the carbonate rocks, and of the minerals forming them, even those minerals regarded traditionally as detrital. . . . It is clear that diagenetic readjustment of sedimentary mineral constituents does take place, and can be thought of as the very beginning of metamorphism.

Incorporation of Mg diagenetically, or authigenetically, in a phyllosilicate under probably higher energy conditions than those which produce vermiculite–chlorite is demonstrated by the formation of talc (not detrital) in evaporites, as was observed by Stewart (1949). These occurrences offer, it seems to me, indubitable evidence of diagenetic Mg phyllosilicates.

As I see it, the key to the formation of diagenetic illite, glauconite, chlorite–corrensite–vermiculite, and talc is an adequate chemical energy (activity) of K^+, Fe^{2+} and Fe^{3+}, and Mg^{2+}, respectively, accompanied by adequately large amounts of those elements. The energy probably derives from both the ionic activity in the solutions surrounding the colloidal solid clay phase and the binding energy of the clay solid. These energies must exceed the activation energy necessary to mobilize and transfer ions within the clay lattice. These energies may be aided by thermal energy and mechanical energy (higher pressure), but as the last two are increased the environment and process grades into what geologists call metamorphism. On the other hand, if we geologists would call all processes of mineral change metamorphism and subdivide it into katamorphism and anamorphism, following Van Hise (1904), I think we would view them more broadly, and as natural history rather than as areas circumscribed by conflicting artificial boundaries.

To effect diagenetic transformations in the second stage in the basic lattice structures of phyllosilicates requires mobility and transfer of ions and charge distribution by processes not now entirely understood, or at least not understood by me. Nevertheless, I see enough straws in the wind to make me think such changes are possible, not solely in phyllosilicates, but in mineral structures in general, including the meso-silicate, olivine, and in the transition of mixed–layer proto–dolomite to dolomite. Peterson (1962) found diagenetic upgrading in the ordering, i.e., geometric morphology, and chemical purity in dolomite concurrently accompanying the diagenesis of corrensite in the carbonate rocks of Tennessee. As a model of the type of changes that occur in the solid state of minerals, and which may be analogously comparable to dia-genetic processes in clay minerals, I cite the following conclusions of Gay and Le Maitre (1961) with reference to olivine altering to idding-site: " 'Iddingsitization' is a continuous transformation in the solid state during which the original olivine crystal may pass through various stages of structural and chemical change; it may be possible at any stage to recognize embryonic structural arrangements, some of which ap-proximate to normal ordered mineral structures, but the altered olivine is at all times a disordered, irregular arrangement which cannot be described as a simple sub-microscopic mineral intergrowth."

I would like to suggest that diagenesis, i.e., diagenetic changes, oc-curs in clay minerals most likely by conversion of certain layers, prob-ably usually randomly situated, for which activation energy for con-version is lowest. Random mixed–layering would then represent reac-tion rate change, or, less frequently, equilibrium conditions in both diagenesis and weathering.

Next, I want to generalize on the process of diagenesis in an effort to categorize it, if not to define it. First, I suggest that geologists have brought trouble on themselves by trying to define diagenesis in terms of geologic environment instead of geochemical environment or process, and by trying to set it up with arbitrary, artificial boundaries instead of a stage in the petrologic, or rock, cycle.

Can we identify diagenesis as follows: the chemical process operating in sedimentology by which cations dominantly other than H^+, and a few oxide groups, are introduced and incorporated into the sediment?

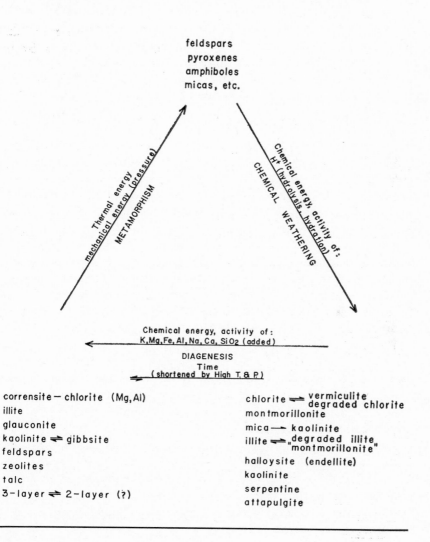

Figure 1.

I have in mind the addition and incorporation of K as in glauconite, Mg as in corrensite, V as in vanadium–rich micaceous clays, Na and Ca as in zeolites and feldspars, SiO_2 as in kaolinization of bauxite, silicification of shales, and various other silicifications. Chemical weathering, in contrast to diagenesis, may be characterized by the addition and incorporation dominantly of H into the given rock or mineral.

Insofar as the preceding generalization is useful, we may relate the processes of weathering, diagenesis, and metamorphosis by the dominant energy drive in the preceding diagram (Fig. 1) of a sedimentary–metamorphic subcycle.

Diagenesis of clay minerals by silication

Diagenesis of clay minerals also includes silication of clay. Two examples of diagenesis of clay minerals by addition of silica may be cited. The high alumina minerals of bauxite were found by Harrison (1934) in British Guiana, and by Gordon, Tracey, and Ellis (1958) in Arkansas, to be resilicated by combination with silica in solution, thereby forming kaolinite. The reaction and evidence for it appear to be straightforward.

More elusive, but now thought to be proved, is the silication of 3–layer clay minerals by condensation of colloidal silica with clay colloids (Keller, 1957, p. 79). It was envisaged that degraded clays, partially disrupted and degenerated clay lattices, "silicate wreckage," and "amorphous gels," characterized by dominating surface properties (as described by Bradley and Grim, 1961, for illite), might encounter small flocs of colloidal silica and condense, via bridging oxygens of silica tetrahedra, the silica and silicate (clay mineral) at least temporarily. Such condensation might occur readily on the floor of a depositional basin (especially where silica was released by hydrolyzing silicate minerals or volcanic ash), or in a sinking floccule from suspension. Even though the condensation was transitory in nature, if covering sediments quickly buried it, the silica and clay might be so closely associated that a "siliceous shale" would result.

Proof, or at least support, of the reaction just described was reported by Bisque (1962). Certain dolomitic carbonate rocks containing disseminated illitic clay were shown to be susceptible to a type of "silicification" whereby the clay particles are polymerized into a 3–dimensional network by the introduction of silicon from an outside source. Bisque and Lemish (1959, p. 41) described the silicification process as "the 'tying together,' or polymerization of clay particles" by hydrated silica tetrahedra. Siliceous shales in which excess silica determined chemically is not resolvable microscopically or separable mechanically from the clay may be formed in this way. It is theoretically possible that some siliceous illitic shales might have been montmorillonites originally from which silica was expelled as Al substituted for Si in the tetrahedral layer (Towe, 1962).

The weathering, katamorphism, and anamorphism of clay minerals

Clay mineralogists and petrologists are concerned not only with processes by which clay minerals originate from a nonclay mineral parent material, but also with the alteration of one clay mineral to another, or complete destruction by weathering of some clay minerals and the building up of other clay minerals (anamorphism).

Discussion of the weathering of clay minerals may begin with illite; this means it may begin with biotite and muscovite because they can be constituents of illite. Biotite may alter to chlorite, hydrobiotite, or vermiculite, depending upon conditions of alteration. Petrologists have observed in thin sections for many years the alteration of biotite to chlorite—with some observers being uncertain whether the alteration was deuteric or was caused by weathering. Stephen (1952), however, reported on weathering of pegmatitic biotite in the Malvern Hills as follows: "It appears therefore that on weathering the biotite breaks down into a polycrystalline aggregate of a chloritic material." Rolfe and Jeffries (1952) wrote that "Mica weathering is essentially a process of potassium depletion. Vadose water actively enters into hydrolytic interplay with the interface K^+ of the mica lattice." Mortland, Lawton, and Vehara (1956) showed that biotite could be altered to vermiculite by the action of plants. Bassett (1959) described the alteration of biotite at Libby, Montana, by supergene waters, by which K was removed in part and Ca and Mg added to yield hydrobiotite. By continued and further similar reaction, hydrobiotite was transformed to vermiculite, but no chlorite was observed by Bassett at Libby. In ion exchange experiments at room temperature, Bassett, using .001M Ca and Mg solutions, changed biotite to vermiculite, provided the concentration of K did not exceed .04M (even at 100°C.). Oxidation of ferrous iron and conversion of the ferric ion in the silicate structure to ferric oxide which, because of its low solubility in oxidizing supergene waters, is essentially nonreactive and therefore out of the chemical system, also takes place concurrently with the depletion and removal of interlayer K.

When K is removed from muscovite, and replaced by H^+, or H_3O^+, the lattice expands in the c–axis direction yielding minerals that expand, as does montmorillonite, but collapse upon treatment with K or Mg considerably more than does montmorillonite derived from framework structure material, and muscovite may yield a dioctahedral vermiculite having a basal spacing of about 14.5–14.7 A (Rich, 1958). Numerous investigators have documented the formation of such an expandable mineral (degraded, or "open" illite), as in a report by Murray and Leininger (1956) on the weathering of clay minerals in a residual soil and on tills of Illinoian and Wisconsin ages, and in another excellent paper by Droste (1956), who traced the weathering of both illite and chlorite to mixed layer montmorillonite—illite and vermiculite, respectively.

Stephen (1952) interprets the weathering of chlorite to vermiculite when reacting at pH less than 5 by H^+ moving in, as Mg^+ moves out, and combining with OH^- to form H_2O. In this way, the brucite layer in chlorite is changed to a layer of hydrated Mg. The mobility and solubility of Mg in silicates are likewise greatly increased as the partial pressure of CO_2 in the system increases (Keller, Balgord, and Reesman, 1962).

First stages in the weathering of micas are typically characterized chemically by removal of K and Mg by dissolution and Fe by oxidation, and structurally by loosening and expanding of the crystal lattice to form expanding illite–montmorillonite and vermiculite (Rich, 1958). The next reaction is typically desilication, whereby a member of the kaolin group of minerals is formed. The statement just made, i.e., "the reaction is typically desilication," should be taken with some reservation, especially with respect to the environment of acid soil where dissolution or at least mobilization of Al (i.e., "dealumination") occurs.

Al has long been considered relatively insoluble and relatively immobile by geologists in numerous geologic situations, and for sound reasons, because it(Al) stays there. On the other hand, there are other occurrences in geologic systems where Al is found to be highly mobile. How can this contradiction be resolved? There may be several answers, but I want to suggest one or two possibilities.

(1) At high pH, say 9.5 and up, Al solubility is highly increased, and if solutions do not become too concentrated the Al may be transported in solution.

(2) On the lower side of the pH scale, say about 4 to 4.5, Al becomes relatively soluble and mobile. It would like to go away, but if any clay is in its path it is preferentially sorbed by the clay because of the very high binding cation exchange energy that clay has for Al. Thus, the solubility of Al is overridden by immobility due to cation exchange, and we commonly say incorrectly that the Al is insoluble. This is analogous to K fixation; highly soluble K is sorbed by clay, and if we geologists relied solely on the relative amounts of K and Na in the ocean, we would say K was much less soluble than Na in geologic environments.

Aluminum in exchange sites may hydrolyze, however, and produce gibbsite–like substances and "be transported through weathering zones only as complex ions or perhaps as protected sols" (Coleman, 1961). This means of transportation may be that by which, in the first part of this paper, Al was shown to move. We know less about dealumination than about desilication of rocks and clay minerals.

Desilication of clay minerals

In the examples of kaolinization in the preceding section, the parent rocks immediately involved were igneous in origin, but another type in which rocks of only immediate sedimentary origin are involved is also important, both geologically and economically. I refer to a group of blanket type sedimentary clays, particularly those which contain flint clay, or a flint–clay facies, and which typically are exploited as fire clay. Examples of such rocks are the Cheltenham clays of Missouri (McQueen, 1943; Keller, 1952; Keller, Westcott, and Bledsoe, 1954), the Mercer clay of Pennsylvania (Bolger and Weitz, 1952), the Olive Hill clays of Kentucky (Patterson and Hosterman, 1960; Hosterman and Patterson, 1961), parts of the Dakota formation (Waage, 1955), and some underclays and seat rocks (Huddle and Patterson, 1961).

Because I am most familiar with the Missouri deposits, I will review for you my interpretation of their origin. Since the same general leaching mechanism that I will describe was thought by Bolger, Hosterman, Huddle, Patterson, and Weitz to have operated in the formation of the deposits they investigated, the generalities are applicable to all the occurrences, but certain specific reactions and details that I propose may not be applicable to all the deposits or acceptable to those investigators.

The Cheltenham clays of Missouri contain in part, to dominantly, kaolinite (*b*–axis disordered) mixed with a relatively high content of low–K illite in the deposits of the plastic to semiplastic clays in the northern part of the fire clay district, well–ordered kaolinite in flint clay across the district, and a relatively high content of diaspore or boehmite in some of the deposits in the southern part of the fire clay district. The clays were formed in karst–type topography developed on limestones and dolomites of Mississippian and Ordovician ages at a time (pre–early Allegheny) when the region was marshy and low lying. North central Missouri was probably receiving marine shale, but farther south, up-ward on the Ozark structural dome, the land must have been slightly above sea level (McQueen, 1943). The landscape in Cheltenham time may have been somewhat like the Everglades region in Florida today, although of course the flora was radically different.

Limestones that were undergoing erosion and supplying sediment during Cheltenham time contained illite, expandable clay called mont-morillonite in 1952, and a clay that yielded a diffuse 7 A reflection re-ferred to as "kaolinite(?)" by Robbins and Keller (1952; a time when expanding "open" illite, and the possibility of a 7 A reflection from chlorite was not common knowledge among clay mineralogists). Many of the diffraction patterns were weak, indicating possibly imperfect crystallization or the presence of material amorphous to X radiation. It is inferred that these clay minerals, and probably dissolved alumina and silica, were moved by slope wash and shallow, sluggish streams to the marsh region. Vegetation was present, perhaps prolific, as indicated by occasional coal, dark-gray color, and few wood fragments (Keller, 1938) in the clay. It is logical that the vegetation may have grown on higher land at the edges of marshes and that the water moving slowly past the plants was filtered of most coarse particles so that mostly colloidal clay and fine quartz silt and sand entered the marshy basins. The plants no doubt extracted alkali and alkaline metal ions as nutrient ions from the clay, and furnished H ions at their roots by way of car-bonic and humic acids as the vegetable matter decomposed. Silica also may have been extracted in considerable quantity by plants, such as sedges and rushes. Lovering (1959) has shown that desilication of soil and translocation of silica, by action of plants, are important geo-chemical processes, possibly contributing much to bauxitization and laterization, that have been overlooked by geologists. Rainfall has been described as being heavy in Cheltenham (Pennsylvanian) paleoclimate.

Under the foregoing conditions, at least three processes of argil-lation are thought to have occurred simultaneously: (1) leaching of Me ions from the 3–layer clays, (2) desilication first of 3–layer and then of

2–layer clays, and (3) crystallization of kaolin clays and boehmite and diaspore from mobilized silica, alumina, and clay colloids. Gibbsite is conspicuously absent; it has never been observed in clays of Cheltenham age in Missouri. That leaching of Me ions (K, Mg, Ca, Na) from illitic parent clay has been extensive is shown by their scantiness in the chemical composition of the fire clay, and refractoriness of the high–illite fire clay. Whereas typical illite is comprised ordinarily of H–K muscovite (a prototype of high–K illite), which contains 9 to 11 per cent total oxides of the Me ions (Grim, 1953) and fuses (in a pyrometric cone) at 1400°C., or less (Searle, 1924), a high–illite Cheltenham clay rarely contains more than 3 per cent total Me oxides, and fuses above 1625°C. Keeling (1961, p. 682) found an inverse relationship between K_2O and combined water in fine fractions of fire clay composed of illite, disordered kaolinite, and well–ordered kaolinite. Thus, depotassication of clays is a common weathering process in soils and sediments (Jackson, *et al.,* 1948, 1952) and in sedimentary rocks (Van Houten, 1953).

To explain the leaching of cations from the clay residue, which was illitic and mixed with other silicate detritus, deposited in these old, low–lying marshes, I break with the geologic tradition of a downward leaching process through sediments, and alternatively propose that upward dialysis, leaching, and flushing off the top of the marshes were equally, or more, effective than downward leaching. In the Cheltenham deposits, usually the more kaolinitic and more refractory clay (i.e., the more highly leached part) occupies the lower part of the clay seam, whereas in soils and various geologic deposits known to be leached by downward movement of water the most highly leached zone is at the top. Moreover, if the marshes were low lying near sea level and relatively heavy salt water stood near the level of the water in the marshes, I doubt that fresh water could circulate effectively downward through the relatively impervious colloidal clay lining in the pits, against the weight–pressure gradient of the salt waters. Therefore, I propose that the Me cations, especially K and lesser amounts of Mg, as well as Ca and Na, moved by dialysis out of the illitic material into the water and upward where fresh rainfall flushed off the top of the marsh water and dissolved ions. This leaching occurred over a long time, simultaneously with the filling of the basin with mud.

The energy for dialysis of the clay is that which drives toward the so–called Donnan equilibrium (Bolam, 1932). The mobile and diffusible ions, as I visualize the system, are K from the clay, H from the water and plant–derived acids, and OH from the water. The alumino–

silicate complex is nondiffusible material forming its own semipermeable membrane. K will move from the illite to the water and H from the water will replace it, resulting in the depotassication of the clay, "refining it of impurities (fluxes)" and increasing its refractoriness. Regardless of whether the Me ions were flushed off the top, as I visualize the process, or moved downward through already refined, relatively impervious clay leaving no evidence of their passage, the overall process is one of clay mineral alteration. Iron was taken out as FeS_2.

Apart from fire clay, Missouri or elsewhere, the process of desilication of clay minerals tends to occur under weathering conditions in temperate (and tropical) climates, if for no other reason than at pH 6 to 6.5, which is the pH of many streams and within the range of abrasion pH of kaolin minerals, silica is many times more soluble in fresh water than is alumina. In warmer climates desilication is speeded up with respect to the rate in temperate climate. Mead's (1915) classic study of the formation of bauxite in Arkansas from kaolinite (an explanation accepted by Gordon, Tracey, and Ellis for part of the bauxite) and geochemical data on bauxitization and dissolved loads of streams cited by Clarke (1924) provide adequate evidence and formal documentation of the process.

Combined depotassication and desilication of illite may yield kaolinite —probably the *b*–axis disordered variety, formerly called "fire clay" mineral by Brindley and Robinson (1946, 1947). Desilication of kaolinite, and/or a 3–layer clay mineral, may yield boehmite or diaspore as in the Cheltenham clay of Missouri, or gibbsite in certain other leached argillaceous rocks. Gibbsite is commonly formed under conditions of strong leaching and good drainage, as in soil above the water table. The oxidation potential is high here. The Missouri diaspore and boehmite deposits were formed presumably below water (below the ground water table) and in association with carbon and occasionally pyrite, which is interpreted as being at a lower pH than that typical of laterization and gibbsite formation in soil. It is speculative whether an underwater, low pH environment was responsible for boehmite– diaspore rather than gibbsite, or whether gibbsite was first formed and inverted upon aging (Bridge, 1952, p. 212) to boehmite (regarded as unstable by Kennedy, 1959) or diaspore. Because gibbsite has never been found in Missouri high alumni clay (gibbsite was reported by Allen in 1935, p. 17, but disclaimed later in oral communication to me), and I have not seen anything interpreted as relic structure of gibbsite, I find most appealing the interpretation that boehmite–diaspore formed at the outset in the environment described above, but not as an alteration of gibbsite.

Anamorphism of clay minerals

By the anamorphism of clay minerals I mean the building up of clay minerals from smaller or simpler units such as alumina and silica gels, perhaps also by polymerization of aluminosilicates and recrystallization of tiny clay mineral crystals to larger crystals or books of crystals. Flint clays of Cheltenham age in Missouri are typically so fine grained as to be cryptocrystalline, but in their harder varieties, tiny pockets or clusters, commonly 0.5 to 2 mm. in diameter, or clean white kaolinite platelets, usually in books or vermiform shapes, may be abundantly (perhaps 5 to 10 per cent) scattered through the fine grained clay. Spatial and textural relations indicate without doubt that the platelets are crystallized, or recrystallized, from fine–grained parent clay material.

The more plastic (than flint clay) variety of Cheltenham clay contains *b*–axis disordered kaolinite in fine grains mixed intimately with illite. We suspect that some of this is detrital kaolinite from limestone–derived soil, and that other parts of it originated by combination of dissolved and/or colloidal silica and alumina carried into the depositional basins. Burst (1952) proposed that this plastic fire clay mineral was crystallized from silica and alumina, giving rise to a characteristic space group represented by one of the polymorphs, "position B," of Gruner's (1932) several alternative stackings in dickite. In view of the considerable progress in crystal structure work and information on clay mineral polymorphism during the last 10 years, it is possible that Burst might wish to re-examine the particular space group he proposed, but this does not diminish the logic of his argument that kaolin–type clays originate from the combination of silica and alumina in depositional basins. This type of kaolinite formation in the field has a laboratory counterpart in the synthesis of kaolinite by De Kimpe, *et al.* (1961, 1964), although the yield of kaolinite from their experiments was too low to permit X–ray diffraction to determine the kaolinite polymorph. The chemical environment in the Cheltenham–type marshes of the northern part of the Missouri fire clay district is interpreted to be such that illites were depotassicated and desilicated toward kaolinite (higher in Al than illite), and simultaneously alumina and silica were combined to produce kaolinite; in other words, kaolinite was the equilibrium phase. In the deposits located higher on the geologic structure, apparently boehmite–

diaspore was the chemical phase at or near equilibrium, and in some of the dominantly flint clay deposits it is inferred that well–ordered kaolinite was the most stable phase. The concept of both katamorphism and anamorphism of clay minerals occurring in a given deposit was expressed by Gordon and Tracey (1952, p. 23) in a discussion of the origin of the Arkansas bauxite, as follows: "In some places, bauxite was changed to kaolin; in others kaolin was changed to bauxite. The two processes went on simultaneously," and "whether the end product was bauxite or kaolin was determined by the local physical–chemical environment." Harrison (1934, p. 9) implied the same reactions in his summary: "The process of primary laterization is succeeded by one of resilication, gradually resulting in the vast masses of lateritic earths or argillaceous laterite." Jackson, *et al.* (1948, 1952) show the reversible reaction type of relationship between weathering and sediments.

The reconstitution of undoubtedly vast amounts of illite and chlorite by sorption of K and Mg ions, respectively, is an anamorphic change in clay minerals. The degradation of illite and chlorite by weathering, resulting in a relatively slow loss of K^+ and Mg^{2+} and substitution of them by H^+ or H_3O^+, and expansion of their structure, is the reverse or katamorphic change.

Hydrothermal argillation

Occasional reference has been made in this discussion to clays of hydrothermal origin—e.g., the Cornwall or Cornish kaolin in England, its probable counterpart in central France (at Echassieres), kaolinite at Etzatlán, Mexico, and others. These illustrations barely touch the subject of hydrothermal argillation in connection with the deposition of metallic ores. Rising steam and hot waters which carry dissolved metals such as Au, Ag, Sn, Cu, Zn, Pb, and others, and anions, such as S^{2-}, F^-, Cl^-, SO_4^{2-}, polysulfides, arsenides, and antimonides, driven off from freezing magmas, move upward and outward under pressure through enclosing country rock. Lowering of temperature and reaction with country rock cause deposition of the metals transported. The reaction of these solutions with silicate country rock commonly results in some to extensive argillation. Argillation may occur without necessarily accompanying mineralization, but commonly the two processes are interrelated.

The presence of argillation, usually in an aureole about the ore body, and the intensity of alteration which may be indicated by the volume and type of clay mineral or mica formed, may be used as a guide to ore (Sales and Meyer, 1948, 1950; Lovering, 1949, 1950; Schwartz, 1955, 1956; Bonorino, 1959) either for finding new ore or enlarging reserves of a previous mineral discovery. For this reason, certain economic geologists have studied rock alteration and argillation, and have contributed significantly to the body of knowledge about clay minerals.

The basic physical–chemical principles that apply to argillation are obviously no different for hydrothermal reaction than for weathering, but a few environmental differences that modify the process in degree, but hardly in kind, characterize hydrothermal argillation as follows:

Table 9. Characteristics of hydrothermal argillation

1. Temperature of solutions is relatively high
2. Volatiles (steam and gases) are abundant
3. Water is scarcely fresh; not repeatedly renewed as pure, distilled (rain) water
4. $S^=$, Cl^-, $SO_4^=$, F^-, arsenides and antimonides may exceed CO_2 compounds
5. Metal ions, as of Au, Sn, Ag, Cu, Zn, Pb, etc., may be abundant
6. The system is moderately confined chemically
7. Dissolved products of alteration are carried outward from zone of most intense alteration and imposed on surrounding country rock
8. pH of solutions may change significantly, as from acid to alkaline, due to reaction (hydrolysis) products
9. Alkaline polysulfides may change to acid sulfates by near–surface oxidation
10. Hydrothermal flow may be intermittent or pulsatory, and composition of solutions likewise pulsatory or changing
11. Supergene argillation may be imposed upon hydrothermal alteration

One of the most important features of hydrothermal argillation is the confining nature of the chemical solutions imposed by the rock system which, in turn, is responsible for holding, at least temporarily, within the surrounding rocks the dissolved products of alteration. Because of variations in this aspect of the geochemistry, apparently at different localities, two concepts of hydrothermal alteration expressed as two mechanisms have arisen.

One proposed mechanism is a periodic, wave–like, or multi–stage alteration, by which, for example, chloritization or sericitization may take place, followed by kaolinization, or montmorillonitization, and silicification.

Another suggested mechanism is a continuous (not periodic) process of soaking and alteration in which sequential mineral zoning of phyllosilicate minerals is developed. The mineral zones appear as fronts in chemical attack outward from the veins and fissures. Highest intensity of alteration is nearest the veins—for example, sericite or hydromica, and grading outward through orthoclase, then kaolinite, montmorillonite, and on the outside border possibly carbonate minerals and silica. Chlorite may occur with the kaolinite. The minerals actually formed are a function of the composition of the parent rock (especially whether containing orthoclase, plagioclase, or mica), the content of the solutions (which includes pH), and the temperature prevailing during alteration. Since these may be interdependent and yet vary from occurrence to occurrence, there is no single unchanging sequence applicable to all systems of hydrothermal argillation. Graphic illustrations of argillic alterations outward from the vein show at a glance what has occurred; see, for example, Bonorino (1959), or earlier reports by Sales and Meyer, and Lovering.

Conclusion

May we conclude that clay minerals are formed under conditions that eventually should be defined clearly in physical–chemical terms, i.e., in terms of materials and energy, and that geologic interpretations and predictions of argillation will then be as good as the geologist or pedologist is able to reconstruct the geologic and pedologic conditions in terms of physical chemical parameters.

References cited

Abbott, Agatin T. (1958) Occurrence of gibbsite on the island of Kauai, Hawaiian Islands: *Ec. Geol.*, v. 53, pp. 842-53.

Allen, V. T. (1935) Mineral composition and origin of Missouri flint and diaspore clays: Appendix IV, 58th An. Rpt., Mo. Geol. Surv. and Water Resources, pp. 5-24.

Allen, V. T. (1937) A study of Missouri glauconite: *Am. Min.*, v. 22, pp. 1180-83.

Allen, Victor T. (1952) Petrographic relations in some typical bauxite and diaspore deposits: *Bull. Geol. Soc. Amer.*, v. 63, pp. 649-88.

Bailey, S. W., Hurley, P. M., Fairbairn, H. W., and Pinson, W. H., Jr. (1962) K-Ar dating of sedimentary illite polytypes: *Bull. Geol. Soc. Amer.*, v. 73, pp. 1167-70.

Barber, S. A., and Marshall, C. E. (1951) Ionization of soils and soil colloids: II. Potassium-calcium relationships in montmorillonite group clays and in attapulgite: *Soil Sci.*, v. 72, pp. 373-85.

Barber, S. A., and Marshall, C. E. (1952) Ionization of soil and soil colloids: III. Potassium-calcium relationships in illite, kaolinite, and halloysite: *Soil Sci.,* v. 73, pp. 403-13.

Bardossy, Gy. (1959) The geochemistry of Hungarian bauxites, parts III and IV: *Acta Geologica* (Hungarian Academy, Budapest 62), Tomus VI, Fasc. 1-2, pp. 1-53.

Barshad, I. (1954) Cation exchange in micaceous minerals: I. Replacement of interlayer cations of vermiculite with ammonium and potassium ions: *Soil Sci.,* v. 77, pp. 463-72.

Bassett, W. A. (1959) Origin of the vermiculite deposit at Libby, Montana: *Am. Min.,* v. 44, pp. 282-300.

Bates, T. F. (1960) Rock weathering and clay formation in Hawaii: *Mineral Industries,* Pennsylvania State Univ., v. 29 (No. 8), p. 1.

Bates, T. F. (1962) Halloysite and gibbsite formation in Hawaii: *Clays and Clay Min.,* 9th Conf., Pergamon Press, New York, pp. 315-28.

Beavers, A. H. (1950) The cataphoresis of clay minerals and factors affecting their separation: Ph.D. Thesis, Univ. Mo. Agr. Library, Columbia, Mo.

Beavers, A. H., and Marshall, C. E. (1951) The cataphoresis of clay minerals and factors affecting their separation: *Soil Sci. Soc. Am. Proc.,* v. 15, pp. 142-45.

Bieger, T. (1952) Über Verwitterungsversuche am Albit: Dissertation, Göttingen.

Bisque, R. E. (1962) Clay polymerization in carbonate rocks: in *Clays and Clay Minerals.* Ninth Conf., Pergamon Press, New York, pp. 365-73.

Bisque, R. E., and Lemish, J. (1959) Silicification of carbonate aggregates in concrete: Natl. Acad. Sci.-Natl. Res. Council pub. 725, *Highway Res. Board Bull.* 239, pp. 41-55.

Bolam, T. R. (1932) *The Donnan Equilibrium:* G. Bell and Sons, London.

Bolger, R. C., and Weitz, J. H. (1952) Mineralogy and origin of the Mercer fire clay of North-Central Pennsylvania: *Problems of Clay and Laterite Genesis,* Symposium AIME, pp. 81-94.

Bolz, D. F. (1958) *Colorimetric determination of nonmetals:* Interscience Pub., New York, Chapter 3, p. 47-74.

Bonorino, F. G. (1959) Hydrothermal alteration in the Front Range mineral belt, Colorado: *Bull. Geol. Soc. Amer.,* v. 70, pp. 53-90.

Botinelly, T., and Fischer, R. P. (1959) Mineralogy and geology at the Rifle and Garfield Mines, Garfield County, Colorado: In Geochemistry and mineralogy of the Colorado Plateau uranium ores: *U. S. Geol. Survey,* Prof. Paper 320, pp. 213-30.

Bradley, W. F., and Grim, R. E. (1961) Mica clay minerals: in *X-ray Identification and Crystal Structures of Clay Minerals,* Chap. V, G. Brown, Editor, Min. Soc., London, p. 544.

Bradley, W. F., and Weaver, C. E. (1956) A regularly interstratified chlorite-vermiculite clay mineral: *Am. Min.,* v. 41, pp. 497-504.

Bridge, Josiah (1952) Discussion in *Problems of Clay and Laterite Genesis:* Symposium AIME, pp. 212-14.

Brindley, G. W., and Radoslovich, E. W. (1956) X-ray studies of the alteration of soda feldspar: in *Clays and Clay Minerals,* Natl. Acad. Sci.-Natl. Res. Council, pub. 456, pp. 330-36.

Brindley, G. W., and Robinson, K. (1946) Randomness in kaolin clays: *Trans. Farad. Soc.,* v. 42B, pp. 198-205.

Brindley, G. W., and Robinson, K. (1947) Fireclay: *Trans. Brit. Ceram. Soc.,* v. 46, pp. 49-52.

Burst, J. F. (1952) New clay mineral evidence concerning the diagenesis of some Missouri fire clays: AIME Symposium, *Problems of Clay and Laterite Genesis,* p. 139.

Burst, J. F. (1958a) "Glauconite" pellets: their mineral nature and applications to stratigraphic interpretations: *Bull. Amer. Assn. Petrol. Geol.,* v. 42, pp. 310-27.

Burst, J. F. (1958b) Mineral heterogeneity in "glauconite" pellets: *Am. Min.,* v. 43, pp. 481-97.

Burst, J. F., Jr. (1959) Postdiagenetic clay mineral environmental relationships in the Gulf Coast Eocene: in *Clays and Clay Minerals,* 6th Conf., Pergamon Press, New York, pp. 327-41.

Carlson, A. B., and Banks, C. V. (1952) Spectrophotometric determination of silicon: *Anal. Chem.,* v. 24, p. 472.

Carroll, D., and Starkey, H. C. (1960) Effect of sea-water on clay minerals: in *Clays and Clay Minerals,* 7th Conf., Pergamon Press, New York, pp. 80-101.

Clarke, F. W. (1924) The data of geochemistry: *U.S. Geol. Survey Bull.,* 770.

Clarke, F. W., and Washington, H. S. (1924) The composition of the earth's crust: *U. S. Geol. Survey,* Prof. Paper 127, p. 117.

Cloud, P. E. (1955) Physical limits of glauconite formation: *Bull. Amer. Assn. Petrol. Geol.,* v. 39, pp. 484-94.

Coleman, N. T. (1961) Decomposition of clays and the fate of aluminum: Abst., program, 1961 meeting. *Geol. Soc. Amer.,* p. 30A (see also next article).

Coleman, N. T. (1962) Decomposition of clays and the fate of aluminum: *Econ. Geol.,* v. 57, pp. 1207-18.

Correns, C. W. (1963) Experiments on the decomposition of silicates and discussion of chemical weathering: in *Clays and Clay Minerals,* 10th Conf., Pergamon Press, New York, pp. 443-59.

De Launay, L. A. (1901) Les kaolins de l'Allier: *La Nature,* v. 29, 1446, pp. 161-63.

De Kimpe, C., Gastuche, M. C., and Brindley, S. W. (1961) Ionic coordination in alumino-silicic gels in relation to clay mineral formation: *Am. Min.,* v. 46, pp. 1370-82.

De Kimpe, C., Gastuche, M. C., and Brindley, G. W. (1964) Low temperature synthesis of kaolin minerals: *Am. Min.,* v. 49, pp. 1-16.

De Mumbrum, L. E. (1959) Exchangeable potassium levels in vermiculite and K-depleted micas, and implications relative to potassium levels in soils: *Soil Sci. Soc. Amer. Proc.,* v. 23, pp. 192-94.

De Vore, G. W. (1959) The surface chemistry of feldspars as an influence on their decomposition products: in *Clays and Clay Minerals,* 6th Conf., Pergamon Press, New York, pp. 26-42.

Droste, J. B. (1956) Alteration of clay minerals by weathering in Wisconsin tills: *Bull. Geol. Soc. Amer.,* v. 67, pp. 911-15.

Earley, J. W., Brindley, G. W., McVeagh, W. J., and Vanden Heuvel, R. C. (1956) Montmorillonite-chlorite: *Am. Min.,* v. 41, pp. 258-67.

Fieldes, M. (1955) Clay mineralogy of New Zealand soils, Part II: Allophane and related mineral colloids: *N. Z. Jour. Sci. and Tech.,* v. 37, pp. 336-50.

Foster, M. D. (1956) Correlation of dioctahedral potassium micas on the basis of their charge relations: *U. S. Geol. Survey Bull.,* 1036-D, pp. 57-67.

Foster, M. D. (1959) Chemical study of the mineralized clays, in geochemistry and mineralogy of the Colorado Plateau uranium ores: *U. S. Geol. Survey,* Prof. Paper 320, pp. 121-32.

Foster, M. D. (1962) Interpretation of the composition and a classification of the chlorites: *U. S. Geol. Survey,* Prof. Paper 414-A, p. 33.

Frederickson, A. F., and Cox, J. E. (1954a) "Solubility" of albite in hydrothermal solutions: *Am. Min.,* v. 39, pp. 738-50.

Frederickson, A. F., and Cox, J. E. (1954b) The decomposition products of anorthite attacked by pure water at elevated temperatures and pressure: in *Clays and Clay Minerals,* Natl. Acad. Sci.-Natl. Res. Council, pub. 327, pp. 111-20.

Galliher, E. W. (1935) Geology of glauconite: *Bull. Amer. Assn. Petrol. Geol.,* v. 19, pp. 1569-1601.

Galliher, E. W. (1939) Biotite-glauconite transformation and associated minerals: *Recent Marine Sediments,* ed. P. D. Trask, Amer. Assn. Petrol. Geol., Tulsa, Okla., pp. 513-15.

Garrels, R. M. (1957) Some free energy values from geologic relations: *Am. Min.,* v. 42, pp. 780-92.

Garrels, R. M., and Howard, Peter (1959) Reactions of feldspar and mica with water at low temperature and pressure: in *Clays and Clay Minerals,* 6th Conf., Pergamon Press, New York, pp. 68-89.

Garrels, R. M., and Thompson, M. E. (1962) A chemical model for seawater at 25°C. and one atmosphere total pressure: *Amer. Jour. Sci.,* v. 260, pp. 57-66.

Garrels, R. M., Thompson, M. E., and Siever, R. (1961) Control of carbonate solubility by carbonate complexes: *Amer. Jour. Sci.,* v. 259, pp. 24-45.

Gay, P., and Le Maitre, R. W. (1961) Some observations on iddingsite: *Am. Min.,* v. 46, pp. 49-112.

Gordon, M., Jr., and Tracey, J. I., Jr. (1952) Origin of the Arkansas bauxite deposits: *Problems of Clay and Laterite Genesis,* Symposium AIME, pp. 12-34.

Gordon, M., Jr., Tracey, J. I., Jr., and Ellis, M. W. (1958) Geology of the Arkansas bauxite region: *U. S. Geol. Survey,* Prof. Paper 299.

Griffin, G. M. (1960) Clay mineral facies development in recent surface sediments of the northeastern Gulf of Mexico: Unpublished Ph.D. Thesis, Rice University, Houston, Texas.

Griffin, G. M. (1962) Regional clay-mineral facies—products of weathering intensity and current distribution in the northeastern Gulf of Mexico: *Bull. Geol. Soc. Amer.*, v. 73, pp. 737-68.

Griffin, G. M., and Ingram, R. L. (1955) Clay minerals of the Neuse River Estuary: *Jour. Sed. Petrol.*, v. 25, pp. 194-200.

Grim, R. E. (1953) *Clay Mineralogy:* McGraw-Hill Book Co., New York.

Grim, R. E. (1958) Concept of diagenesis in argillaceous sediments: *Bull. Amer. Assn. Petrol. Geol.*, v. 42, pp. 246-53.

Grim, R. E. (1962) Clay mineralogy: *Science*, v. 135, pp. 890-98.

Grim, R. E., and Bradley, W. F. (1955) Structural implication in diagenesis: *Geolog. Rund.*, Band 43, Heft 2, pp. 469-74.

Grim, R. E., Bray, R. H., and Bradley, W. F. (1937) Mica in argillaceous sediments: *Am. Min.*, v. 22, pp. 813-29.

Grim, R. E., Dietz, R. S., and Bradley, W. F. (1949) Clay mineral composition of some sediments from the Pacific Ocean off the California coast and the Gulf of California: *Bull. Geol. Soc. Amer.*, v. 60, pp. 1785-1808.

Grim, R. E., Droste, J. B., and Bradley, W. F. (1961) A mixed-layer clay mineral associated with an evaporite: in *Clays and Clay Minerals*, 8th Conf., Pergamon Press, New York, pp. 228-35.

Grim, R. E., and Johns, W. D. (1954) Clay mineral investigation of sediments in the Northern Gulf of Mexico: in *Clays and Clay Minerals*, Natl. Acad. Sci.-Natl. Res. Council, pub. 327, pp. 81-103.

Gruner, J. W. (1932) Crystal structure of dickite: *Z. Krist.*, v. 83, pp. 394-404.

Harder, E. C. (1952) Examples of bauxite deposits illustrating variations in origin: *Problems of Clay and Laterite Genesis*, Symposium AIME, p. 244.

Harrison, J. B. (1934) The katamorphism of igneous rocks under humid tropical conditions: British Guiana, *Imp. Bur. Soil Sci.*, Rothamsted Exp. Sta. Harpenden, Pub., St. Albans.

Hathaway, J. C. (1959) Mixed-layer structures in vanadium clays, in geochemistry and mineralogy of the Colorado Plateau uranium ores: *U. S. Geol. Survey*, Prof. Paper 320, pp. 133-38.

Hay, R. L. (1959) Origin and weathering of late Pleistocene ash deposits on St. Vincent, B. W. I.: *Jour. Geol.*, v. 67, pp. 65-88.

Hemley, J. J. (1959) Some mineral equilibria in the system $K_2O - Al_2O_3 - SiO_2 - H_2O$: *Am. Jour. Sci.*, v. 257, pp. 241-70.

Hendricks, S. B., and Ross, C. S. (1941) Chemical composition and genesis of glauconite and celadonite: *Am. Min.*, v. 26, pp. 683-708.

Holmes, R. J. (1950) Reference clay localities—Europe: *Amer. Petrol. Inst.*, Project 49, Amer. Petrol. Inst. New York, Prelim. Rpt. 4, p. 101.

Hosterman, J. W., and Patterson, S. H. (1961) Mineralogy of the Olive Hill clay bed, Kentucky: *U. S. Geol. Survey*, Prof. Paper 424-B, pp. 280-83.

Howe, J. A. (1914) A handbook to the collection of kaolin, China-clay, and

China-stone in the museum of practical geology: *Mus. Pract. Geol.,* London, p. 271.

Howell, J. V. (1957) Glossary of Geology and Related Sciences: *Amer. Geol. Inst.,* under NAS-NRC, Washington, D. C.

Hower, J. (1961) Some factors concerning the nature and origin of glauconite: *Am. Min.,* v. 46, pp. 313-34.

Huddle, J. W., and Patterson, S. H. (1961) Origin of Pennsylvania underclay and related seat rocks: *Bull. Geol. Soc. Amer.,* v. 72, pp. 1643-60.

Hurley, P. M., Cormier, R. F., Hower, J., and Fairbairn, H. W., Jr. (1960) Reliability of glauconite for age measurement by K-Ar and Rb-Sr methods: *Bull. Amer. Assn. Petrol. Geol.,* v. 44, pp. 1793-1808.

Jackson, M. L., Tyler, S. A., Willis, A. L., Bourbeau, G. A. and Pennington, R. P. (1948) Weathering sequence of clay size minerals in soils and sediments: *Jour. Phy. and Colloid. Chem.,* v. 52, pp. 1237-60.

Jackson, M. L., Hseung, Y., Corey, R. B., Evans, E. J., and Vanden Heuvel, R. C. (1952) Weathering sequence of clay size minerals in soils and sediments, II. Chemical weathering of layer silicates: *Soil Sci. Soc. Am. Proc.,* v. 16, pp. 3-6.

Jarusov, S. S. (1937) Mobility of exchangeable cations in the soil: *Soil Sci.,* v. 43, pp. 285-303.

Keeling, P. S. (1961) A new concept of clay minerals; geochemistry of common clay minerals: *Trans. Brit. Ceram. Soc.,* v. 60, pp. 449-75, 678-89.

Keller, W. D. (1936) Clay colloids as a cause of bedding in sedimentary rocks: *Jour. Geol.,* v. 44, pp. 52-59.

Keller, W. D. (1938) Diaspore clay cast of fossil wood in a Missouri diaspore pit: *Am. Min.,* v. 23, pp. 461-63.

Keller, W. D. (1952) Observations on the origin of Missouri high-alumina clays: *Problems of Clay and Laterite Genesis,* Symposium AIME, pp. 115-34.

Keller, W. D. (1956) Clay minerals as influenced by environments of their formation: *Bull. Amer. Assn. Petrol. Geol.,* v. 40, pp. 2689-2710.

Keller, W. D. (1957) *Principles of Chemical Weathering:* Lucas Bros., Pub., Columbia, Mo., p. 111.

Keller, W. D. (1958) Glauconitic mica in the Morrison formation in Colorado: in *Clays and Clay Minerals,* Natl. Acad. Sci.-Natl. Res. Council, pub. 566, pp. 120-28.

Keller, W. D. (1961) Mineral and chemical alluviation in a unique pedologic example: *Jour. Sed. Petrol.,* v. 31, pp. 80-86.

Keller, W. D. (1962) Clay minerals in the Morrison formation on the Colorado Plateau: *U. S. Geol. Survey Bull.* 1150, pp. 1-90.

Keller, W. D. (1963) Hydrothermal kaolinization (endellitization) of volcanic glassy rock: in *Clays and Clay Minerals,* 10th Conf., Pergamon Press, New York, pp. 333-43.

Keller, W. D., Balgord, W. D., and Reesman, A. L. (1963) Dissolved products of artificially pulverized silicate minerals and rocks, Part 1: *Jour. Sed. Petrol.,* v. 33, pp. 191-204.

Keller, W. D., and Frederickson, A. F. (1952) Role of plants and colloidal acids in the mechanism of weathering: *Am. Jour. Sci.,* v. 250, pp. 594-608.

Keller, W. D., Westcott, J. F., and Bledsoe, A. O. (1954) The origin of Missouri fire clays: in *Clays and Clay Minerals,* Natl. Acad. Sci.-Natl. Res. Council, pub. 327, pp. 7-46.

Kennedy, G. C. (1959) Phase relations in the systems $Al_2O_3 - H_2O$ at high temperatures and pressures: *Amer. Jour. Sci.,* v. 257, pp. 563-73.

Kesler, T. L. (1952) Occurrence and exploration of Georgia's kaolin deposits: in *Problems of clay and laterite genesis,* Symposium at the meeting of the Am. Inst. of Mining and Metallurgical Eng., St. Louis, Mo., Feb. 1951.

Knechtel, M. M., and Patterson, S. H. (1962) Bentonite deposits of the northern Black Hills district, Wyoming, Montana, and South Dakota: U.S. Geol. Survey Bull., 1082-M, pp. 893-1030.

Kohler, E. (1903) Die Amberger Erzlagerstatten: K. Bayer. Oberbergamts, Geognost. Jahreschefts, Jahrg., 15(1902), pp. 11-56.

Krauskopf, Konrad (1959) The geochemistry of silica in sediments: *Soc. Econ. Paleo. and Mineral.,* Spec. pub. No. 7, pp. 4-20.

Levinson, A. A. (1955) Studies in the mica group: Polymorphism among illites and hydrous micas: *Am. Min.,* v. 40, pp. 41-49.

Light, M. A. (1952) Evidence of authigenic and detrital glauconite: *Science,* v. 115, pp. 73-75.

Lilley, E. R. (1932) The geology of some kaolins of Western Europe: AIME Tech. pub. 475, pp. 11-13.

Lippman, F. (1954) Corrensite: *Heidelberg. Betr. Min.,* v. 4, pp. 130-34.

Lippman, F. (1956) Clay Minerals of Trias: *Jour. Sed. Petrol.,* v. 26, pp. 125-39.

Logan, W. N. (1919) Kaolin of Indiana: Indiana Dept. of Conservation, pub. 6, p. 131.

Lovering, T. S. (1949) Rock alteration as a guide to ore—East Tintic district, Utah: *Econ. Geol. Mon.,* 1, p. 65.

Lovering, T. S. (1950) The geochemistry of argillic and related types of alteration: *Colo. School Mines Quart.,* v. 45, no. 1B, pp. 231-60.

Lovering, T. S. (1959) Significance of accumulator plants in rock weathering: *Bull. Geol. Soc. Amer.,* v. 70, pp. 781-800.

MacEwan, D. M. C., Amil, A. R., and Brown, G. (1960) Interstratified clay minerals: Chap. XI, in Brown, G. *X-ray Identification and Crystal Structures of Clay Minerals,* Min. Soc., London.

Martin-Vivaldi, J. L., and MacEwan, D. M. C. (1957) Triassic clays: *Clay Min. Bull.,* v. 3, p. 177-83.

Marshall, C. E. (1954) Multifunctional ionization as illustrated by the clay minerals: in *Clays and Clay Minerals,* Natl. Acad. Sci.-Natl. Res. Council, pub. 327, pp. 364-85.

McLean, E. O. (1950) Interrelationships of potassium, sodium, and calcium as shown by their activities in a beidellite clay: *Soil Sci. Soc. Amer. Proc.,* v. 15, pp. 102-6.

McQueen, H. S. (1943) Fire clay districts of east central Missouri: *Mo. Geol. Survey and Water Resour.,* 2nd series, v. 23.

Mead, W. J. (1915) Occurrence and origin of the bauxite deposits of Arkansas: *Jour. Geol.,* v. 10, pp. 28-54.

Millot, G. (1949) Relations entre la constitution et al genese des roches sedimentares argileuses: *Bull. l'Assn. des Ingen. Geol. de l'univ.* Nancy, Tome 11, Parts 2, 3, 4, Nancy, France.

Milne, I. H., and Early, J. W. (1958) Effect of source and environment on clay minerals: *Bull. Amer. Assn. Petrol. Geol.,* v. 42, pp. 328-38.

Mohr, E. C. J., and Van Baren, J. (1954) *Tropical Soils:* Interscience, Publishers, New York.

Morey, G. W., and Chen, W. T. (1955) The action of hot water on some feldspars: *Am. Min.,* v. 40, pp. 996-1000.

Morey, G. W., and Fournier, R. O. (1961) Decomposition of microcline, albite, and nepheline in hot water: *Am. Min.,* v. 46, pp. 668-700.

Mortland, M. M., and Gieseking, J. E. (1951) Influence of the silicate ion on potassium fixation: *Soil Sci.,* v. 71, pp. 381-85.

Mortland, M. M., Lawton, K., and Vehara, G. (1956) Alterations of biotite to vermiculite by plant growth: *Soil Sci.,* v. 82, pp. 477-81.

Mortland, M. M., Lawton, K., and Vehara, G. (1957) Fixation and release of potassium by some clay minerals: *Soil Sci. Soc. Amer. Proc.,* v. 21, pp. 381-84.

Murray, H. H., and Harrison, J. L. (1956) Clay mineral composition of recent sediments from Sigsbee Deep: *Jour. Sed. Petrol.,* v. 26, pp. 363-68.

Murray, H. H., and Leininger, R. K. (1956) Effect of weathering on clay minerals: in *Clays and Clay Minerals,* Natl. Acad. Sci.-Natl. Res. Council, pub. 456, pp. 340-47.

Murray, H. H., and Sayyab, A. S. (1955) Clay mineral studies of some recent marine sediments off the North Carolina coast: *Clays and Clay Minerals,* Natl. Acad. Sci.-Natl. Res. Council, pub. 395, pp. 430-41.

Nash, V. E., and Marshall, C. E. (1956) The surface reactions of silicate minerals, Part I: The reactions of feldspar surfaces with acidic solutions: U. of Mo. Agr. Exp. Sta., Research Bull. 613: Part II, Reactions of feldspar surfaces with salt solutions: U. of Mo. Agr. Exp. Sta., Research Bull. 614.

Nelson, B. W. (1960) Clay mineralogy of the bottom sediments, Rappahannock River, Virginia: in *Clays and Clay Minerals,* 7th Conf., Pergamon Press, New York, pp. 135-47.

Nelson, B. W., and Roy, R. (1958) Synthesis of the chlorites and their structural and chemical constitutions: *Am. Min.,* v. 43, pp. 707-25.

Noll, W. (1936) Uber die Bildungs bedingungen von Kaolin, Montmorillonite, Sericit, Pyrophyllit and Analcim: *Min. Petr. Mitt.,* v. 42, pp. 210-47.

Norin, E. (1953) Occurrence of authigenous illitic mica in the sediments of the central Tyrrhenian sea: *Bull. Geol. Inst. Uppsala,* v. 34, pp. 279-84.

Nutting, P. G. (1943) Absorbent clays, thin distribution, properties, production and uses: *U. S. Geol. Survey Bull.* 928-C, pp. 127-221.

Ojakangas, Richard, and Keller, W. D. (1964) Glauconization of rhyolite sand grains: *Jour. Sed. Petrol.,* v. 34, pp. 84-90.

Okamoto, G., Okura, T., and Goto, K. (1947) Properties of silica in water: *Geochim. et Cosmochim. Acta.,* v. 12, pp. 123-32.

Packham, G. H., and Crook, K. A. W. (1960) The principle of diagenetic facies and some of its implications: *Jour. Geol.,* v. 68, pp. 392-407.

Patterson, S. H., and Hosterman, J. W. (1960) Geology of the clay deposits in the Olive Hill district, Kentucky: in *Clays and Clay Minerals,* 7th Conf., Pergamon Press, New York, pp. 178-95.

Peterson, M. N. A. (1961) Expandable chloritic clay minerals from upper Mississippian carbonate rocks of the Cumberland Plateau in Tennessee: *Am. Min.,* v. 46, pp. 1245-69.

Peterson, M. N. A. (1962) The mineralogy and petrology of upper Mississippian carbonate rocks of the Cumberland Plateau in Tennessee: *Jour. Geol.,* v. 70, pp. 1-31.

Potts, R. H. (1959) Cationic and structural changes in Missouri River clays when treated with ocean water: Unpublished Master's thesis, University of Missouri, Library, Columbia, Mo.

Powers, M. C. (1954) Clay diagenesis in the Chesapeake Bay area: in *Clays and Clay Minerals,* Natl. Acad. Sci.-Natl. Res. Council, pub. 327, pp. 66-80.

Powers, M. C. (1957) Adjustment of land-derived clays to the marine environment: *Jour. Sed. Petrol.,* v. 27, pp. 355-72.

Powers, M. C. (1959) Adjustment of clays to chemical change and the concept of the equivalence level: in *Clays and Clay Minerals,* 6th Conf., Pergamon Press, New York, pp. 309-26.

Pray, L. C. (1960) Composition in calcilutites: Abstract in program, Annual Meeting of Geol. Soc. Amer., Denver, Colo.

Pryor, W. A., and Glass, H. D. (1961) Cretaceous—Tertiary clay mineralogy of the upper Mississippi embayment: *Jour. Sed. Petrol.,* v. 31, pp. 38-51.

Reitemeier, R. F. (1951) The chemistry of soil potassium: *Advances in Agronomy,* Academic Press, N. Y., no. 3, pp. 113-59.

Rich, C. I. (1958) Muscovite weathering in a soil developed in the Virginia Piedmont: in *Clays and Clay Minerals,* Natl. Acad. Sci.-Natl. Res. Council, pub. 566, pp. 203-12.

Rich, C. I. (1960) Aluminum in interlayers of vermiculite: *Soil Sci. Soc. Amer. Proc.,* v. 24, pp. 457-60.

Robbins, C., and Keller, W. D. (1952) Clay and other noncarbonate minerals in some limestones: *Jour. Sed. Petrol.,* v. 22, pp. 146-52.

Rolfe, B. N., and Jeffries, C. D. (1952) A new criterion for weathering in soils: *Science,* v. 116, pp. 599-600.

Rosler, H. (1902) Beitrage zur Kentniss einiger Kaolin Lagerstatten: Neu. Jahrb. fur Mineral., Geol., and Pal., Beil, Bd. 15, pp. 231-393 (281-283).

Ross, C. S., and Hendricks, S. B. (1945) Minerals of the montmorillonite group: *U. S. Geol. Survey,* Prof. Paper 205-B.

Ross, C. S., and Kerr, P. F. (1930) The kaolin minerals: *U. S. Geol. Survey,* Prof. Paper 165-E.

Ross, C. S., and Kerr, P. F. (1931) The clay minerals and their identity: *Jour. Sed. Petrol.*, v. 1, pp. 55-65.

Ross, C. S., and Kerr, P. F. (1934) Halloysite and allophane: *U. S. Geol. Survey*, Prof. Paper 185-G, pp. 133-48.

Sales, R. H., and Meyer, Chas. (1948) Wall rock alteration at Butte, Montana: AIME Tech. Pub. 2400, p. 25.

Sales, R. H., and Meyer, Chas. (1950) Interpretation of wall rock alteration at Butte, Montana: *Colo. School Mines Quart.*, v. 45, no. 1b, pp. 261-73.

Sand, L. B. (1956) On the genesis of residual kaolins: *Am. Min.*, v. 41, pp. 28-40.

Schatz, A. (1955) Bodenbildung and Ertragssteigerung durch "Chelatisierung": Umschau, Heft 24, pp. 746-48.

Schatz, A., Cheronis, N. D., Schatz, V., and Trelawney, S. (1954) Chelation (sequestration) as a biological weathering factor in pedogenesis: *Proc. Penn. Acad. Sci.*, v. 28, pp. 44-51.

Schatz, A., Schatz, V., and Martin, J. J. (1957) Chelation as a biochemical weathering factor: *Bull. Geol. Soc. Amer.*, v. 68, pp. 1792-93.

Schwartz, G. M. (1955) Hydrothermal alteration as a guide to ore: *Econ. Geol.*, v. 50, pp. 300-323.

Schwartz, G. M. (1956) Argillic alteration and ore deposits: *Econ. Geol.*, v. 51, pp. 407-14.

Searle, A. B. (1924) *Refractory materials:* Chas. Griffin and Co. Ltd., London.

Shen, M. J., and Rich, C. I. (1962) Aluminum fixation in montmorillonite: *Soil Sci. Soc. Amer. Proc.*, v. 26, pp. 33-36.

Sherman, G. D., and Ikawa, H. (1959) Occurrence of gibbsite amygdules in Haiku bauxite area of Maui: *Pacific Science*, v. 13, pp. 291-94.

Shively, R. R., Jr., and Weyl, W. A. (1951) The color change of ferrous hydroxide upon oxidation: *Jour. Phys. and Colloid Chem.*, v. 55, pp. 512-15.

Siever, R. (1962) Silica solubility, $0°-200°C.$, and the diagenesis of siliceous sediments: *Jour. Geol.*, v. 70, pp. 127-50.

Slaughter, M., and Milne, I. H. (1960) The formation of chlorite-like structures from montmorillonite: in *Clays and Clay Minerals,* 7th Conf., Pergamon Press, New York, pp. 114-24.

Stahl, A. (1912) Die Verbreitung der Kaolin Lagerstatten in Deutschland, K. Preuss. Geol. Landesangstalt, Archiv. fur Loger Forsch., Heft 12, p. 135 (pp. 86-96).

Stelle, V. (1907) Zeitschur: *Naturwiss.*, v. 79, pp. 321-23, *Vide* Ross and Kerr, 1930.

Stephen, I. (1952) A study of weathering with reference to the soils of the Malvern Hills, Part 1: Weathering of biotite and granite: *Jour. Soil Sci.*, v. 3, p. 20.

Stevens, R. E., and Carron, M. K. (1948) Simple field test for distinguishing minerals by abrasion pH: *Am. Min.*, v. 33, pp. 31-50.

Stewart, F. H. (1949) The petrology of the evaporites of the Eskdale no. 2

boring, East Yorkshire, 1. The lower evaporite bed: *Min. Mag.,* v. 28, pp. 621-75.

Sudo, T. (1954) Clay mineralogical aspects of the alteration of volcanic glass in Japan: *Clay Min. Bull.,* v. 2, pp. 96-104.

Sudo, T. (1959) *Mineralogical study of clays of Japan:* Maruzen Co., Ltd., Tokyo, p. 328.

Sudo, T., and Ossoka, J. (1952) Hydrated halloysite from Japan: *Jap. J. Geol. Geograph.,* v. 22, pp. 215-29.

Sujkowski, Zb. L. (1958) Diagenesis: *Bull. Amer. Assn. Petrol. Geol.,* v. 42, pp. 2692-2717.

Takahashi, J. (1939) Synopsis of glauconitization: Recent Marine Sediments: *Amer. Assn. Petrol. Geol.,* pp. 503-15.

Tamura, T., and Jackson, M. L. (1953) Structural and energy relationships in the formation of iron and aluminum oxides, hydroxides, and silicates: *Science,* v. 117, pp. 381-83.

Tarr, W. A., and Keller, W. D. (1936) Dickite in Missouri: *Am. Min.,* v. 21, pp. 109-14.

Tarr, W. A., and Keller, W. D. (1937) Some occurrences of kaolinite deposited from solution: *Am. Min.,* v. 22, pp. 933-35.

Towe, K. M. (1962) Clay mineral diagenesis as a possible source of silica cement in sedimentary rocks: *Jour. Sed. Petrol.,* v. 32, pp. 26-28.

Ussher, W. A., Barrow, G., MacAlister, D. A., and Flett, J. S. (1949) The geology of the country around Bodmin and St. Austell (Explanation of sheet 347): *Geol. Sur. Gr. Britain,* Mem., p. 131.

Van Andel, Tj. H., and Postma, H. (1954) Recent sediments in the Gulf of Paria: *Verh. Kon. Nederlandse Akod. V. Wetensch.,* Afd. Nat., 1st reecks, v. 20, no. 5, pp. 1-246.

Van der Marel, H. W. (1954) Potassium fixation in soils: Mineralogical analyses: *Soil Sci.,* v. 78, pp. 163-79.

Van der Marel, H. W. (1955) Potassium fixation in soils: Potassium Symposium, International Potash Institute, Berne, Switzerland, pp. 157-201.

Van der Marel, H. W. (1959) Potassium fixation, a beneficial soil characteristic for crop products: *Zeitsch. fur Pflanzenernahrung, Dungung, Bodenkunde,* 84 Band, Heft 1-3, pp. 51-62.

Van Hise, C. R. (1904) A treatise on metamorphism: *U. S. Geol. Survey,* Mon. 47, p. 1286.

Van Houten, F. B. (1953) Clay minerals in sedimentary rocks and derived soils: *Amer. Jour. Sci.,* v. 251, pp. 61-82.

Vartia, K. O. (1950) On antibiotic effects of lichens and lichen substances: Helsinki Univ. Finland (from Schatz *et al.,* 1954).

Volk, N. J. (1934) The fixation of potash in difficult available forms in soils: *Soil Sci.,* v. 37, pp. 267-87.

Waage, K. M. (1955) Dakota Group in northern Front Range foothills, Colorado: *U. S. Geol. Survey,* Prof. Paper 274-B, pp. 15-51.

Walker, G. F. (1950) Trioctahedral minerals in soil clays: *Min. Mag.,* v. 29, pp. 72-84.

Walker, T. R. (1962) Reversible nature of chert—carbonate replacement in sedimentary rocks: *Bull. Geol. Soc. Amer.*, v. 73, pp. 237-42.

Wallace, A. (1963) Role of chelating agents on the availability of nutrients to plants: *Soil Sci. Soc. Amer. Proc.*, v. 27, pp. 176-79.

Warshaw, C. M. (1957) The mineralogy of glauconite: Ph.D. Thesis, Pennsylvania State Univ., p. 155.

Wear, J. L., and White, J. L. (1951) Potassium fixation in clay minerals as related to crystal structure: *Soil Sci.*, v. 71, pp. 1-14.

Weaver, C. E. (1958a) A discussion on the origin of clay minerals in sedimentary rocks: in *Clays and Clay Minerals*, Natl. Acad. Sci.-Natl. Res. Council, pub. 566, pp. 159-73.

Weaver, C. E. (1958b) The effects and geologic significance of potassium "fixation" by expandable clay minerals derived from muscovite, biotite, chlorite, and volcanic material: *Am. Min.*, v. 43, pp. 839-61.

Weaver, C. E. (1958c) Geologic interpretation of argillaceous sediments: *Bull. Amer. Assn. Petrol. Geol.*, v. 42, pp. 254-71.

Weaver, C. E. (1959) The clay petrology of sediments: in *Clays and Clay Minerals*, 6th Conf., Pergamon Press, New York, pp. 154-87.

Weaver, C. E. (1960) Possible uses of clay minerals in search for oil: *Bull. Amer. Assn. Petrol. Geol.*, v. 44, pp. 1505-18.

Weaver, C. E. (1961) Clay mineralogy of the late cretaceous rocks of the Washakie Basin: Guide book sixteenth Ann. Conf. Wyo. Geol. Assn., pp. 148-54.

Weinstein, L. H., Robbins, W. R., and Perkins, H. F. (1954) Chelating agents and plant nutrition: *Science*, v. 120, pp. 41-43.

Wermund, E. G. (1961) Glauconite in early Tertiary sediments of Gulf coastal province: *Bull. Amer. Assn. Petrol. Geol.*, v. 45, pp. 1667-96.

Weyl, W. A. (1951) Light absorption as a result of two states of valency of the same element: *Jour. Phys. and Colloid Chem.*, v. 55, pp. 507-12.

Whitehouse, U. G. (1951/1952) Progress reports for the API Research Project 51: Oceanogr. Dept., Texas A & M College, *Vide* Van Andel and Postma, 1954.

Whitehouse, U. G., and Jeffrey, L. M. (1955) Peptization resistance of selected samples of kaolinitic, montmorillonitic, and illitic clay minerals: in *Clays and Clay Minerals*, Natl. Acad. Sci.-Natl. Res. Council, pub. 395, pp. 260-81.

Whitehouse, U. G., Jeffrey, L. M., and Delbrecht, J. D. (1960) Differential settling tendencies of clay minerals in saline waters: in *Clays and Clay Minerals*, 7th Conf., Pergamon Press, New York, pp. 1-80.

Wilson, H., and Threasher, R. D. (1938) Preliminary report of some of the refractory clays of Western Oregon: Ore. Dept. Geol. and Min. Ind. Bull. 6, p. 96.

Woodruff, C. M. (1955a) Ionic equilibria between clay and dilute salt solutions: *Soil Sci. Soc. Amer Proc.*, v. 19, pp. 36-50.

Woodruff, C. M. (1955b) The energies of replacement of calcium by potassium in soils: *Soil Sci. Soc. Amer. Proc.*, v. 19, pp. 167-71.

Yaalon, D. H. (1959) Weathering reactions: *Jour. Chem. Ed.,* v. 36, pp. 73-76.

Yoder, H. S., and Eugster, H. P. (1954) Phlogopite and synthesis range: *Geochim. et Cosmochim. Acta,* v. 6, pp. 157-85.

Yoder, H. S., and Eugster, H. P. (1955) Synthetic and natural muscovites, *Geochim. et Cosmochim. Acta,* v. 8, pp. 225-80.

Zen, E-An. (1959a) Clay mineral-carbonate relations in sedimentary rocks: *Am. Jour. Sci.,* v. 257, pp. 29-43.

Zen, E-An. (1959b) Mineralogy and petrography of marine bottom sediment samples off the coast of Peru and Chile: *Jour. Sed. Petrol.,* v. 29, pp. 513-39.

II... Structure and Mineral Analysis of Soils

Roy Brewer

Foreword

The following notes formed the basis for a series of lectures given at an "Advanced Seminar in Clay Mineralogy" at Virginia Polytechnic Institute, Blacksburg, Virginia. The fact that the number of lectures was limited rectricted the scope of the material, particularly the detail which could be given in regard to background, reasons for the use of certain principles and classification schemes in preference to others, and consideration of the interpretation of the morphological and quantitative data. Similarly, lack of time has restricted the preparation of these notes although it was felt, in any case, that they should not go beyond what was delivered during the lectures. A much expanded and more complete treatment of the subject is being published (1964) as a textbook by John Wiley and Sons, Inc., New York, under the proposed title of *Fabric and Mineral Analysis of Soils*.

The nature of soils

Soils in relation to geology

It is generally accepted that soils are the result of alteration of a so-called "parent material" due to exposure at the earth's surface. Jenny's

(1941, pp. 1-20) assessment of soils as a function of five major soil–forming factors (climate, time, parent material, organisms, relief) is acceptable in a general way. By itself, however, this is a narrow view of soils and of their importance as records of recent events in landscape development. Also, it can be misleading in that every soil profile has a history of development so that the parent material may not have been like the material immediately underlying the profile, the climate during the major part of the development of the profile may have been unlike the present climate, the profile may have been partly truncated, or buried, and so on.

Now, the majority of soils are formed by either: (1) alteration of hard rocks *in situ* by weathering, or (2) alteration of unconsolidated sediments (i.e., transported materials) which were derived from other unconsolidated sediments or from weathered hard rocks. In both these cases, the soils are relatively loose materials which provide source material for the formation of subsequent sedimentary bodies. In fact, studies in the United States and Australia (e.g., Ruhe 1956; Butler 1958, 1959; van Dijk 1959; Walker 1959) indicate that the recent history of landscape development in many regions is dominated by recurrent cycles of erosion and deposition followed by stable periods during which soil formation took place.

Soils, therefore, are rocks, or rather they are rocks which have been altered due to exposure at the earth's surface. They are records of the minor cycles of erosion and stability between the larger geological cycles, and also of the environment during the periods of stability when soil formation took place. They are formed on hard rocks and on unconsolidated sediments, and they are the source material for other sediments and soils formed during subsequent cycles of erosion and stability. Older soils may be preserved by burial under younger sediments, they may escape erosion in parts of some landscapes, or they may be truncated or completely removed.

Soil formation, therefore, is a form of diagenesis when it takes place in unconsolidated sediments before burial and consolidation, while in other cases it is simply alteration of a previously existing rock by weathering, whether the rock is a hard sediment or igneous rock, or an unconsolidated sediment. If soils are viewed in this way, the applicability of petrographic methods to the study of soils becomes apparent. On the one hand there is petrology, which includes petrogenesis and petrography, and on the other its analogue, pedology, which includes pedogenesis and pedography.

Profile trends

Like rocks, soils vary in their characteristics both horizontally and vertically, but their main attribute is a much more rapid change in properties vertically than horizontally. This has some similarities with sedimentary rock series, but, because soils are formed due to exposure at the earth's surface, certain characteristic vertical variations can be expected which do not occur generally in sedimentary series. This has been the basic reason for choosing the soil profile as the unit of study. It also means that a single handspecimen from a soil profile is a very incomplete sample of the unit as a whole—even more incomplete and misleading than would be a handspecimen of a sedimentary bed. It is necessary, therefore, to study a number of samples in vertical sequence to describe the characteristics of the unit and to identify typical soil profiles; that is, it is necessary to study vertical profile trends.

Since soils are formed by exposure at the earth's surface, the curves to be expected for vertical profile trends are of the forms shown in Fig. 1(a), depending on the characteristic chosen. That is, the processes causing the profile trends should be most severe at the surface and decrease in intensity in something of an exponential way with depth. This is the simplest possible case, however, and it is well known that there are innumerable variations from this ideal. For example, the curves for percentage of clay–size material and for percentage of carbonates can have a number of forms with quite prominent inflections, such as the forms shown in Fig. 1(b). These variations from the expected simple curves demand investigation and explanation.

The study of pedogenesis, therefore, involves, first, the identification and characterization of the parent material, and, second, examination of the characteristic properties of soil materials and their variation with depth. On these bases, hypotheses can be presented concerning the origin of the phenomena observed and the reasons for their particular distribution with depth in the profile. Any of the many properties of soil materials can be studied in this way, and fabric and mineral analyses are powerful tools for such studies.

The nature of soil materials

The constituents—From this point the discussion concerns soil materials rather than soil profiles; these can be thought of as being the

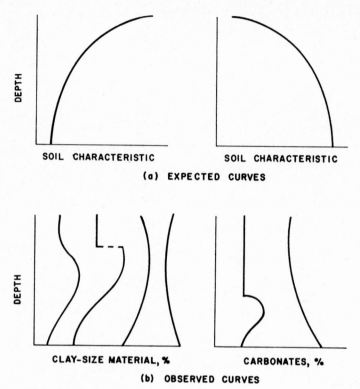

Figure 1. *Profile trends.*

analogues of handspecimens of rocks. That is, they are representative samples of the soil horizons which make up a profile.

Consider first the nature of the constituents of soil materials. They consist essentially of minerals, which can be divided conveniently, on the basis of differences in their properties, into the two groups:

(1) Skeleton grains are individual, relatively stable grains which are not readily translocated, concentrated, or reorganized by soil–forming processes. They include mineral grains and resistant siliceous and organic bodies larger than colloidal size (Brewer and Sleeman 1960, after Kubiena 1938). Complex grains are not considered as skeleton grains but as pedological features, which are discussed later. The skeleton grains are relatively immobile except for extreme processes such as washing down cracks, but they are capable of weathering to form plasma.

(2) Plasma is that part of a soil material which is capable of being (or has been) moved, reorganized, and/or concentrated by the processes of soil formation. It includes all the mineral and organic material of colloidal size, and relatively soluble material which is not bound up in the skeleton grains (Brewer and Sleeman 1960, after Kubiena 1938). The material need not be in a suitable state for translocation or concentration at present to be termed plasma. For example, colloid–size clay minerals which occur as aggregates stabilized by iron oxides are still part of the plasma, as are the iron oxides, since their characteristics are such that under certain conditions they are capable of translocation, reorientation, and concentration. The plasma is the potentially active, mobile part of the soil material, and it is this mobility which causes many of the phenomena observed in soil materials.

Besides these two groups of constituents, a sample of a soil material often contains living and dead plant roots and various species of *flora* and *fauna*. These are not considered as part of the soil material in fabric and mineral analysis; the soil material is regarded simply as the medium for their activities, although its characteristics may be affected by these activities. Similarly, recognizable undecomposed organic remains are not considered. The characteristics of these materials are so different from those of the mineral constituents that they require a different method of treatment which is not within the scope of fabric and mineral analysis. Organic constituents released by humification, however, *are* part of the plasma, and resistant siliceous bodies of organic origin are part of the skeleton.

The units of organization—The soil–forming processes cause a reorganization of the constituents in soil materials as compared with the organization in the parent material. For example, fractionation and translocation of the plasma may occur with reorganization of the various fractions. This may result in formation of concentrations of certain fractions of the plasma on the walls of voids which have acted as conducting channels for the movement of solutions or suspensions, or it may cause cementing of parts of the soil material by some fraction of the plasma, and so on. All these features, too, may have various kinds of internal arrangements of the constituents. Other processes cause the formation of recognizable composite aggregates of the soil material, which may be packed together in different arrangements compatible

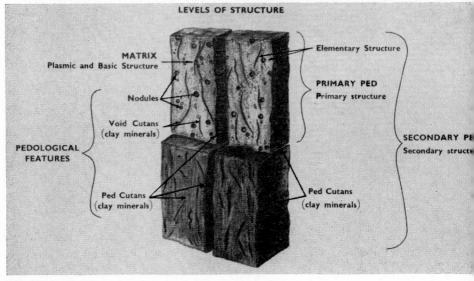

Figure 2. Levels of structure.

with their size and shape. In addition, certain features may be inherited from the parent rock or parent material.

Many soil materials, therefore, have an extremely complex organization, and the problem is to devise an orderly, systematic method of describing this complexity. This can be achieved by using the concepts of *units of organization* and *levels of organization* which allow the study and description of any part of this complex organization without detailed reference to any other part, and by naming the units and levels and specific examples of them.

The units of organization which have been chosen are *peds, pedological features,* and *s–matrices*[1]. It is also possible to deal with the pore spaces, or *voids,* quite independently. The units are defined as follows (see Fig. 2):

(1) Peds are individual natural soil aggregates consisting of clusters of primary (individual) particles and separated from adjoining peds by surfaces of weakness which are recognizable as voids or natural surfaces (Sleeman 1963). Thus, peds are units which are recognizable by the characteristics of their surfaces, as distinct from previous definitions

1. S-matrices replaces "matrices" as used in the lectures to avoid confusion with sedimentary petrological terms.

which recognized so–called peds on the occurrence of a population of units of similar size and shape after the application of a force to a soil material (U.S.D.A. 1951, pp. 225-30).

(2) Pedological features are recognizable units within a soil material which are distinguishable from the enclosing material for any reason such as origin (deposition as an entity), differences in concentration of some fraction of the plasma, or differences in arrangement of the constituents (Brewer and Sleeman 1960). Thus, pedological features reflect the result of specific soil–forming processes.

(3) S–matrix of a soil material is the material within primary peds, or composing unaggregated soil materials, in which the pedological features occur. Certain pedological features recognized by differences in arrangement of constituents (the plasma separations of Brewer and Sleeman 1960; see Plate 4) are essentially part of the s–matrix (Brewer 1960b).

Each of these units of organization has levels of organization within it, and each contributes toward levels of organization within a soil material. These aspects are discussed later under the levels of structure and fabric.

Structure and fabric analysis

Concepts of structure and fabric

There are considerable differences between the various definitions proposed for soil structure, which apparently depend on the interests of the people who proposed the definitions. In the field, structure is used generally to mean the size, shape, and arrangement of peds (U.S.D.A. 1951, pp. 225-30). On the other hand, the physicists use structure to mean the arrangement of any of the recognizable units— both compound aggregates such as peds, and single grains such as plasma and skeleton grains (Baver 1948, p. 126). Since all the constituents of soil materials have the attributes of size and shape, and occur in various arrangements, it is reasonable to have some term for the physical constitution of soil materials in these terms, and so the following terms have been defined (Brewer and Sleeman 1960):

(1) Soil structure is the physical constitution of a soil material as expressed by the size, shape, and arrangement of the solid particles and

Table 1. Relationships of proposed concepts to current concepts (after Brewer and Sleeman 1960)

Characteristics	Soil components*	Proposed Pedological usage					Current Pedological Usage						Geological Usage					
		Field grading	Pedality	Fabric	Structure	Texture	Field texture (U.S.D.A. manual)	Fabric (Kubiena)	Structure (Zakharov)	Structure (Baver)	Structure (U.S.D.A. manual)	Grade	Packing	Fabric (sedimentary)	Fabric (igneous)	Structure† (sedimentary)	Texture† (sedimentary)	Texture (igneous)
Crystallinity	Skeleton grains	×				×											×	×
	Plasma					×												×
Size	Skeleton grains	×		×	×	×	×										×	×
	Peds		×	×	×	×			×		×	×						
	Pedological features			×	×	×												
	Plasma grains	×		×	×	×	×										×	×
	Voids			×	×	×							×					
Shape	Skeleton grains			×	×	×									×		×	×
	Peds		×	×	×	×			×		×	×						
	Pedological features			×	×	×												
	Plasma grains			×	×	×								×	×		×	×
	Voids			×	×								×					
Arrangement	Skeleton grains			×	×	×		×		×					×		×	×
	Peds		×	×	×	×		×		×	×		×			×		
	Pedological features			×	×	×		×						×	×			
	Plasma			×	×	×		×		×				×	×	×	×	×
	Voids			×	×								×	×		×		

* For geological usage substitute rock components, viz., solid elements and voids
† Restricted usage, e.g., oolitic structure, equivalent to sedimentary features

voids, including both the primary particles to form compound particles and the compound particles themselves.

(2) Soil fabric is the physical constitution of a soil material as expressed by the spatial arrangement of the solid particles and voids; thus, fabric is a part of structure.

(3) Pedality is the physical constitution of a soil material as expressed by the size, shape, and arrangement of the peds. This term accommodates the need for a term to deal with peds separately, especially in the field.

Two other terms (texture and field grading) have been defined. "Texture" has been used in the field in pedology as a term for the assessment of particle–size distribution of a soil material. Even earlier, however, it was used in geology in the sense of the definition set out below, which is also more like its normal English usage. "Field grading" is used to replace the old concept of texture.

(4) Soil texture is the physical constitution of a soil material as expressed by its structure, and by the degree of crystallization (crystallinity) of the soil particles.

(5) Field grading is the assessment of the particle–size distribution by the method of moistening and manipulating of the soil material in the field.

The relationships of these definitions to those now in use in geology and pedology are shown in Table 1.

Levels of structure

The levels of organization in a soil material can be dealt with as their equivalent levels of structure, which includes the aspect of arrangement or soil fabric. The first need is to select a standard level or unit, and the most appropriate one is the *primary ped,* which is the simplest recognizable ped in a soil material which cannot be broken into simpler natural units. Its equivalent in an apedal soil material is the whole soil material. Within the primary ped there are plasma, skeleton grains and voids (which together make up the s–matrix), and pedological features. In addition, the peds can be packed in various ways to make up successively more complex units (higher levels of peds). On this basis, the following levels of structure have been recognized (after Brewer and Sleeman 1960, Brewer 1960b). Their relationships are illustrated in Fig. 2.

(1) Plasmic structure is the size, shape, and arrangement of the plasma grains and associated simple packing voids in the s–matrix. These voids, of course, are too small to resolve with a light microscope.

(2) Basic structure is the size, shape, and arrangement of simple grains (plasma and skeleton grains) and the associated voids within the s–matrix. The larger voids in the s–matrix can be resolved with a light microscope.

(3) Primary structure is an integration of the size, shape, and arrangement of all the pedological features enclosed in the s–matrix and the basic structure, or structure of the s–matrix.

(4) Elementary structure is a simplified level of primary structure; it is an integration of a *characteristic* size, shape, and arrangement of *specific* pedological features and the basic structure.

(5) Secondary structure is the size, shape, and arrangement of the primary peds, their interpedal voids, and associated interpedal pedological features.

(6) Tertiary structure is the size, shape, and arrangement of the secondary peds, their interpedal voids and associated interpedal pedological features.

Pedological features can exhibit levels of structure analogous to those of soil materials. They may be compound features in which a large feature (the host pedological feature) may contain smaller features (the included pedological features) in the same way that the s–matrix of a soil material includes pedological features. The host feature then exhibits the plasmic, basic, elementary, and primary levels of structure, while the included features (if they are simple features) may exhibit plasmic and basic levels of structure.

Principles of structure analysis

Size and shape analyses—There are a number of standard works which deal exhaustively with size and shape analyses, but there are a number of additional considerations which are pertinent to the interpretation of the analyses for soil materials.

(1) Size. The objective of size analysis usually is to estimate the degree of sorting of the mineral grains and, in sedimentary petrology, to interpret this sorting coefficient and measures of kurtosis and skewness in terms of the origin of the sediment. Such interpretations are based on a vast amount of data which has been accumulated for sedi-

ments of known origin. The basic assumption is that the source material was capable of supplying a wide range of sizes so that the degree of sorting is the result of the processes of transportation and sedimentation, and is not inherited from the source material. Soil materials, however, have been acted upon by the soil–forming processes, and so the effects of these processes on the particle–size distribution of the materials must be considered in the interpretation of the analyses. One common effect is a progressive reduction in particle size, due to physical fracturing of the mineral grains along planes of weakness which are due to strain, cleavage, and inclusions (Brewer 1955, Raeside 1959). This is apparent even in field observations; many soil materials developed from hard, coarse–grained rocks contain a high percentage of clay– and silt–size grains. Carried to extremes, these processes may result in the majority of the mineral grains occurring in the finer fractions. That is, they cause a significant decrease in the size range of grains; size analysis may then indicate a high degree of sorting which is due to weathering and not to transportation and sedimentation. Kurtosis, skewness, and other measures may distinguish this kind of sorting due to weathering, but no systematic investigations have been made. One obstacle to attempting such studies is the difficulty of being certain of the original uniformity of the parent material throughout a soil profile, and of its derivation from the underlying rock.

If the proposed definition is accepted, it is possible to make size analyses of peds. This could not be done previously because peds were recognized only if they occurred as populations of units of similar size so that a simple statement of the modal size was all that was required. Such analyses may provide correlations with other factors so as to indicate the genesis of the peds. Similarly, size analyses can be made of pedological features, especially those which occur as relatively stable, discrete entities, such as some nodules and concretions. The results of such analyses can be expected to correlate with some of the factors of formation of the features. For example, the modal size and size distribution of accretionary features depends on the frequency of suitable foci for deposition, the total and rate of supply of the accreting fraction of the plasma, and the time during which accretion progressed. No studies have been made on the significance of the size distribution of either peds or pedological features.

The usual method of size analysis of voids is to measure the amount of water displaced from a saturated soil material at successively increasing tensions and/or pressures, and to calculate from this the size frequency distribution of the voids on the assumption that all voids in soil materials are circular capillaries. Thin sections of soil materials have shown that the voids are usually quite irregular in shape, and few indeed even approximate such a shape. Such analyses, therefore, are not factual statements of the size distribution. Void size, however, is difficult to measure in other ways; cross–sectional area can be obtained from sections, but it is virtually impossible to measure the third dimension. In addition, void size changes significantly with moisture content. It would seem, therefore, that little can be expected from the measurement of void–size distribution, and, in fact, the most significant data concerning the genesis of voids is likely to be obtained from studies of shape and distribution.

(2) Shape. There are three aspects of the shape of an entity: the *sphericity* and *roundness* (Wadell 1932, 1933, 1935; Sneed and Folk 1958), which are respectively measures of the degree of conformity of the shape to that of a standard form (a sphere or a triaxial ellipsoid) irrespective of the sharpness of edges and corners, and of the sharpness of the edges and corners irrespective of the sphericity, and the *conformation* of the faces, for which descriptive terms such as botryoidal, tuberose, lenticular, and so on, are used.

As with size analysis, interpretation of the data on roundness and sphericity of pebbles and grains may be complicated by the effects of the soil–forming processes. Interpretation again depends on the assumption that the observed characteristics were not inherent in the source material, and, to interpret the data in terms of degree and kind of transport, it is necessary to be assured that the observed characteristics are not due to the processes of soil formation. No studies have been made on the modifications of sphericity and roundness which can be achieved by soil formation.

The roundness and sphericity of peds, pedological features, and voids can be described. For peds, sphericity is the more important property; roundness measures are difficult to apply, but in some instances they may be important. Many pedological features lend themselves admirably to studies of roundness and sphericity, and studies of the shapes of voids in relation to measurements of "pore–size distribution" by tension methods are very desirable. No such studies of shape have been made on features other than mineral grains and pebbles, so there is no data on which to base hypotheses of the significance of shape analysis of other entities. Correlations can be expected, however, between the shape analyses of pedological features and peds and their mode of formation, and between certain voids of particular shape (e.g., the almost spherical vesicles) and their origin.

Fabric analysis—There are two aspects of fabric analysis or the description of arrangement: the *distribution pattern* and the *orientation pattern,* each of which can be subdivided into: *basic, referred,* and *related* patterns (Brewer and Sleeman 1960). The *basic* patterns refer simply to the distribution or orientation of like individuals with regard to each other. For example, the distribution and orientation patterns of skeleton grains can be described by treating them as individuals—that is, whether they are scattered randomly throughout the s–matrix or exhibit some specific distribution pattern, and whether they have any degree of preferred orientation. The *referred* patterns are, as the name implies, distribution and orientation patterns of like individuals with regard to some specific reference feature; the reference features are chosen to reveal specific patterns. For example, iron–rich nodules may be distributed in some specific way related to the horizontal or to the top of a planosolic B horizon which then becomes the reference feature for the distribution of the nodules. Similarly, the anisotropic clay–mineral grains in the plasma may be oriented parallel to the surfaces of peds or particular kinds of voids. The *related* patterns are distribution and orientation patterns of like individuals referred to the patterns of other individuals. For example, two groups of pedological features may have distribution patterns which are related to each other.

(1) Distribution pattern. The treatment of distribution patterns entails little more than the recognition, description, and classification of the entities, and the selection and definition of adequate terms for observed patterns. As far as is possible, such terms should be general ones so that they can be applied to any of the entities recognizable in soil materials. Basic patterns may be referred to as *banded, clustered, radial, concentric,* and so on. Referred patterns can be described as *normal* (perpendicular to the specific reference feature, *parallel* (to the specific reference feature), *inclined* (at a constant angle to the reference feature), *cutanic* (associated with natural surfaces in the soil material —see cutans later), and *subcutanic* (parallel and close to adjoining natural surfaces). Related patterns can be described as *normal, parallel,* or *inclined* since they are patterns which are referred to the basic pattern of another group of entities.

(2) Orientation pattern. Description of the orientation pattern is an assessment of the kind and degree of preferred orientation of the

individuals. If the individuals are physically anisotropic, the direction of one of their axes (usually the long or short axis) can be measured and plotted on polar coordinate paper, or if they are optically anisotropic one of the optical axes can be plotted. Then the degree of clustering of points indicates the degree of preferred orientation, or the *basic* orientation pattern. Now, if the reference feature is a flat plane, it also can be plotted on the polar diagram, and so the *referred* orientation pattern is shown. If the reference feature is a curved surface and the units are oriented parallel to that surface, the normal polar diagram may not indicate a high degree of preferred orientation. However, if such a reference feature is treated as a flat plane and plotted at the center of the diagram, and then the individuals are plotted in relation to this curved surface, the high degree of referred orientation will be apparent in the diagram.

Although this method is suited to megascopic individuals which can be measured, other techniques must be used for microscopic individuals such as plasma grains. The simplest microscopic method is interpretation of the extinction phenomena under crossed nicols in thin section. This depends on a knowledge of the optical properties of the mineral species involved. The majority of the minerals in the plasma which exhibit preferred orientation are those with a layer–lattice structure and/or an elongated or platy form. Most of these have a number of optical and physical properties in common. In particular, they exhibit straight extinction. Thus, if the preferred orientation is strong and linear, the entity which is composed of oriented grains will extinguish as a unit; all the grains extinguish in the one position. If, however, the grains have a strong preferred orientation which follows a curve, the high degree of orientation is expressed by the occurrence of strong dark extinction bands which move in an orderly manner across the section of the entity as the microscope stage is rotated. As the degree of preferred orientation of the grains decreases, the sharpness of the extinction phenomena also decreases. However, since the individual plasma grains are less than the two microns equivalent diameter, and a thin section is approximately 25 to 30 microns thick, any anisotropy in the clay minerals of the plasma in thin section must be due to some degree of optical orientation of the smaller anisotropic grains—that is, preferred orientation of the individual grains with regard to each other.

The plasma grains in soil materials commonly occur as compound units which may be so small that they are recognizable only at high magnifications. Thus, basic orientation of the plasma can be described at two levels: the orientation of the individual grains with regard to each other (the *degree* of basic orientation), and the orientation of the compound units, or plasma aggregates, with regard to each other (the *pattern* of basic orientation). The degree of basic orientation can be described, according to the extinction phenomena in thin section, as *strong* (dark extinction lines run across the aggregates, or they extinguish as a unit), *moderate* (the extinction is "mottled," reminiscent of the extinction of some micas), *weak* (birefringence is weak, and extinction is wavy or undulose), and *unoriented* (the plasma is isotropic because of the low degree of preferred orientation). The pattern of basic orientation can be described as *continuous* (the mass of plasma exhibits extinction lines or extinguishes as a unit), *striated* (the plasma aggregates exhibit a lineal or curved lineal arrangement with a "striated" extinction pattern), and *flecked* (the plasma aggregates are randomly arranged and exhibit a "flecked" extinction pattern). Examples of these patterns are shown in Figures 3 and 6. The referred orientation pattern can be described as unrelated, normal, parallel, or inclined.

Classification of the units of organization

Voids

In order to classify voids, it is necessary to treat them as individuals even though they are always interconnected with other voids. In most soil materials, a significant proportion of the voids are connected to others of comparable size by a population of very much smaller voids, and so the large ones can be treated as entities. Where voids of similar size are interconnected, as in the simple packing of sand grains, significant constrictions must be taken as the boundaries of the individual voids.

Size—In practice, it is very difficult to measure the size of voids. The pore–size measurements made by tension methods are not entirely satisfactory, and measurements on thin sections can be made only in two dimensions. It is proposed, therefore, that the classification of voids according to size should be standardized on the length of the shortest dimension since this parameter has the greatest effect on the movement of water through voids, and this is an important factor both in soil formation and for plant growth. The following size classes are based on proposals by Jongerius (1957, p. 86) and Johnson, *et al.* (1960):

(1) Macrovoids: shortest dimension is greater than 75 μ.
(2) Mesovoids: shortest dimension is between 30 and 75 μ.
(3) Microvoids: shortest dimension is between 5 and 30 μ.
(4) Ultramicrovoids: shortest dimension is less than 5 μ.

Each of these groups can be subdivided, especially the macrovoids and ultramicrovoids.

Morphological classification—The following classes of voids have been recognized on the basis of their distribution and orientation patterns, shape (ratios of axes), and conformation (Brewer 1960b, Sleeman 1963):

(1) Packing voids are due to the random packing of single grains (simple packing voids) or compound units such as peds which do not accommodate each other (compound packing voids).

(2) Vughs occur in the s–matrix and are significantly larger than voids which would result from the normal packing of single grains.

(3) Vesicles differ from vughs principally in that their walls consist of smooth, simple curves.

(4) Chambers differ from vughs and vesicles in that they are interconnected through channels and usually have a characteristic shape (subspherical or hemispherical).

(5) Planes are simply voids which would be classified as planar in shape according to the ratios of their principal axes; *joint planes* occur as parallel sets and series, *skew planes* traverse the soil material in an irregular manner, and *craze planes* are essentially irregular planar voids which occur as an intricate network.

(6) Channels are significantly larger than voids which would result from the normal packing of single grains, and have a generally tubular form; they may exhibit a number of branching patterns such as *dendroid* (branching without rejoining), *anastomosing* (branching and rejoining), and *trellised* (horizontal branches joined by short vertical branches).

Voids can also be classified, according to the smoothness of the walls, into:

(1) Orthovoids, whose walls appear morphologically to be due to the unaltered, normal, random packing of plasma and skeleton grains, and

(2) Metavoids, whose walls appear morphologically to be significantly smoother than would be due to the normal, random packing of

plasma and skeleton grains; they may be referred to as *smoothed* or *slickensided*.

Peds

Size—The size of peds can be measured by sieving or by measurement of the lengths of the principal axes. Sieving gives a series of grade classes which can be treated mathematically just as any other particle–size distribution. Measurement of the principal axes is much more tedious but gives more detail, and grade classes can be set up according to their true volume which is generally considered to be the only true measure of size (Wadell 1932).

Morphological classification—A number of the terms used for the shape of peds are used in a very loose way. For example, to most soil workers the term "prismatic" denotes an elongated ped with plane faces, oriented with its long axis vertical. The definition of a prism, however, is simply that the bases, or ends, are similar plane figures, and the sides are parallelograms; there is no qualification concerning the number of faces, the orientation of the unit, or the relative lengths of the axes. It is possible, therefore, to have elongated, acicular prisms and very short platy prisms. These terms, therefore, describe quite separate features. "Prismatic" refers to the *basic form* of the entity, while "platy" and "acicular" refer to the relative lengths or *ratios of the principal axes*. Similarly, the distinction between peds which have curved faces and those which have only flat, plane faces has not been entirely satisfactory.

The following classes of peds have been recognized on the basis of shape (ratio of principal axes, number and shape of faces, presence or absence of re–entrant angles) and arrangement (orientation in space, degree of accommodation of adjoining peds); they conform, as far as possible, with the classes set up by the U.S.D.A. (1951, pp. 225-30) and Butler (1955).

(1) Blocky: equant[2] ($b/a > 2/3$, $c/b > 2/3$) peds having a number of plane faces and no re–entrant angles.

(2) Subrounded blocky: equant peds having mixed curved and plane faces; re–entrant angles are absent or weakly developed.

2. *a*, *b*, and *c* are the principal axes, mutually at right angles, such that *a* is the longest, *c* is the shortest and *b* is intermediate.

(3) Rounded blocky: like subrounded blocky except that all faces are curved.

(4) Multiangular blocky: equant peds having dominantly plane faces and strongly developed re–entrant angles.

(5) Cuboid: peds with six plane faces whose ratios of the principal axes are restricted to $b/a > 9/10$ and $c/b > 9/10$. The angles between adjoining faces are approximately right angles, and the principal axes are parallel to the vertical and horizontal.

(6) Pyramoidal: equant peds bounded by four plane faces.

(7) Mammillated: equant to prolate peds with all faces curved and strongly developed re–entrant angles.

(8) Columnar: prolate and acicular ($b/a < 2/3$, $c/b > 2/3$) prismatic peds having plane faces; re–entrant angles are absent or rare; the longest axis is vertical. Variants of columnar are *parallelo–columnar* (the bases are parallelograms) and *trapezocolumnar* (the bases are trapeziums).

(9) Cuneate: wedge–shaped; prismatic peds in which the bases are triangles or trapeziums, and the axis of the zone of parallelogram faces is horizontal.

(10) Platy: planar ($b/a > 2/3$, $c/b < 1/10$) prismatic peds with the longest and intermediate axes in the horizontal plane.

(11) Lenticular: peds consisting of two curved faces which intersect in an ellipse or circle.

(12) Domed: an adjective to qualify columnar, or other appropriate specific names, for forms in which the *upper* face is a curved surface, convex upwards.

Pedological features

The pedological features which have been observed to date have been classified into a number of broad morphological groups, principally on the basis of their mode of occurrence and shape. Within each group, subclasses have been set up on the basis of shape, composition, fabric (including sharpness of boundary), degree of adhesion to the soil s–matrix, and degree of separation (contrast in fabric and/or composition with the soil s–matrix).

Cutans—Cutans were defined and classified by Brewer (1960a). They are modifications of the texture, structure, or fabric at natural surfaces in soil materials due to concentration of particular components or *in situ* modification of the plasma; cutans can be composed of any of the component substances of plasma. Those which are the result of deposition or diffusion of plasmic material are *plasma concentrations,* while those formed by *in situ* modification of the plasma are *plasma separations.*

Although this definition is strongly genetic, cutans are recognized by their location as evidenced by a change in concentration, structure, or fabric, and by their shape, which conforms to the shape of the natural surfaces with which they are associated. The following classes have been recognized on the basis of the characteristics of the surfaces affected:

(1) Grain cutans are associated with the surfaces of skeleton grains or other discrete units, such as nodules. *Free grain* cutans occur on the surfaces of grains which form the walls of voids as in a loosely packed sand, and *embedded grain cutans* occur on the surfaces of grains embedded in a relatively dense matrix of plasma.

(2) Ped cutans are associated with the surfaces of peds.

(3) Channel cutans are associated with the walls of channels.

(4) Plane cutans are associated with the walls of planar voids.

(5) Normal void cutans are associated with the walls of normal, equant, triaxial, and prolate voids within the soil s–matrix. They can be subdivided on the basis of the morphological classification of voids into vugh, vesicle, and chamber cutans.

Cutans can be classified further according to the mineralogical nature of the cutanic material into classes such as:

(1) Argillans are composed dominantly of clay minerals. These can be subdivided according to significant amounts of contaminants (e.g., ferri–argillans are clay mineral—iron oxide mixtures, organo–argillans are clay mineral—organic matter mixtures), or they may be single pure clay minerals (e.g., kaolinans, palygorskans).

(2) Sesquans are composed of sesquioxides or hydroxides.

(3) Mangans are composed of manganese oxides or hydroxides.

(4) Soluans are composed of crystalline salts such as carbonates, sulphates, and chlorites of calcium, magnesium, and sodium. They can be subdivided into gypsans (gypsum), calcitans (calcite), and halans (halite).

(5) Silans are composed of various forms of silica; the most common forms are silt– or clay–size quartz (quartzans), and poorly crystalline chalcedony (chalcedans). Such cutans composed of a single min-

eralogical and/or chemical substance, or of a uniformly intimate mixture are *simple* cutans; *compound* cutans are composed of alternate layers of mineralogically and/or chemically different substances, or of different fabrics.

Additional description of cutans can be made according to the sharpness of the boundary between the cutanic material and the soil s–matrix, according to the plasmic fabric of the cutan and the referred orientation of the plasma of the cutan with reference to the cutanic surface with which it is associated, according to the degree of separation (i.e., the contrast in fabric or concentration of material between the cutanic material and the soil s–matrix), and according to the degree of adhesion (i.e., the strength of adhesion between the cutanic material and the soil s–matrix).

In addition to this morphological classification, cutans can be subdivided into the following four major groups on the basis of interpretation of the process of formation:

(1) Illuviation cutans are formed by movement of the cutanic material in solution or suspension, and subsequent deposition.

(2) Diffusion cutans are concentrations at a surface due to diffusion.

(3) Stress cutans are *in situ* modifications of the plasma due to differential forces such as shearing; they are not true coatings.

(4) Complex cutans are formed by a combination of more than one of the above processes.

Micrographs of cutans are shown in Fig. 3.

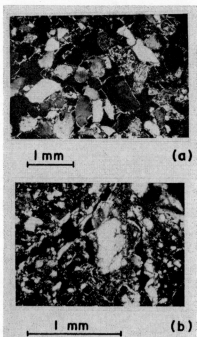

Figure 3. (a) Strongly oriented (continuous orientation pattern) free grain argillans (cutans composed of clay minerals); (b) Strongly oriented (continuous orientation pattern) channel argillans (cutans composed of clay minerals).

Pedotubules[3]—Pedotubules have been defined and classified by Brewer and Sleeman (1963). They are pedological features which consist of soil material (skeleton grains or skeleton grains plus plasma, as distinct from concentrations of fractions of the plasma) and which have a tubular external form, either single tubes or branching systems of tubes. Their external boundaries with the enclosing soil material are relatively sharp. Tubular form, in this context, means that the pedotubule as a unit, or its impression in the enclosing soil material, has a relatively uniform cross–sectional size and shape, most commonly circular or elliptical. Pedotubules are distinguished from similarly shaped crystallized material (the crystal tubes of Kubiena, 1938) and thick illuviation cutans by their internal fabric which is comparable to that of a soil material (at the level of basic or primary fabric). On this basis the following classes have been recognized:

(1) Granotubules consist essentially of skeleton grains without plasma, or all the plasma occurs as pedological features.

(2) Aggrotubules consist of skeleton grains and plasma which occur essentially as aggregates within which there is no directional arrangement with regard to the external form.

(3) Isotubules consist of skeleton grains and plasma which are not organized into recognizable aggregates, and within which the basic fabric shows no directional arrange-

3. Pedotubule replaces "tubule", as used in the lectures, to avoid confusion with geological terms.

2 cm   (a)

1 mm   (b)

Figure 4. (a) Discrete, single isotubule: a pedotubule without branches, with a dense internal fabric, composed of plasma and skeleton grains, and which is entirely free of adhering soil material when removed gently from the enclosing soil material; (b) Internal fabric of an isotubule: dense soil material in which aggregates or a directional arrangement cannot be recognized.

ment with regard to the external form.

(4) Striotubules consist of skeleton grains and plasma which are not organized into recognizable aggregates, but exhibit a basic fabric which has a semi–ellipsoidal arrangement with the walls of the pedotubule approximately tangential to the semi–ellipsoid. A subclass, *cleavage striotubules*, is characterized by a closely spaced "parting" which occurs in the form of the typical semi–ellipsoidal arrangement.

Additional description of pedotubules can be made according to the composition of their plasma compared with that of the enclosing soil s–matrix; they can be described as organic, sesquioxidic, siliceous, calcareous, organic–deficient, carbonate–deficient, and so on. They can also be classified according to the degree of adhesion of the soil material to the pedotubule, and according to their branching patterns:

(1) Single pedotubules consist of single tubes without branches.

(2) Dendroid pedotubules branch "after the manner of a tree" (Rice 1954, p. 102).

(3) Anastomosing pedotubules branch and rejoin to form an irregular network.

(4) Trellised pedotubules branch and rejoin to form a regular network of long horizontal tubes interconnected by shorter vertical tubes.

(5) Chamber pedotubules consist of chambers connected by tubes of smaller diameter.

In addition to this morphological classification, pedotubules can be classified according to evidence for the source of the tubulic material into:

(1) Orthotubules consist of material derived from the soil material of the horizon in which they occur.

(2) Metatubules consist of material derived from the soil material of another horizon.

(3) Paratubules consist of material quite unlike that of the soil materials of any of the horizons in the profile.

Examples of pedotubules are shown in Fig. 4.

Glaebules—A glaebule is a three–dimensional unit within the soil material, apparently not associated as a whole with a void, and usually approximately prolate to equant in shape (Brewer and Sleeman, 1964). It is recognized as a unit either because of a greater concentration of some constituent and/or a difference in fabric compared with the enclosing soil material, or because it has a distinct boundary with the enclosing soil material. Thus, glaebules include Pettijohn's (1957, p. 196-211) nodules, concretions, septaria and related forms, but not his spherulites and other regular crystal growths which occur in voids. They also include Kubiena's (1938) invasion amygdali, but not his amygdalus types formed in voids, or his crystal growths. Besides these, additional classes are necessary to accommodate all the types which occur in soil materials. The following classes have been recognized primarily on the basis of their internal fabric, on their shape, sharpness of boundaries, and degree of adhesion of enclosing soil material:

(1) Nodules have an undifferentiated internal fabric; in this context, undifferentiated fabric includes normal rock and soil fabrics. *Normal* types have relatively sharp boundaries and smooth curved surfaces. *Irregular* types have an irregular shape. *Diffuse* types have diffuse external boundaries and the enclosing soil material usually adheres rather strongly to their surfaces.

(2) Concretions have a generally concentric fabric about a point, a line, or a plane. Normal, irregular, and diffuse types occur.

(3) Septaria have a series of radiating cracks crossed by a series of concentric cracks; the crack pattern is often highly irregular. They are usually spheroidal.

(4) Pedodes have a hollow interior, often with a drusy lining of crystals; there may be associated veins or an outer layer of chalcedonic silica.

(5) Glaebular haloes are weak accumulations of some fraction of the plasma surrounding much stronger glaebular features, and having an undifferentiated fabric and relatively diffuse external boundaries.

(6) Papules consist dominantly of clay minerals which exhibit a strong preferred orientation and/or lamellar fabric; they have sharp external boundaries, and are usually prolate to equant and sub–rounded to well–rounded.

These classes of glaebules can be qualified further according to the composition of their plasma, compared with the enclosing soil material (e.g., sesquioxidic, manganiferous, calcareous, gypseous, siliceous, argillaceous, and so on), and specific shape names may be useful, such as those listed by Read (1948, pp. 37-38) (e.g., amygdaloidal, bladed, botryoidal, ellipsoidal, lenticular, lamellar, mammillated, reniform, spherical, tuberose, irregular, convolute, and so on). Examples of some types of glaebules are shown in Fig. 5.

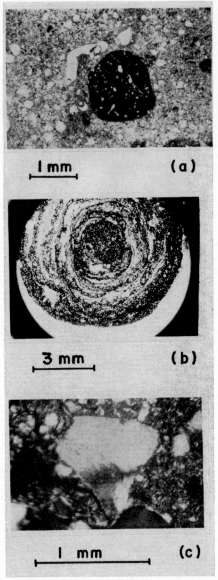

Figure 5. (a) A nodule of iron oxides with an undifferentiated internal fabric and sharp external boundaries; (b) a concretion of iron oxides with a concentric internal fabric and

Crystallaria—Crystallaria are single crystals or groups of crystals of relatively soluble, pure fractions of the plasma which do not enclose the s–matrix of the soil material and which form cohesive masses; they are usually formed in voids. The following classes have been recognized primarily on the basis of shape, and follow those of Kubiena (1938);

(1) Crystal tubes occur in channels of simple or branching tubular form; they usually show evidence of crystallization from the walls inward by preservation of a central void.

(2) Crystal chambers are usually prolate to equant crystallaria formed in vughs.

(3) Crystal sheets are planar shaped crystallaria formed in planes.

(4) Intercalary crystals consist of single large crystals of groups of a few large crystals set in the soil material and apparently not associated with voids of equivalent size or shape; the crystals are euhedral to subhedral. These classes of crystallaria can be subdivided according to the arrangement of the crystals within them, and the mineralogical nature of the crystals.

sharp external boundaries; (c) a papule of clay minerals with sharp external boundaries and a continuous internal orientation pattern.

Subcutanic plasma concentrations—Subcutanic plasma concentrations occur within the s–matrix of a soil material but have obvious relationships with the surfaces of voids; they follow the general shape of voids in the soil material. Two classes have been recognized on the basis of their relationships with the voids:

(1) Neocutans are subcutanic plasma concentrations within the s–matrix adjacent to voids; the varieties observed to date were composed of calcite, iron oxides or hydroxides, or manganese oxides.

(2) Quasicutans are subcutanic plasma concentrations which occur in association with voids but at some distance from the walls of the void; they are commonly composed of iron oxides or hydroxides.

Faecal pellets—Faecal pellets occur commonly both as *single faecal pellets* and as groups or aggregates of pellets which are "welded" together so that the individuals have lost their form over the area where they adjoin each other (*welded faecal pellets*).

S–matrices

By definition, the s–matrix of a soil material is the material within peds, or composing unaggregated soil materials, in which the pedological features occur; it consists essentially of skeleton grains, plasma, and the intrapedal voids.

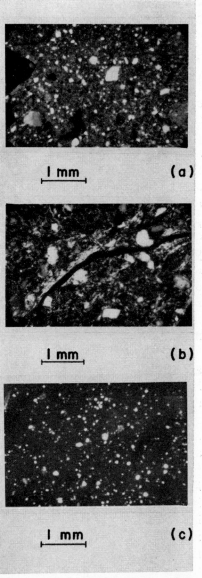

Figure 6. (a) Argillasepic fabric showing a flecked extinction pattern; (b) vosepic fabric showing striated extinction pattern associated with the walls of a planar void (plasma separation); (c) undulic fabric.

Pedological features also have s–matrices. S–matrices, therefore, are classified on the fabric of the plasma grains (plasmic fabric), the characteristics of the voids and skeleton grains, and their relationships to each other.

Plasmic fabric—Since plasma grains are generally too small to see even microscopically, their orientation patterns must be inferred from their extinction phenomena in thin section under crossed nicols on a petrological microscope, unless more direct methods, such as electron microscopy, are used. The first optical expression of preferred orientation of the plasma grains is a "flecked" appearance under crossed nicols and a "twinkling" effect as the stage is rotated (*flecked extinction pattern*); this is due to the presence of plasma aggregates within which the plasma grains have a preferred orientation, but which have a random orientation with regard to each other. If the plasma aggregates have a preferred orientation with regard to each other, varying degrees of a *striated extinction pattern* become apparent. If the plasma is isotropic, or birefringence is masked by organic matter or sesquioxides, the thin section appears isotropic under crossed nicols. These are the basic criteria on which the following classes of plasmic fabric have been recognized.

(1) Asepic[4] plasmic fabrics: the extinction pattern is flecked; there are virtually no plasma separations. Asepic fabrics can be subdivided into *argillasepic* fabric in which the plasma consists dominantly of anisotropic clay minerals and has a flecked extinction pattern, and *silasepic* fabric in which the plasma has a flecked extinction pattern but high proportions of silt–size grains make it difficult to recognize plasma aggregates.

(2) Sepic plasmic fabrics: striated extinction patterns are present in some part of the plasma. Sepic plasmic fabrics can be subdivided into *insepic* fabric, in which the striated extinction pattern occurs as isolated patches or islands; *mosepic* fabric, which is an extreme development of insepic fabric in which the striated patches are numerous and may even adjoin each other; *vosepic* fabric, in which the striated extinction pattern is associated with voids; *skelsepic* fabric, in which the striated pattern is close to and parallel to the surfaces of skeleton grains and/or glaebules; *masepic* fabric, in which the striated pattern occurs in zones through the s–matrix but is not associated with voids; *lattisepic*

4. "Sepic" is derived from "separation"; "sepic" means "with plasma separations", and "asepic" means "without plasma separations".

fabric, in which the striated pattern occurs as two sets of short prolate areas approximately at right angles to each other; and *omnisepic* fabric, in which all the plasma exhibits a complex striated extinction pattern.

(3) Undulic[5] plasmic fabric: the plasma is weakly anisotropic with faint undulose extinction; anisotropic plasma aggregates are not recognizable, or are indistinct, even at high magnification.

(4) Isotic[6] plasmic fabric: the plasma appears isotropic.

(5) Crystic[7] plasmic fabric: the plasma is usually anisotropic and consists of recognizable crystals, usually of the more soluble plasma fractions.

Each of these named plasmic fabrics is characterized by a single kind of pattern; this is an idealized concept since soil materials usually exhibit combinations of such fabrics. Thus, a material with striated orientation associated with skeleton grains and voids may be termed *vo–skelsepic* if the rest of the material is argillasepic, or *vo–skelsepic undulic* if the rest of the material is undulic, and so on. Examples of plasmic fabrics are shown in Fig. 6.

Voids—The plasmic fabric names can be qualified by adjectives to describe the void pattern (e.g., vughy, vesicular, channelled, jointed, fractured, and crazed, where the voids are vughs, vesicles, channels, joint planes, skew planes, and craze planes, respectively).

Related distribution of plasma and skeleton grains—The plasmic fabrics can also be qualified as being *porphyroskelic*[8] where the skeleton grains are set in a dense plasma, *agglomeroplasmic*[9] where the plasma forms loose masses between the skeleton grains, *intertextic* (Kubiena 1938) where the plasma forms bridges between skeleton grains, and *granular* where there is no plasma.

Characteristics of the skeleton grains—The plasmic fabrics can be qualified further according to the distribution pattern of the skeleton grains (e.g., regular, banded, clustered, and so on).

5. "Undulic" is derived from "undulose" which describes the extinction pattern.
6. "Isotic" is derived from "isotropic".
7. "Crystic" is derived from "crystallized".
8. Porphyroskelic replaces "porphyritic" as used in the lectures to avoid confusion with geological terms.
9. Agglomeroplasmic replaces "agglomeratic" as used in the lectures to avoid confusion with geological terms.

Mineral analysis

This section deals only with those mineral analyses which can be made with the petrological microscope, and the principal uses to which such analyses can be put in the study of soils. Basically, such analyses are used to relate soil materials to their parent materials, to establish the uniformity (or otherwise) of the parent material of soil profiles, and to assess changes in the profile due to soil–forming processes. These objectives can be achieved only by quantitative mineral analyses.

Methods of estimation

Grain counts—The usual method of estimating the proportions of the various mineral species is by counting grains in size separates. The accuracy of such counts has been considered by a number of authors, most of whom based their conclusions on considerations put forward by Dryden (1931, 1935). The situation is that a balance must be struck between the probable percentage error (P), the confidence interval (k), the mineral species as a fraction of the sample (p), and the total number of grains counted (n). Without going into its derivation, the equation relating these values is:

$$n = \left(\frac{1-p}{p}\right)\left(\frac{100k}{P}\right)^2$$

A number of workers have suggested that it is necessary to count a total of only 300 grains in each sample, but this is based on a confidence interval of only 50 per cent (k = 0.6745). That is, the true value will lie between the limits of the estimated value plus or minus the probable percentage error in only one case out of two. Even if this level were acceptable, Table 2 shows that there must be between 30 and 40 per cent of the species being estimated in the sample to achieve a probable percentage error of 5 per cent, and between 10 and 15 per cent for a probable percentage error of 10 per cent. Therefore, as a balance between time and accuracy, it is suggested that a minimum of 1500 grains should be counted in each sample (see Table 2).

Estimation of volume and weight—Percentage by weight can be estimated by making pure separates, which is a time–consuming operation. Percentage by volume is estimated by measuring areas in grain mounts.

Table 2. Relationship between number of grains counted, probable percentage error, confidence interval, and percentage of the mineral species in the sample

Mineral species as a fraction of sample	Probable percentage error = 5 per cent			Probable percentage error = 10 per cent		
	Confidence Interval 50 per cent	Confidence Interval 80 per cent	Confidence Interval 95 per cent	Confidence Interval 50 per cent	Confidence Interval 80 per cent	Confidence Interval 95 per cent
.005	36,019	130,345	305,863	9,055	32,636	76,416
.01	16,119	64,848	152,163	4,504	16,236	38,016
.02	8,869	32,095	75,313	2,230	8,036	18,816
.05	**3,439**	12,445	29,203	865	3,116	7,296
.10	**1,629**	5,895	15,370	406	**1,476**	3,456
.15	1,029	3,712	8,709	258	929	2,176
.20	724	2,620	6,148	182	656	**1,536**
.25	543	1,965	4,611	136	492	1,152
.30	422	**1,528**	**3,586**	106	383	896
.40	271	983	2,306	68	246	576
.50	181	655	**1,537**	46	164	384
.60	121	437	1,025	30	109	256
.70	78	281	659	20	70	165
.80	45	164	384	11	41	96
.90	20	73	171	5	18	43

Rosiwal's (1898) method consisted simply of making line traverses and measuring the length along these lines occupied by each mineral species. Two sets of measurements are made along sets of lines perpendicular to each other, and percentages by area are estimated simply by adding the linear measurements and reducing them to 100. Friedman (1958) used a similar method, while Chayes (1956) used a point grid and counted the number of points enclosed by the grains of each mineral species. Percentage by weight can be estimated from percentage by volume if the specific gravities of the mineral species are known.

Calculation of soil formation

The parent material—The first essential for making quantitative estimations of soil formation is that the parent material must have been uniform throughout the profile; the second is that the true parent material must be preserved. Changes in kind of mineral species with depth in the profile can be taken to indicate lack of uniformity of parent material, but changes in percentage of mineral species cannot be used by themselves since the soil–forming processes normally cause such changes. Probably the best criterion for uniformity is a constant ratio throughout the profile of two mineral species which are essentially stable under the conditions of soil formation; zircon and tourmaline are commonly accepted as most suitable for this purpose. Failing this, the most dependable criterion is a gradual, progressive change in mineral composition, particularly in specific mineral ratios, with depth and a constancy for some depth in the parent material. Even so, abrupt horizon boundaries which are due to soil formation will cause abrupt changes in mineral ratios, even though the parent material is uniform, unless the mineral species used are relatively resistant to weathering. If these criteria are used, it becomes apparent that the only true parent material of soil profiles is the unweathered rock, whether it be a hard rock or an unconsolidated sediment.

The stable constituent—Calculations of soil formation are based on measurement of some characteristic of the parent material which is considered to have remained constant during soil formation. The characteristics which have been used are chemical (e.g., percentage of silica, alumina, or titanium depending on the climatic zone—see Merrill 1921, Muir 1951, Joffe 1936, Nikiforoff and Drosdoff 1943), mineralogical (e.g., percentage of zircon, quartz, fine sand, tourmaline, and so on— see Haseman and Marshall 1945, Brewer 1955, Barshad 1955), or physical (e.g., constant volume—see Wild 1961). Although there is probably no such thing as absolute immobility and stability of minerals or chemical constituents, the percentage of zircon is probably the most generally dependable characteristic on which to base calculations. Although zircon is known to weather under some conditions, apparently satisfactory results have been obtained when the estimates of zircon are based on the larger size fractions in which it occurs. It often occurs in igneous rocks in two generations, one as relatively large crystals and one as very small inclusions in other minerals, and there is some evidence that where weathering of zircon has been recorded it has taken place principally in the small grains. Certainly, the percentage of zircon should be more dependable than composite characteristics such as the fine sand fraction, while the selection of a chemical characteristic depends on a knowledge that the particular characteristic has been stable, not only in the present environment, but during any changes in environment during the history of development of the profile. Certainly, it can be demonstrated, on the basis of numbers of skeleton grains per unit volume, that volume is not constant during soil development in many profiles.

Calculations—Having proved uniformity of parent material and selected a constant characteristic, calculations can be made concerning change in volume, weight, and thickness of each soil horizon and of the whole profile, and gains and losses of specific constituents. The equations involved are:

(1) Changes in volume:

$$V_p - V_s = V_p - \frac{K \cdot V_p}{R_s \cdot D_s}$$

where V_p = volume of parent material which forms V_s
V_s = volume of present–day soil horizon formed from V_p
K = a constant = the product of the percentage by weight of the stable constituent in the parent material and its bulk density.
R_s = percentage by weight of the stable constituent in the present–day soil horizon.
D_s = bulk density of the present–day soil horizon.

(2) Change in weight:

$$W_p - W_s = V_p \cdot D_p - \frac{K \cdot V_p}{R_s}$$

where W_p = weight of parent material which forms W_s
W_s = weight of present–day soil horizon formed from W_p
D_p = bulk density of parent material

(3) Change in thickness:

$$T_p - T_s = T_p - \frac{K \cdot T_p}{R_s \cdot D_s}$$

where T_p = thickness of parent material which forms T_s
T_s = thickness of present–day soil horizon formed from T_p

(4) Gain or loss of a constituent:

$$X_g = \frac{V_s \cdot D_s}{100} \left(\frac{R_s \cdot P'_x}{R_p} - P_x \right)$$

where X_g = weight in gms of constituent X lost or gained during formation of the present–day horizon.

P_x = percentage by weight of constituent X in the present–day
soil horizon.

P'_x = percentage by weight of constituent X in the parent material.

Rp = percentage by weight of stable constituent in the parent
material.

Evaluation of weathering

It is often desirable to assess the so–called "degree of weathering"
of soil materials and soil profiles. There are two important aspects to
this question: the factual measurement of the amount of weathering of
the constituent minerals (*absolute weathering*), and an estimate of the
relative stability of the minerals weathered, the kind of secondary minerals formed, and the effect of grain size, fracturing, and so on, on
the rate of weathering (*intensity of weathering*).

Absolute weathering—The absolute weathering can be measured by
using the calculations of soil formation to estimate the amounts of the
various mineral species which have been lost during soil formation.
These estimates should be quoted as actual amounts lost rather than
percentages of the amounts originally present, because they should be
estimations of the actual amount of weathering due to soil formation.

Intensity of weathering—The assessment of the intensity of weathering is the measure of the amount of primary minerals of known relative
stability which has been weathered, and of the effectiveness of leaching
as expressed by the kind of secondary mineral formed. Jackson and
Sherman (1953) introduced the concept of a *weathering mean* to assess
intensity of weathering. It was derived from the equation:

$$m = \frac{\Sigma (pS)}{\Sigma (p)}$$

where m = the weathering mean

p = the percentage of a mineral species in the soil

S = the weathering stage of the mineral species to which p refers (according to Jackson and Sherman's [*loc. cit.*] weathering sequence table).

$\Sigma =$ "the summation of."

This weathering mean is based entirely on the kind of secondary mineral formed, and takes no account of the clay–size minerals which may have been present in the parent material, or of the relative stabilities of the primary minerals. A more comprehensive weathering mean can be calculated from the equation

$$m = m_s - m_p$$

where $m_s = \dfrac{\Sigma\,(pS)}{\Sigma\,(p)}$ for the soil material

$m_p = \dfrac{\Sigma\,(pS)}{\Sigma\,(p)}$ for the parent material

and *p* refers to both the primary and secondary minerals with *S* taken from Jackson and Sherman's table for secondary minerals and from Pettijohn's (1941) table of persistence for primary minerals.

The role of fabric and mineral analysis

The role of fabric and mineral analysis is obvious from the foregoing discussion. Fabric analysis is a powerful tool for description and classification of soil materials and soil profiles; it describes in detail most important morphological features which have been ignored in the past. These features, too, are susceptible to interpretation, both directly from the data obtained from fabric analysis, and because fabric analysis presents the information necessary for the proper planning of experimental work designed to elucidate the genesis of the various fabric features. It also supplies the means of checking whether particular experiments, in fact, do reproduce the features which occur in soil materials. There are several phases to such experiments: first, the simple reproduction of observed fabric features which will point to the general kind of process involved, and, second, elucidation of the details of the actual mechanisms involved. The latter is likely to be a much more difficult and time–consuming study for specialist physical chemists, chemists, and physicists. The data of fabric analysis is directly applicable to the first phase of such studies, but is of lesser importance in the second stage even though it is based on the first stage.

Such studies in genesis of fabric features, and so of soil profiles, depend on identification of the kinds of constituents involved in the features, and knowledge of the properties and reactions of such constituents. The techniques of fabric analysis make it possible to locate and isolate these constituents so that they can be identified in relation to their location in the soil material and in the soil profile.

The importance of fabric analysis in soil physics is self–evident in the definition of soil fabric and the kinds of properties it describes. It deals with the size, shape, and arrangement of the constituents and voids, and, if the nature and behavior of the constituents are also known, fabric analysis will obviously lead to a knowledge of the physical behavior and properties of soil materials. It is obvious, too, that since they control the environment of the plant roots, such characteristics are of prime importance to the growth of plants.

Of themselves, fabric and mineral analyses are essential tools in the study of the origin and uniformity of soil parent materials and the genesis of soil profiles in terms of the degree of weathering minerals, losses and gains in the profile, and the general processes involved, such as segregation of constituents, illuviation, diffusion, and crystallization. From the data of fabric analysis, hypotheses can be put forward on the general processes of formation of voids, the various kinds of pedological features, and the various levels of structure, especially the important levels of plasmic and secondary structure. The data and hypotheses derived in this way can be applied to various kinds of soil profiles, and so hypotheses concerning their genesis can be put forward.

Such studies are in their infancy, and so it is probable that many hypotheses which seem sound on present data will need modification as more data is obtained. This data will come partly from the work of specialists in the study of the details of mechanisms operative in soil formation, but it will also come from the accumulation of data from fabric and mineral analyses on a wide range of soil profiles.

References

Barshad, I. (1955) *Chemistry of the Soil:* I. Soil development: Reinhold Publ. Corp., New York (Edited by F. E. Bear), pp. 1-52.

Baver, L. D. (1948) *Soil Physics:* Chapman-Hall, Ltd., London, p. 308.

Brewer, R. (1955) Mineralogical examination of a yellow podzolic soil formed on granodiorite: *C.S.I.R.O. (Aust.) Soil Publ.*, No. 5, p. 28.

Brewer, R. (1960a) Cutans: their definition, recognition and classification: *Jour. Soil Sci.*, v. 11, pp. 280-92.

Brewer, R. (1960b) The petrographic approach to the study of soils: in *Trans. 7th Intl. Cong. Soil Sci.,* Madison, v. 1, pp. 1-13.

Brewer, R. and Sleeman, J. R. (1960) Soil structure and fabric: their definition and description: *Jour. Soil Sci.,* v. 11, pp. 172-85.

Brewer, R. and Sleeman, J. R. (1963) Pedotubules: their definition, classification and interpretation: *Jour. Soil Sci.,* v. 14, pp. 156-66.

Brewer, R. and Sleeman, J. R. (1964) Glaebules: their definition, classification and interpretation, *Jour. Soil Sci.,* v. 15, pp. 66-78.

Butler, B. E. (1955) A system for the description of soil structure and consistence in the field: *Jour. Aust. Inst. Agr. Sci.,* v. 21, pp. 239-49.

Butler, B. E. (1958) Depositional systems of the Riverine Plain in relation to soils: *C.S.I.R.O. (Aust.) Soil Publ.,* No. 10, p. 35.

Butler, B. E. (1959) Periodic phenomena in landscapes as a basis for soil studies: *C.S.I.R.O. (Aust.) Soil Publ.,* No. 14, p. 20.

Chayes, F. (1956) *Petrographic Modal Analysis:* John Wiley and Sons, Inc., New York, pp. 4-16.

Dijk, D. C. van (1959) Soil features in relation to erosional history in the vicinity of Canberra: *C.S.I.R.O. (Aust.) Soil. Publ.,* No. 13, p. 41.

Dryden, L. (1931) Accuracy in percentage representation of heavy mineral frequencies: *Proc. Nat. Acad. Sci.,* v. 17, pp. 233-38.

Dryden, L. (1935) A statistical method for the comparison of heavy mineral suites: *Amer. Jour. Sci.,* v. 29, pp. 393-408.

Friedman, C. M. (1958) Determination of sieve-size distribution from thin-section data for sedimentary petrological studies: *Jour. Geol.,* v. 66, p. 394.

Haseman, J. F. and Marshall, C. E. (1945) The use of heavy minerals in studies of the origin and development of soils: *Mo. Agr. Exp. Sta. Res. Bul.,* No. 387, p. 75.

Jackson, M. L. and Sherman, G. D. (1953) Chemical weathering of minerals in soils: *Adv. in Agronomy,* No. 5, pp. 219-318.

Jenny, H. (1941) *Factors of Soil Formation:* McGraw-Hill, New York, p. 281.

Johnson, W. M., *et al.* (1960) Classification and description of soil pores: *Soil Sci.,* v. 89, pp. 319-21.

Jongerius, A. (1957) Morphologic investigation of soil structure: Bodemkundige Studies No. 2: Mededelingen van de Stickting voor Bodemkartering, Wageningen, p. 93.

Kubiena, W. L. (1938) *Micropedology:* Collegiate Press Inc., Ames, Iowa.

Merrill, G. P. (1921) *Rocks, Rock Weathering, and Soils:* Macmillan, New York.

Muir, A. (1951) Notes on the soils of Syria: *Jour. Soil Sci.,* v. 2, pp. 163-82.

Nikiforoff, C. C. and Drosdoff, M. (1943) Genesis of a clay-pan soil: *Soil Sci.,* v. 55, p. 459.

Pettijohn, F. J. (1941) Persistence of heavy minerals and geologic age: *Jour. Geol.,* v. 49, pp. 610-25.

Pettijohn, F. J. (1957) *Sedimentary Rocks:* Harper, New York, p. 718.

Raeside, J. D. (1959) Stability of index minerals in soils with particular reference to quartz, zircon, and garnet: *Jour. Sed. Petrol.*, v. 29, pp. 493-502.

Read, H. J. (1948) *Rutley's Elements of Mineralogy:* Thomas Murby and Co., London, p. 525.

Rice, C. M. (1954) *Dictionary of Geological Terms:* Edwards Bros., Inc., Ann Arbor, Michigan, p. 461.

Rosiwal, A. (1898) Ueber geometrische Geistens analysen. Ein enfacher Weg Quantitatsverhaltnisses der Mineralbestandtheile gemengter Gesteine: *Verhandl K. K. Geol. Reichsanstalt*, Wien, p. 143.

Ruhe, R. V. (1956) Geomorphic surfaces and the nature of soils: *Soil Sci.*, v. 82, pp. 441-55.

Sleeman, J. R. (1963) Cracks, peds, and their surfaces in some soils of the Riverine Plain, N.S.W.: *Aust. Jour. Soil Res.*, v. 1, pp. 91-102.

Sneed, E. D. and Folk, R. L. (1958) Pebbles in the lower Colorado River, Texas: a study in particle morphogenesis: *Jour. Geol.*, v. 66, pp. 114-50.

U.S.D.A. (1951) *Soil Survey Manual:* U.S. Dept. Agr. Handbook No. 18, p. 503.

Wadell, H. (1932) Volume, shape and roundness of rock particles: *Jour. Geol.*, v. 40, pp. 443-51.

Wadell, H. (1933) Sphericity and roundness of rock particles: *Jour. Geol.* v. 41, pp. 310-31.

Wadell, H. (1935) Volume, shape, and roundness of quartz particles: *Jour. Geol.*, v. 43, pp. 250-79.

Walker, P. H. (1959) A study of cyclic soils, their relation to landscape and their development on the South Coast of New South Wales: M. Sc. Thesis, University of Sydney.

Wild, A. (1961) Loss of zirconium from 12 soils derived from granite: *Aust. Jour. Agr. Res.*, v. 12, pp. 300-305.

III . . . X-ray Diffraction Analysis of Soil Clays and Structures of Clay Minerals

(Abstracts of Lectures)

W. F. Bradley

I. Introduction to principles of diffraction and absorption of X rays

The diffraction analysis of crystalline solids is a consequence of the physical coincidence that the periodic nature of the arrangements of atoms (with their individual electron configurations) in crystals exhibit periodicities of magnitudes comparable with the wave lengths of the electromagnetic radiations called X rays.

Diffraction methods for identification and estimations of soil minerals make use of rather complex series of factors, some inherent in the principles of diffraction, and some consequent to the nature of the soil minerals, which bear upon and require scanning of rather small diffraction angles. Taken together these have an over–all effect of producing the highest intensity features in the low–angle range. In fact any contrary observation may be taken as an automatic signal of improper specimen alignment. In the course of my discussions, I will try to furnish an elementary picture of the various principles involved.

First and simplest is the matter of polarization. An electromagnetic wave has an electric vector in a plane normal to its direction of propagation that may be considered as resolved into two component amplitudes at right angles to each other. These are analogous to the two polarized components of visible light that are separated by a Nicol prism. If the interaction of an electromagnetic wave with an electron be viewed in the direction of propagation of the wave, both polarized components are viewed at their full amplitudes, but at any other direction of observation, only one component is seen at its full amplitude, and the other is seen foreshortened by the cosine of the angle between the observer and the direction of propagation. Intensity effects, which are squares of amplitudes, are therefore subject to the relation: $I \propto 1 + \cos^2 \emptyset$, where $\emptyset$ is the angle of deviation. We will later call this angle 2Θ.

If electrons were utterly unrelated to each other, the intensity of a signal from n electrons would simply be n times the signal from one electron. In solids, however, electrons are clumped in meticulously prescribed shells according to the atomic numbers of the positive nuclei with which they are associated. In such clumps it is still true that the intensity of a signal in the direction of propagation is directly proportional to the number of electrons, but at all inclined directions of observation, phase differences between the signals from individuals result in reduced efficiency.

If two equal atoms be considered, a line connecting their centers can be a bisectrix to the angle between incident radiation and diffracted radi-

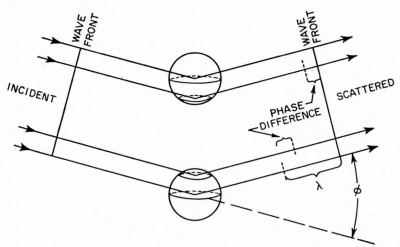

Figure 1. Phase relationships for radiation scattered by electrons at illustrative levels within two typical spherical atoms.

tion as observed at some point ($180° - \emptyset$). Then, when radiation is incident in the direction indicated in Fig. 1, a maximum signal is received in the scattered direction when the path length through the second atom is exactly one, or some integral number of wave lengths of radiation longer than that through the first atom. But of all the electrons in each given clump the exact relation can hold only for those in the horizontal great circle reference sections of the atoms. Their signals differ by whole phases, but electrons elsewhere in the clump furnish amplitudes which either lag or lead the great circle contributions by phase angles proportional to their displacement from the reference. Total signal amplitudes are the sum of the individual contributions by the cosines of their phase angles, and these sums decrease notably as the angle $\emptyset$ (or 2Θ) increases. Every atom therefore has an atom scattering factor (available in amplitude tabulations in X–ray diffraction texts) which varies from its atomic number at a zero–degree scattering angle to about half that for directions for which $\dfrac{\sin\Theta}{\lambda}$ is on the order of 0.4 The corresponding intensity decline is to one fourth.

The geometry of Bragg's law, $n\lambda = 2\,d\,\sin\Theta$, emerges from Fig. 1 by the addition of infinite arrays of like atoms whose horizonal great circle sections are coplanar with either of the two individuals shown or with additional parallel planes displaced by the same translation d in either direction from the two planes indicated. (Additional remarks with respect to diffraction geometry will be deferred to Section III.)

Absorption geometry furnishes a concept of prime significance to people with soils interests.

As X–radiation penetrates solid matter the rate of attenuation of intensity is proportional to the flux of radiation. This is formulated in a familiar "first order" equation:

$I/I_o = e^{-\mu t}$, where I_o is intensity incident, I intensity transmitted through t, the length of the solid path, and μ a coefficient of linear absorption characteristic of the composition of the solid penetrated. Absorption coefficients are normally tabulated on basis of mass, and are related to linear coefficients by the relation: $\mu_{linear} = \mu_{mass} \times \rho$, where ρ is the density of the solid. For complex compositions, μ_{mass} is the sum of μ_{mass} for each of the several chemical species in the compound times their fractional abundances in the compound.

For common (iron–free) soil mineral compositions μ_{linear} for Cu radiation is about 100. It increases rapidly with the presence of iron to a maximum of about 1200 for hematite.

Specimen calculations indicate that, if a diffracted intensity commensurate with the diffracting ability of a common soil sample is to be realized in spectrometer techniques, the solid path length should be of the order of 200 microns. Thin specimens, prepared to accomplish maximum degrees of preferred orientation, easily afford desirable solid path lengths at small angles of inclined incidence, but rapidly become excessively transparent as angle of incidence increases. A slide 10 μ thick and 5 cm. long provides an "in–bound" path of 200 μ for diffraction angle of 6° (2Θ), but only 100 μ at 12° (2Θ), and only 10 μ at 90° (2Θ). When definitive data for identification of minerals is required at moderately large diffraction angles, slides need be thickened to levels commensurate with the absorptive requirement, even at sacrifice in the efficiency with which preferred orientation in the slide can be developed. Extended treatments of the foregoing principles are available in chapters II and III of Klug and Alexander (1954).

II. Crystal-chemical aspects of layer silicates

The clay mineral structures in which we are interested are quite lucidly described in Chapter IV of *Clay Mineralogy* by R. E. Grim. Rather than be repetitious of this reference and of the subject matter of the other lectures in this course, I will instead call attention to some of the not too rigorously inferred features of such structures.

The backbone feature of the layer silicates is an articulated array of silica tetrahedra in which each silicon atom is surrounded by 4 oxygens in tetrahedral disposition, and each oxygen is shared, either within a layer by 2 silicons, or by extra–layer condensation, between a silicon and octahedral ions. The array affords an infinite net of 6–membered rings which consist of bases of tetrahedra all coplanar, with one apex of each tetrahedron in a plane about 2.2 A removed from the basal net. Analyses have disclosed that the silicons are indeed very nearly centrally located in their respective tetrahedra, and from this and other considerations it is inferred that a large degree of covalent bonding characterizes the complex. Each silicon is bound to oxygen by its sp^3 tetrahedral hybrid orbitals, and the silicons have the same disposition relative to oxygen of 2 of the oxygen sp^3 bonding orbitals. The basal plane oxygens participate in only 2 bonds, and they are polarized, presenting a definite negative aspect on the side of the plane opposite the silicons. The apical oxygens bond (but more weakly) to 3 or 2 octahedral neighbors, also disposed in their sp^3 hybrid orbital directions.

Two equal tetrahedral nets, with apices facing each other, form a motif, together with hydroxyl ions, which affords octahedral environment to additional metal ions (mainly Al, Mg, and Fe^{++} but often including many other comparable sized species). The octahedral ion–oxygen associations have some unspecified but lesser degree of covalency in their nature and have more ionic nature than do the Si–O associations.

A Si–O bond is only about 1.60 A long, and when Al appears as a tetrahedral ion the Al–O bond is about 1.78 A long. Bonds from octahedral ions (including Al also) are from about 1.95 to 2.1 A long. The familiar "three–layer" sandwich of 2 tetrahedral levels articulating between them 1 octahedral level thus consists of 2 strongly associated sheets supporting 1 which is somewhat less strongly associated. The sandwich presents a negative aspect to the outside world, and conceals its positive nature within.

A lateral unit of this crystallization scheme consists of 24 oxygens in 4 parallel planes, and normally has associated with it 4 protons as members of O–H$^-$ groups. The summed cation valencies are demanded to total 44, and the sites available to them are 8 tetrahedra and 6 octahedra. Two compositions achieve this perfect balance; pyrophyllite with 8 Si, 4 Al, and 2 unoccupied octahedra; and talc, with 8 Si and 6 Mg. The other compositions of interest to us fail to furnish a full complement of 44 charges in the 14 possible sites, and any deficiency must be made up by the collection of other positively charged ions in space exterior to the sandwich. These comprise the exchange ions. They may have a bewildering array of specific identities, they may exhibit greatly variable degrees of exchangeability, and they may condition supplemental accumulations of water in interlayer space, but they always involve less intimate bonding than that which characterizes the tetrahedral and octahedral associations of the fundamental structure.

When immersed in water, materials which conform to this basic structure enter into heterogeneous equilibria with the liquid phase, furnishing the highest activity to the solution for interlayer ions, activities of lesser magnitude for octahedrally coordinated ions, and still lower activities for the ions which were tetrahedrally coordinated. You may note that these relationships may be altered by the more rigorous conditions imposed in various sample benefication procedures treated by Professor Jackson.

The great permissible latitudes of composition of the 3–layer soil minerals, as contrasted with the narrow composition ranges of the kaolin minerals, is of fundamental importance in soil fertility, and leads us to concentrate attention on them. The ultimate kaolin bodies will probably never assume any importance in agriculture.

III. The intensity of diffracted X-radiation

A very useful concept in the description of diffraction processes is that of a reciprocal lattice. The orientation of any plane in space is conveniently represented by a vector normal to that plane. For the periodically arranged families of planes which characterize crystalline nature, the same vector is normal to the whole family, and by assigning to it a length reciprocal to the family interplanar distance, both the orientation and spacing are specified. A set of three intersecting noncoplanar vectors and their combinations affords an imaginary space–permeating set of points, named a reciprocal lattice, which are a property of any crystal.

The construction by which this lattice is equated to the Bragg law is illustrated in Fig. 2 (Klug and Alexander, Figs. 3–8, p. 123). By choos-

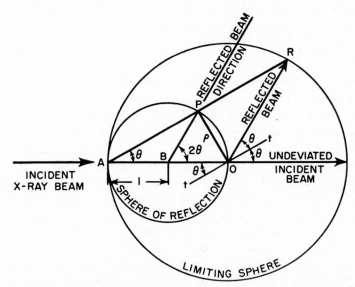

Figure 2. Geometrical relationships between a reciprocal lattice node and incident and reflected X = radiation for the condition $\rho d = \lambda$. AO and OR are incident and reflected directions, θ is the Bragg angle, and P is the reciprocal lattice node for which $OP = \rho$ (Adapted from J. D. Bernal, Proc. Roy. Soc., London, 113A, 117).

ing the reciprocal relation that $\rho d = \lambda$, $\rho = 2 \sin \Theta$, and the position of any vector terminal, called a node, lies in the surface of a sphere of radius 1 when the Bragg equation is satisfied. This sphere is called the sphere of diffraction.

In powder diffraction, enough crystals are present in the aggregate to insure that a given node in the reciprocal lattice for some one crystal in the aggregate takes every possible position on the surface of a sphere of radius ρ, and diffraction occurs for all cases in which ρ terminates in the circular intersection of this sphere with the sphere of diffraction. This circular intersection varies in circumference with the magnitude of ρ, and the fraction of the population of nodes which can be coincident with a given site on the circular intersection is proportional to $\dfrac{1}{\sin \Theta}$. Similarly, a reflected cone of radiation is distributed about a circular section of a limitary sphere which has a circumference of $4\pi \sin 2\Theta$, and the fraction of the diffracted cone which can be received in a slit of length l is proportional to $l/\sin 2\Theta$. These two efficiency factors complete the combined Lorentz and polarization factors which are conveniently tabulated as a function $\Xi = \dfrac{1 + \cos^2 2\Theta}{\sin^2 \Theta \cos \Theta}$. This function has numerical values of several thousand at 2° or 3° of diffraction angle, but declines rapidly to only about 100 at 16°. In order to appraise the relative importance of diffraction features from the standpoint of the crystal, intensities need be reduced by correction for this factor which arises only from the conditions for observation.

A final, rather massive, consideration in the intensity of diffraction effects is the geometrical structure factor, F. This factor is normally developed on a three dimensional basis, but in the soils analyses only one dimension is found to be critically useful, so we will take advantage of the simplification. In the Fig. 1 in which we looked at atom factors, only one species was present, and we extended it by adding equals in arrays in the same horizontal planes. In complex compositions, other atomic species participate in the total structures, and we have seen that they tend to be arranged in planes other than the reference levels, constituting various interleavings. Just as we found the need to consider the efficiency of signal from out–of–reference plane electrons in that case, we must now consider the signal from out–of–plane atoms. In the structures we study, reference planes include centers of symmetry, and the amplitude of scattered radiation for a whole complex structure is a sum of the amplitudes contributed by all the entities in a given unit times the cosine of the phase angle by which their amplitudes lag or lead the signals from the reference position. In our one dimensional summation, $F_{ool} = \Sigma_i f_i \cos 2\pi l z_i$. In most of the clays, individual atoms group in only a few planes, and sums are arrived at by carrying only 5 or 6 terms. The profile views of common compositions illustrated in Grim's (1953) text aid in visualization of the summation process.

Again, it is true that an undeviated beam carries a signal of amplitude equal to the sum of the amplitudes for all components, or the sum of their atomic numbers. No other direction can receive a stronger signal, and in general, signals are much weaker.

As a principle in crystallography, it is also true that thermal vibrations of atoms, involving displacement from ideal sites, attenuate diffracted intensities with increasing diffraction angles, but in the clays the effect is not observed separately from attenuations due to actual irregular displacements in the solids, and the principle need not be treated here.

In these several developments we are noting: that although the best definitive data for X–ray diffraction analysis are those collected at rather large diffraction angles, the features which are of sufficient intensity that we can manage any observations, even in the heterogeneous assemblages which comprise our soils, are the ones which occur at relatively small angles. A considerable requirement for artistry is imposed on the soil mineralogist. Additional pertinent reading on the subject may be found in Chapter III of Klug and Alexander (1954).

IV. The application of Fourier transform concepts to data analysis

The "3–layer" packet which we have found common to a large number of mineral structures has the uniform geometric feature that each set of 6 octahedral sites, taken as a plane of origin, are surrounded, above and below by 6 oxygens in planes about 1.1 A distant, by 4 silicons in planes about 2.7 A distant, and by 6 oxygens in planes about 3.3 A distant.

For any one composition the amplitude of a wave scattered by one layer in the direction defined by its normal can be calculated for all possible diffraction angles. This function is the Fourier transform of the layer along its normal, and it exists in reciprocal space with the same aura of reality as the reciprocal lattice nodes of a bona fide crystal

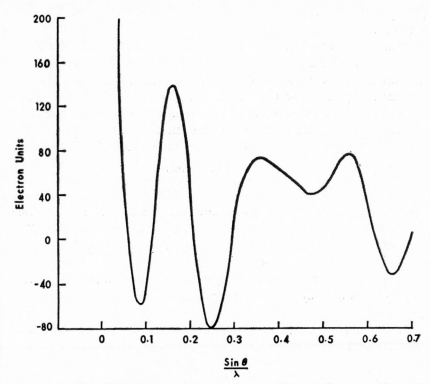

Figure 3. The Fourier transform of a single talc layer evaluated along the C* reciprocal space axis.

exist. It includes both the single value F_{ool} amplitudes summed in Section III and all intermediate points.

The Fourier transform for one layer of talc is illustrated in Fig. 3. Its shape is essentially constant for the other compositions, but its relation to the base line varies with the compositions of the octahedral reference plane. Amplitudes for more complicated arrays are derivable from it by direct addition of the effective amplitudes of the complicating matter. For example, this curve furnishes a transform for vermiculite if it is added to a transform for interlayer water and exchangeable Mg, or a transform for phlogopite if it is added to a transform for interlayer K.

For each proper crystal structure the discrete reciprocal lattice nodes (00*l*) are windows through which the continuous transform curve is viewed at the corresponding precise points. Illustrations were provided for related structures which afforded many nodes, because of their complexity, and few nodes because of simplicity of structures as projected onto (00*l*) reciprocal vectors.

The utility of the transform arises in the application of Fourier methods to data analysis. Observations are always in terms of intensity, and are reducible to terms of relative importance by application of Lorentz and polarization corrections, but geometric factors are summed in terms of amplitudes which are square roots of intensities. The Fourier formulation, reduced to one dimension states that

$$\rho_{(z)} = \frac{1}{L_c} \sum_{+\infty}^{-\infty} F_{ool} \cos 2\pi \frac{l_z}{c}$$

where ρ is the electron density in any plane parallel to the reference plane and F_{ool} are the amplitudes of signals at successive reciprocal lattice nodes. The sign of each F entry must be established independently from a transform of a proper model. It is noted in Fig. 3 that both positive and negative regions exist, and for those few cases where extraneous interlayer matter may influence a sign, proper choices can be made by trial and error.

The mechanics of electron density summations at specific points were illustrated in the laboratory.

V. Methods of analysis applicable to mixed-layer systems

The conventional methods of crystal structure analysis are, quite naturally, strictly applicable to crystals. In our soils, which develop from crystals by varying degrees of and diverse paths of deterioration, much mineral matter is encountered which no longer retains a constant crystalline character.

It is extremely fortunate then that so much of this mineral matter derives from the three–layer structural arrangements, and that it retains enough of its character that recognizable diffraction effects can be observed.

Attacks on soil mineralogy may be made, on one hand, by chemical treatments which attempt to remove the worst deteriorated matter, seeking the best grades in residues, or which attempt to regrade to a relatively constant condition; or, on the other hand, by seeking to interpret scattering from inconstant assemblages. Partial successes in both attacks supplement each other. The interpretations of scattering from mixed layer assemblages constitutes the second attack.

Each specific layer mineral has its own set of reciprocal lattice nodes, which are integrally spaced in sequences of windows through which their layer transform can be seen. The windows are specific positions which can be tabulated for all individual species. For any mixed assemblage, then, the windows belonging to properly chosen species can be scaled together along a single reciprocal lattice line. When windows exactly coincide, the transform (which is essentially the same for both species) is seen undistorted at that point. Near coincidences afford slightly out of focus views, and widely spaced windows permit only very vague glimpses. Such a co–linearly scaled pair of sets is illustrated in Fig. 4. Black dashes denote the nearer coincidences, and the shortness of each relates to the sharpness of focus, or the relative sharpness of a possible scattering feature. The position of actual observed maxima within each black dashed range is proportional to the relative abundance of the specific layers present. The arrangement for random sequences in mixed systems was also formulated analytically by Hendricks and Teller. Analyses are best conducted graphically by constructing nodes for assumed pairs (or triplets, etc.) until a match for an observed record is achieved.

As was true in crystal analysis, the effects to be realized from a model may be calculated for comparison with observed data, or observed data may be subjected to the Fourier analysis to produce a model.

The direct synthesis of a mixed system model is accomplished by the MacEwan transform method (Brown, 1961). This analysis is also formulated to say that the frequency with which one layer occurs displaced from any reference layer by a given number of angstroms is the sum of the relative importances of each scattering maximum by the

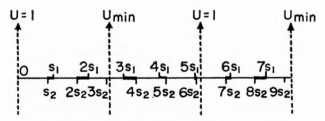

Figure 4. The device utilized by Mering (Acta Cryst. 2, 374) to depict co–linearly the positions of hypothetical nodes for each of the two components in a mixed system.

cosine of the phase angle at that point of the period it represents. This analysis, too, is best conducted graphically. Cosine waves of amplitude proportional to importance and wave length equal to apparent d are superposed on a single scale, and are added algebraically point by point. Importance at any given point is evaluated by dividing the actual observed intensity at that point by the Lorentz and polarization correction and the amplitude squared of our already familiar Fourier transform for the three–layer structure. The several pertinent references are reviewed together by MacEwan, Ruiz and Brown, in chapter XI in the Mineralogical Societies Monograph edited by Brown (1961).

Additional reading

Section	Source
I.	Klug, H. P. and Alexander, L. E. (1954) *X-ray Diffraction Procedures:* John Wiley & Sons, Inc., N. Y.
II.	Grim, R. E. (1953) *Clay Mineralogy:* McGraw-Hill Book Co., N. Y.
III.	Klug, H. P. and Alexander, L. E. (1954) *Diffraction Procedures:* John Wiley & Sons, Inc., N. Y.
IV.	*International Tables for Crystallography:* Kynoch Press, Birmingham, London, 1952.
V.	Brown, George (1961) *X-ray Identification and Crystal Structures of Clay Minerals:* Min. Soc. of London, Chap. XI, N. Y.

IV... The Application of Electron Microscopy in Soil Clay Mineralogy

Thomas F. Bates

Principle of the electron microscope*

The main purpose of an electron microscope is to extend the capabilities of our eyes by magnifying any small object which can be resolved by its lens system until the image, as recorded on a photographic plate, is large enough to be seen. From this statement it is evident that, in discussing the principles of electron microscopy, the two points of major concern are *resolution* and *magnification*. Less fundamental but nevertheless of vital significance are the matters of *depth of field* and *contrast*.

Since light and electron microscopy are similar not only with respect to these principles but also in regard to the arrangement of radiation source, lenses, sample position and image detectors, it is convenient and informative to compare the two methods, pointing out similarities and differences between them.

The principal difference is, of course, the use of an electron rather than a light beam as the type of radiation, and other differences arise from this. Thus, to produce electrons a tungsten filament is heated in a

* Detailed treatment of this subject is provided in many standard texts on electron microscopy such as that by Robert B. Fischer entitled *Applied Electron Microscopy*, published in 1954 by the Indiana University Press.

vacuum which must be maintained not only in the region of the "electron gun" but also in the column through which the electron beam must travel to reach the photographic plate. To achieve sufficient velocity to penetrate a specimen and traverse the column, the electrons are subjected to a potential difference, V, which may be varied to suit the purpose, but in most electron microscopes is commonly 50,000 to 100,000 volts. The condenser, objective, and projector lenses are arranged in the same relative position as are their counterparts in the light microscope but consist of electromagnetic or electrostatic devices for controlling the paths of the electrons. The image in an electron microscope is made visible by a fluorescent screen and recorded on a photographic plate in a camera arrangement for which the screen usually acts as a shutter.

The capability of the electron microscope to reveal objects almost three orders of magnitude smaller than those that can be seen in light microscopy results from the use of electron beams with wave lengths of the order of 0.05 A (as contrasted with 4000 to 7600 A for visible light). Just as in glass lens systems, however, the attainment of the theoretical limits is prevented by the aberrations produced in the lenses.

Most important are spherical aberration and that due to diffraction.

In the latter case, as first shown by Abbé, (1) $d = \dfrac{0.61 \lambda}{n \sin \alpha}$ where λ is

the wave length, n is the index of the medium, α is one–half the aperture angle of the lens, and d may be thought of as the diameter of the disc of light in the image derived from a point source in the object. In the case of spherical aberration, (2) $d = kf\alpha^3$ where k is the constant of proportionality, α is one–half the aperture angle of the lens (in radians), and f is the focal length of the lens. Since, in accord with the DeBroglie

equation (3) $\lambda = \dfrac{12.3}{V}$, wave length can be decreased by increasing the

potential difference V, aberration due to diffraction can be reduced in this manner (equation 1). Unfortunately, however, an increase in V also results in an increase in focal length thereby increasing the amount of spherical aberration (equation 2) and thus requiring a compromise between the two aberration effects in order to obtain optimum resolution. Other types of aberration, such as chromatic, are also important but can be minimized by careful design and construction of lens components. Using aperture angles of about 4.5×10^{-3} radians, electron microscopes now in operation are routinely attaining resolutions of about 5 A and claims of 2 to 3 A resolution have been made.

In order for a tiny particle (e.g., 10 A in diameter) to be made visible, it must not only be resolved but its image enlarged to a diameter of at least 1,000,000 A (0.1 mm.) before the normal human eye can perceive it. Thus, in this example, the "useful" magnification must be 100,000X. This magnification can easily be attained in present day electron microscopes, or if desired, the same total magnification can be produced by enlargement of electron micrographs taken at lower magnification on photographic plates of appropriate grain size.

Sample preparation

General statement

As is the case for a number of scientific instruments, only in rare instances, if ever, will the environment in the electron microscope even remotely resemble that in which the sample existed prior to its removal for study. It is true that frequently the behavior of the sample in the "instrumental environment" may provide much information of scientific value about the material under study, but if one is to interpret from the appearance of the material in the electron microscope what it looked like before being placed in the instrument, either he must assume that the change in environment has had no effect or he must determine or postulate what the changes have been and take them into account. Fortunately in the majority of experiments the change in the characteristics of the sample is either negligible or of little significance in the light of the amount of new information obtained.

Of more importance in many instances—particularly in dealing with soils and the clay minerals in them—is the problem of how to prepare the sample for insertion into the analytical instrument without changing the characteristics one desires to observe. Obviously the choice of sample preparation procedure may be critical and will depend on several factors, among the most important of which are:

1. the sensitivity of the material to change;
2. the object of the investigation;
3. the existing state of the material; and
4. the scope of the investigation and variety of techniques being used.

Thus, in the electron microscope study of soils and the clay minerals therein, the choice of procedure may vary considerably depending upon, for example:

1. Whether the morphology of the clay particles is highly dependent upon the state of hydration, as in the case for montmorillonite minerals, or more independent thereof as is kaolinite;
2. whether the purpose is to study the texture of the aggregate or the size of individual crystallites;
3. whether the sample is received in the natural state or after some type of preliminary chemical or physical treatment;
4. whether the purpose of the study is a quick check on the morphology of the fine fraction or a comprehensive investigation on morphological variability and textural relationships.

Whatever procedure is selected, it is important to bear in mind that the sample being observed in the electron microscope is no longer in its original condition. Since, in any scientific experiment, the data obtained will always be affected in some degree by the nature of the analytical operation, the best that can usually be done is to:

1. describe as completely as possible the nature of the starting material;
2. reduce the preparation procedures to a minimum;
3. discover through experience the effect of various procedures on similar materials; and
4. describe the operational procedure in detail for the benefit of other workers interested in making their own interpretation of the results.

Preliminary treatment for electron microscope study

Chemical and physical means of preparing soil material for electron microscope observation do not differ in most respects from those used to get the material ready for study with other instruments, primarily because the need for disaggregation, fractionation, and purification is common to many methods of evaluation. In most cases the gentlest method is the most preferable. Thus, if ultrasonic vibration satisfactorily disaggregates the particles, this method is much preferred to grinding because of the effect the latter treatment may have on the shape, crystallinity, and surface characteristics of the clay particles. Chemical treatments, for the removal of iron from the soil, for example, may be relatively innocuous in a kaolin–rich soil but drastically affect the morphology of clay particles in montmorillonite–rich material.

Preparation for the electron microscope

The standard preparation techniques are discussed in detail elsewhere (see, e.g., "Techniques for electron microscopy," by Desmond Kay, 1961), and will not be described again here. As in the preliminary treatment, the technique chosen for application to a particular problem should be the one which produces the least change in the condition of the sample. For this reason replica techniques, for example, are especially useful wherever information is sought on the morphological and textural characteristics of crystallites and aggregates received in the dry state. If, on the other hand, information is sought on the size and shape of particles in aqueous suspension, the freeze–dry technique or simple sedimentation upon the substrate may involve the least change in the parameters being measured.

As an example of the type of problem often encountered, reference may be made to Figs. 1 and 2 which illustrate kaolinite when dispersed as contrasted with its appearance in the original lump of clay. It can readily be seen that measurements of particle size may differ depending on the preparation technique employed; particularly since the problem is complicated by the difficulty, particularly in the replica, of defining a particle and its boundaries. A comparison of replicas and dispersions of the same kaolinite specimen commonly indicates that cleavage is an important part of the dispersion process.

Electron micrographs of clay minerals*

General statement

With the exception of attapulgite and sepiolite, the hydrous aluminum and magnesium silicates commonly referred to as clays belong in the

* The material in this section is excerpted from the author's Circular #51 of the Mineral Industries Experiment Station, College of Mineral Industries, The Pennsylvania State University: "Selected Electron Micrographs of Clays and other fine–grained minerals." The reader is referred to this work for other representative illustrations.

structure group known as the layer lattice or sheet structure silicates. As in other cases where layered groups of atoms are stacked in parallel array, the size, degree of order, and crystallographic characteristics of the resulting compound depend in large part upon the amount of strain resulting from the packing of smaller structural units within each layer, and upon the role played by interlayer bonds in counteracting such local strains in order to produce a large, three–dimensional crystal.

In the micas and chlorites, where possible intralayer strain is overcome by a combination of appropriate ion substitution within the layer and relatively strong bonds between adjacent layers, crystals grow to large size and have good three–dimensional order with the attendant development of well–defined crystal faces, cleavage, optical characteristics, and so on. On the other hand, when intralayer strain is not overcome by strong enough interlayer bonds, order in all dimensions is not sufficient to produce large mica–like crystals and fine–grained minerals result. However, since amount of strain, strength of bonds, and consequent degree of order all vary considerably, it is to be expected that within the mineral group referred to as clays there will be a large amount of variation in those properties which reflect the amount of structural order. Morphology is such a property and, because of the size range involved, the electron microscope is the best tool with which to study it.

Because of the variation in structure, composition, and degree of order in the clay mineral groups, the morphological characteristics of the various mineral species vary from those of a mica, at one extreme, to those of an amorphous silica–alumina gel at the other. Similarly because there is a gradation in chemistry and structure between species, a gradation in morphology and other properties is to be expected. In dickite and some kaolinites where interlayer bonds are relatively strong, crystals approach or attain megascopic size, plates are thick and crystallographic faces, angles, and cleavage are prominent and distinctive. Therefore, some crystals of these minerals can be effectively studied with the light microscope as well as at higher magnification. In other clays of the 1:1 structure type, decrease of interlayer bond strength results in the distinctive curved laths and tubes typical of halloysite and chrysotile; and ultimately in the "blobs" and spherules characteristic of allophane.

In the 2:1 minerals where curvature is inhibited by the sandwich arrangement of 2 silicon–oxygen sheets with a "gibbsite" or "brucite" sheet between, lack of strong interlayer bonds results in sheets and laths so thin as to approach unit cell thickness. Thus, montmorillonites are characterized in electron micrographs by barely resolved, thin flakes and shreds of irregular shape, or aggregates with considerable variation in density to the electron beam and frequently rather fuzzy outlines.

As is to be expected, illites occupy a morphological position intermediate between montmorillonites and micas. In dispersion preparations flakes are commonly thick enough to show well–defined edges, but only in lath–shaped varieties do the outlines indicate crystallographic control in directions other than the (001) plane.

Many electron micrographs bring out important morphological differences, even between samples of the same mineral, which result from different techniques used in preparing the material for electron microscope observation. Minerals such as the clays are extremely re-

Figure 1. Kaolinite—Langley, South Carolina (X34,968) Replicas such as this of a fracture surface indicate that crystalline units in the undistributed clay lump are often larger than the angular particles usually observed after dispersion of the material. This suggests that such particles are commonly cleavage fragments rather than true pseudohexagonal crystals.

Figure 2. Kaolinite—Williamsburg, Pennsylvania (X35,821) This dispersion shows typical angular flakes of variable thickness. Light oval areas are holes in the Collodion substrate. The variable thickness of some of the particles suggests that they represent cleavage fragments from larger units.

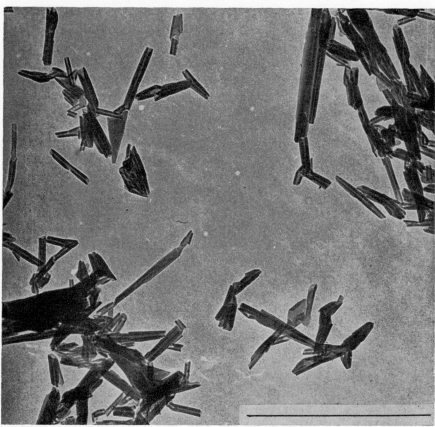

Figure 3. Halloysite—Wendover, Utah (X48,768) The tubular crystals found in samples from this locality tend to be shorter but somewhat better defined than those found in many halloysite samples. There is, however, no evidence of angular terminations and edge "markings," and the outlines of unrolled tubes are quite irregular.

sponsive to external forces and therefore particles seen after dispersion will often appear very different than when viewed in a replica of a fracture surface of the bulk specimen. Obviously the weaker the inter-layer bonds, the greater the effect will be. Consequently some clays will be affected more than others. However, even in kaolinite, comparison of different preparations shows that many of the well–defined, dispersed hexagonal plates assumed to be crystals are probably cleavage fragments from larger crystalline areas seen in replica in the original specimen.

*Figure 4. Kaolinite and halloysite, Clayton deposit—Leaky,
Texas (X24,400) This material consists of well-defined, roughly
equi-dimensional plates of kaolinite and large to small tubes of
halloysite. Some of the latter have "angular" termination and
edge features similar to those reported on elsewhere (Bates and
Comer, 1959).*

As a result it is important that each picture be evaluated in the light of
the method of preparation and its probable effect on the particular
mineral.

The kaolin group (Figs. 1, 2, 3, 4, and 5)

The minerals of this group include nacrite, dickite, kaolinite, halloysite ($2H_2O$), halloysite ($4H_2O$), and allophane. All are characterized

by distinctive morphological features and, except for the last
mentioned, are among the most
photogenic of the clay minerals.
Because the amount of crystalline
order in the direction perpendicular to (001) varies from excellent to nil, and because the
chemistry is not complicated by
appreciable cation substitution,
these minerals illustrate a direct
relationship between morphology
and interlayer bond strength.
Dickite and some kaolinite, with
the strongest bonds, occur in
megascopic "books" which are
easily studied in the light microscope and appear massive in low
magnification electron micrographs. In such cases basal
cleavage is present on the prism
faces but is not always well developed. Occurrences of such
books are rare, however, in comparison to the amount of kaolinite found in microscopic crystals. Nevertheless, bonds are still

*Figure 5. Halloysite—Wendover,
Utah (X75,136) This is a replica
of a fracture surface of the clay
lump showing end sections of
many tubes which intersect the
fracture surface at an angle.
The tubes vary appreciably in
length, thickness, apparent
radius of curvature, and linearity. Some of the tubes lying in
the surface may have become
flattened due to removal of interlayer water in the vacuum
evaporating apparatus during
production of the replica.*

sufficiently strong to give rise to crystals and cleavage forms thick
enough to give well–defined outlines in the most thoroughly dispersed
preparations. Furthermore, the hexagonal outlines provide evidence
not only of relatively strong interlayer bonds but of well–ordered stacking of successive layers in the direction of the c–axis.

Many kaolinite flint clays differ from other kaolins in that, even in
cases where X–ray study shows a minimum of randomness, replicas and
dispersions may reveal little evidence of hexagonal units. It is not definitely known whether this can be attributed to the manner in which the
crystals are packed, the presence of cementing material, failure to develop crystal outlines during formation, or loss of sharp outlines in the
process of formation or subsequent leaching. It is probable that different
factors are involved in different clays.

Halloysites represent the next step in the sequence from dickite to allophane. Until recently evidence indicated that all material characterized morphologically as halloysite originated in nature as tubes of the $4H_2O$ variety. However, study (Bates and Comer, 1958) of replicas of halloysite ($2H_2O$) from several deposits shows that much material giving X–ray patterns indicating the structural randomness characteristic of halloysite occurs in the form of flat to slightly curved laths. The presence on some of these of angular terminations and projections along the edges indicates that crystalline order perpendicular to (001) is greater than that in halloysite ($4H_2O$) tubes. Critical evaluations of chemical analyses of halloysite ($2H_2O$) supports other evidence that

Figure 6. Allophane—Tochigi Prefecture, Japan (X37,600)
This replica of particles allowed to settle on a glass slide
reveals the surface texture of some of the allophane
spherules in the Imaichi Clay. Although the clay contains
halloysite, no definite tubes are visible here.

*Figure 7. Illite—State College, Pennsylvania (X33,728)
This micrograph shows in replica the lath-shaped nature
of much of the illite found in clay fractions of the
Tuscarora and Oswego formations in Central Pennsylvania.*

excess hydrogen and oxygen which can not be removed at 100°C. causes
interlayer bonds to be weaker than in kaolinite (Bates, 1959).

Tubes of halloysite ($4H_2O$) represent the situation where bonds between layers, though very weak, are still sufficiently strong to produce
particles with some of the morphological characteristics of crystals.
Structural control of tube size and shape is evident and makes this material morphologically distinctive.

Finally, in allophane (Fig. 6) the only morphological evidence of
incipient layer structure is the appearance on some of the spherules of
concentric shells which tend to peel off presumably as a result of dehydration.

The illite group (Figs. 7, 8, and 9)

Electron micrographs of illite commonly show more detail than micrographs of montmorillonites but the particles are not as morphologically distinctive as those of the 1:1 minerals. In this group differences in appearance of the material in replica as compared to that in the dispersed state assume a greater degree of importance than in the kaolins. Because of weak interlayer bonds and strain in the layers themselves, crystalline features seen in replicas of bulk material disappear completely when the clay is dispersed. It is evident that more replica work on untreated natural material will provide important information on problems of clay formation and genesis of the soil.

In specimens studied by the author, interesting differences have been noted in the morphology of illites from the midcontinent area as contrasted with those from the Appalachian region. Possibly because of sensitivity to the pressures associated with regional metamorphism, dispersions of illites from shales found in the eastern part of the country commonly show larger, better defined flakes than is the case for material from the area of the type locality. Samples of the latter contain particles that are definitely flaky to elongate but tend to be so thin and small in size that aggregates appear quite "fluffy," in that resolution of the boundaries of each flake is not attained. The possible relationship of illite particle size to de-

Figure 8. Illite—Alexandria, Pennsylvania (X38,923) This morphology is typical of that of illite found in many shales. Plates are appreciably larger than those seen in Fithian material and because of greater thickness the irregular edges are well defined. Occasional hexagons seen in this sample are probably kaolinite.

gree of metamorphism is supported by the fact that illite flakes separated from the slates of northeastern Pennsylvania appear to be larger and better crystallized than material found in shales of the region (Bates, 1947). X–ray studies indicate that degree of orientation of the illite flakes correlates with the amount of metamorphism of the rock.

The K–bentonite found in the limestones of central Pennsylvania and studied by Weaver (1953a) possesses the same morphological characteristics as other typical illites from shales of the region, even though the material is actually a mixed–layer illite–montmorillonite in the proportion 80 to 20 per cent respectively.

A lath–shaped illite also discussed by Weaver (1953b) is common in the fine fractions of some of the quartzites and arkoses of central Pennsylvania. A possible explanation of the unusual morphology is that the material may represent the degradation of mica and the larger angular flakes and laths may result from the partial but incomplete physical breakdown of larger mica sheets.

The montmorillonite group (Figs. 10, 11, and 12)

Of all the clay minerals, those in this group are most sensitive to change in apparent morphology as a result of change in the nature of their surroundings. For this reason the characteristics of size and shape of "individual particles" or aggregates seen in electron micrographs must be carefully evaluated in terms of the method of preparation of the specimen. However, if proper at-

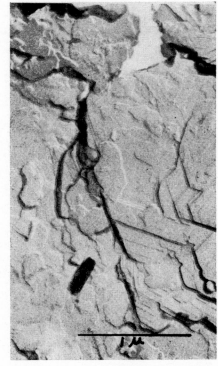

Figure 9. Illite and Kaolinite —Clearfield County, Pennsylvania (X30,294) In this sample of the Allegheny shale, the well–crystallized kaolinite contrasts sharply with the irregular illite surface. The opaque needle was transferred from the fracture surface to the replica and is probably rutile.

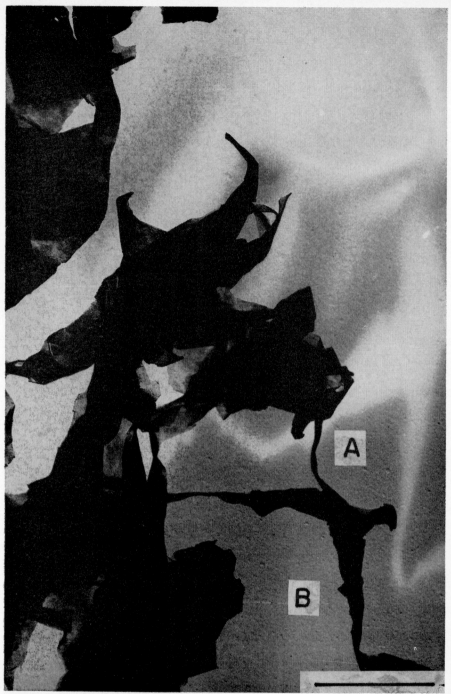

Figure 10. Na-Montmorillonite—Clay Spur, Wyoming (API H-26) (X28,880) This specimen was dispersed by ultrasonics and mounted on the electron microscope screen using the freeze-dry technique. The shadows such as that at "A" cast by the particle at "B" show that much of the clay film does not touch the substrate.

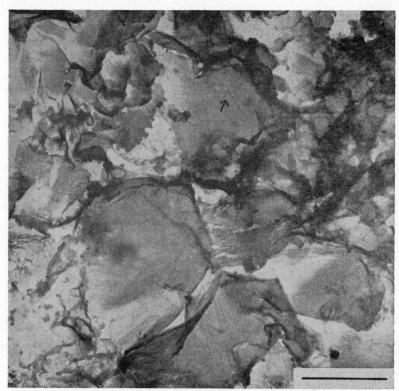

Figure 11. Montmorillonite—Montmorillon, France (X21, 762) An occasional replica reveals the presence of crystallographically oriented striations such as those which intersect at a 60° angle on the surface denoted by the arrow. This type of evidence indicates that three-dimensional order exists in such crystals before dispersion of the sample.

tention is paid to this fact, this very sensitivity of the material to its environment may be used to advantage to predict the behavior of the clay in various applications.

As in the case of illite, replicas of natural bulk material sometimes show evidence of crystalline order that is lost when the clay is dispersed. However, even in replicas of untreated clay lumps, surfaces are commonly completely irregular, characterized only by "broad" undulations suggesting, in some cases, unexpectedly large lateral extent of thin sheets. Obviously, in such cases the appearance of the replica depends not only on the manner in which the material fractures but also upon the condi-

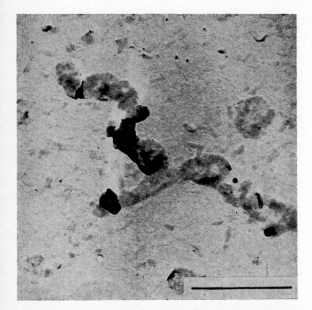

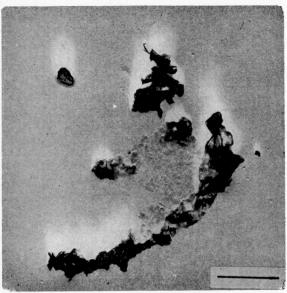

Figure 12. Wyoming Bentonite—Upton, Wyoming: top (X26,384) bottom (X15,606) These micrographs illustrate characteristic shapes resulting from use of the freeze-drying treatment on <400 Å fractions. Thin films and elongate particles are visible in both preparations.

tions of formation of the material. Much more replica work will have to be done, however, before fracture–surface structures can be used to help evaluate conditions of sedimentation or weathering.

Aqueous dispersions of montmorillonite are characterized morphologically by "lumpy" aggregates, extremely thin laths or irregular sheets, and a relatively high percentage of very fine "background" material consisting of barely resolvable specks which tend to aggregate on the substrate into layers resembling, in shape, the thin layers which settle out of suspension.

Usually little information can be gained from the aggregates unless studies are being made to determine degree of aggregation produced by various treatments. Here, as in any quantitative study, great care must be exercised to assure representative sampling of electron microscope fields and areas within fields.

Individual flakes of montmorillonite and of most of the Wyoming bentonite material are extremely thin but vary tremendously in lateral extent. Precise measurements using shadow techniques leave little doubt that sheets approaching a thickness of one or two 2:1 layers are of common occurrence. Yet these units, 10 to 30 A thick, sometimes cover measurable areas in electron micrographs encompassing at least 100 square microns or 10,000,000 square Angstroms. At the other extreme the lateral extent may become so small that the sheet–like character is lost and, as mentioned above, the particles take the form of barely resolved specks appearing as 10 to 30 A spheres. In many micrographs there appears to be a perfect gradation from such individual particles to small two–dimensional groups of these units arrayed in close–packed layers to discrete films of greater lateral extent. Although it is commonly not evident as to whether the small two–dimensional areas settled as such out of suspension or formed by aggregation of smaller specks on the substrate, star–like clusters and thin angular forms indicate that the latter must be the case in some instances. It is significant, if such interpretation is correct, aggregation of tiny units in nontronite tends to produce lath–shaped units while in montmorillonites with equidimensional flakes, layered aggregates are equidimensional in outline.

The freeze–dry technique, whereby the drop of suspension is frozen upon contact with the substrate and the particles settle as sublimation of the ice takes place, provides micrographs which give a better understanding of the shape the particles had in the suspension. This is a potentially productive area for much future work and the pictures included here simply indicate the appearance of material treated in this way. It is apparent that the thin films describe striking convolutions in suspension. In pictures of Wyoming bentonite material of the < 400 A supercentrifuge fraction, the films are themselves aggregates of hundreds of small elongate flakes. A large number of micrographs not included here indicate that, in this material, variation of the exchange cation had little apparent effect on the morphology of the film or of the units that compose it.

The lathlike morphological characteristics of hectorite and nontronite are quite diagnostic of these varieties of the montmorillonite group. The laths are as thin as the flakes of more common montmorillonites, but presumably development of more equidimensional units has been inhibited by strain arising from the incorporation of iron, lithium, and magnesium in the lattice. The two species differ morphologically in the nature of the aggregates as viewed in dispersions.

References

Abeledo, M. J. de, and Galloni, E. E. (1956) Material Saponitico de Calamuchita: *Rev. Assoc. Geol. Argentina*, v. 11, (3) pp. 143-57.

Abeledo, M. J. de (1951) El estudio de las arcillas: *Cienciae e Investigacion,* v. 7, (11) pp. 487-99.

Bates, T. F. (1947) Investigation of the micaceous minerals in slate: *Am. Min.,* v. 32, pp. 625-36.

Bates, T. F., Sand, L. B., and Mink, J. F. (1950) Tubular crystals of chrysotile asbestos: *Science,* v. 111, p. 512.

Bates, T. F., and Comer, J. J. (1955) Electron microscopy of clay surfaces: Proc. 3rd Nat. Conf. *Clays and Clay Minerals,* Nat. Acad. Sci.-Nat. Res. Council Publ. 395, pp. 1-25.

Bates, T. F., and Comer, J. J. (1959) Further observations on the morphology of chrysotile and halloysite: Proc. 6th Nat. Conf. *Clays and Clay Minerals,* Pergamon Press, pp. 237-48.

Bates, T. F. (1961) Electron microscopy of minerals: *Encyclopedia of Microscopy,* ed. G. L. Clark, Reinhold Publ. Corp., pp. 187-200.

Bates, T. F. (1959) Morphology and crystal chemistry of 1:1 layer lattice silicates: *Am. Min.,* v. 44, pp. 78-114.

Behne, W., and Müller, W. (1954) Electronenmikroskopische Untersuchungen Über der Morphologie von Halloysite: *Naturwissenschaften,* v. 41, p. 138.

Beutelspacher, Hans, and van der Marel, H. W. (1961) Kennzeichen zur Identifizierung von Kaolinit, "Fireclay"—Mineral and Halloysit, ihre Verbreitung und Bildung: *Tonind.-Zeit. Zbl.,* v. 85, pp. 1-24.

Birrell, K. S., Fieldes, M., and Williamson, K. I. (1955) Unusual forms of halloysite: *Am. Min.,* v. 40, pp. 122-24.

Bradley, D. E. (1954) Evaporated carbon films for use in electron microscopy: *Brit. J. Appl. Phys.,* v. 5, p. 65.

Bradley, D. E. (1958) Simultaneous evaporation of platinum and carbon for possible use in high-resolution shadow-casting for the electron microscope: *Nature,* v. 181, pp. 875.

Bramao, L., Cady, J. G., Hendricks, S. B., and Swerdlow, M. (1952) Criteria for the characterization of kaolinite, halloysite and related minerals in clays and soils: *Soil Sci.,* v. 73, pp. 273-87.

Brindley, G. W., and Comer, J. J. (1956) The structure and morphology of a kaolin clay from Les Eyzies (France): Proc. 4th Nat. Conf. *Clays and Clay Minerals,* Nat. Acad. Sci.-Nat. Res. Council Publ. 456, pp. 61-66.

Brindley, G. W., Comer, J. J., Uyeda, R., and Zussman, J. (1958) Electron-optical observations with crystals of antigorite: *Acta Cryst.,* v. 11, pp. 99-102.

Brydon, J. E., and Marshall, C. E. (1958) Mineralogy and chemistry of the Hagerstown soil in Missouri: *Univ. Missouri Ag. Expt. Sta. Res. Bull.,* No. 655, pp. 1-56.

Comer, J. J. (1959) The electron microscope in the study of minerals and ceramics: *A.S.T.M. Spec. Tech. Publ.,* No. 257, pp. 94-120.

Comer, J. J., and Turly, J. W. (1955) Replica studies of bulk clays: *J. Appl. Phys.,* v. 26 (3), pp. 346-50.

Cowley, J. M. (1961) Diffraction intensities from bent crystals: *Acta Cryst.,* v. 14, pp. 920-27.

Cowley, J. M., and Goswami, A. (1961) Electron diffraction patterns from montmorillonite: *Acta Cryst.,* v. 14, pp. 1071-79.

DeKeyser, W. L., and Degueldre, L. (1954) Note sur les Rapports entre la Morphologie et la Structure des Kaolins et Halloysites: *Bull. Soc. Belge Geol., Paleo., et Hydrologie,* v. 63, p. 100.

Dwornik, E., and Ross, M. (1955) Application of electron microscope to mineralogic studies: *Am. Min.,* v. 40, pp. 261-74.

Earley, J. W., Osthaus, B. B., and Milne, I. H. (1953) Purification and properties of montmorillonite: *Am. Min.,* v. 38, pp. 707-724.

Eckhardt, Franz-Jörg (1958) Elektronenoptische Untersuchungen an Einkristallen aus tonigen Sedimenten: *Neues Jb. Mineral,* Mh. 1958, pp. 1-17.

Egawa, T., Watanabe, Y., and Sato, A. (1955) Studies on the clay minerals of some upland soils in Japan (English summary): *Bull. Nat. Inst. Ag. Sci.,* Series B, (5), pp. 39-107.

Ferrandis, V. A., and Pena, J. M. G. (1954) Identification en el microscopio electronico de algunas arcillas y caolines espanoles: *Anales de Edafologia y Fisiologia Vegetal,* v. 13, pp. 631-62.

Fieldes, M., and Williamson, K. I. (1955) Clay mineralogy of New Zealand soils: Part 1—Electron micrography: *New Zealand J. Sci. Tech.,* B, v. 37, pp. 314-35.

Fieldes, M. (1955) Clay mineralogy of New Zealand soils: Part II—Allophane and related mineral colloids: *New Zealand J. Sci. Tech.,* B, v. 37, pp. 336-50.

Gastuche, M. C. (1959) Etude de l'alteration de la kaolinite par divers agents chimiques: *Silicates Industriels,* v. 24, pp. 237-44.

Hartman, P., and Perdok, W. G. (1955) The relations between structure and morphology of crystals: *Acta Cryst.,* v. 8, pp. 49-52; 521-29.

Honjo, G., Kitamura, N., and Mihama, K. (1954) A study of clay minerals by means of single-crystal electron-diffraction diagrams. The structure of tubular kaolin: *Clay Minerals Bull.,* v. 2, pp. 133-41.

Huggins, C. W. (1959) Electron micrographs of asbestiform minerals; *U.S. Bur. Mines Rep't. Investigations,* No. 5551, pp. 1-14.

Jagodzinski, H. and Kunze, G. (1954) Die Röllchenstruktur des Chrysotils: *Neues Jb. Mineral.,* Mh. 1954, pp. 95-108 and 113-30 and 137-50.

Jasmund, K., and Riedel, D. (1961) Untersuchungen des tonigen Zwischenmittels im Hauptbuntsandstein der Nordeifel: *Bull. Geol. Inst. Univ. of Uppsala,* v. 40, pp. 247-57.

Kalousek, G. L., and Muttart, L. E. (1957) Studies on the chrysotile and antigorite components of serpentine: *Am. Min.,* v. 42, pp. 1-22.

Kay, Desmond (1961) *Techniques for Electron Microscopy:* Blackwell Scientific Publications, Oxford, England.

Kinter, E. B., Wintermeyer, A. M., and Swerdlow, M. (1952) Electron microscopy of soil clays and related minerals: *Public Roads,* Rep. No. 27, pp. 89-100.

Kittrick, J. A., and Jackson, M. L. (1954) Electron microscope observations of the formation of aluminum phosphate crystals with kaolinite as the source of aluminum: *Science,* v. 120, pp. 508-9.

Kleber, W. (1955) Die Korrespondenz zwischen Morphologie und Struktur der Kristalle: *Naturwiss,* v. 42, pp. 170-73.

Kukovsky, E. G. (1960) Replacement of kaolinite by hydrargillite in the Novo-selitzk kaolin deposits of the Ukraine (English abstract): *Reports to the meeting of the International commission for the study of clays, Acad. Sci. USSR,* pp. 67-76.

Loughnan, E. C., and Craig, D. C. (1960) An occurrence of fully hydrated halloysite at Muswellbrook, N.S.W.: *Am. Min.,* v. 45, pp. 783-90.

Martin-Vivaldi, J. L., and Vilchez, F. G. (1959) A study of the halloysite from Maazza (North Morocco): *Silicate Industriels,* v. 24, pp. 380-85.

Maser, M., Rice, R. V., and Klug, H. P. (1960) Chrysotile morphology: *Am. Min.,* v. 45, pp. 680-88.

Meldau, R., Harsewinkel, and Robertson, R. H. S. (1952) Morphologische Einflusse auf technische staubeigenschaften: *Ber. DKG. u. VDEfa,* v. 29, pp. 27-35.

Nagasawa, K. (1961) Mineralization at the Mikawa mine, northeastern Japan: *Jour. Earth Sci.,* (Nagoya Univ.), v. 9, pp. 129-72.

Nixon, H. L., and Weir, A. H. (1957) The morphology of the Unter-rupsroth montmorillonite: *Min. Mag.,* v. 31, pp. 413-16.

Noll, W. and Kircher, H. (1950) Zur Morphologie der Chrysotilasbestos: *Naturwissenschaften,* v. 37, p. 540.

Noll, W., and Kircher, H. (1951) Über die Morphologie von Asbesten und ihren Zusammenhang mit der Kristallstruktur: *Neues Jb. Mineral.,* Mh. 1951, pp. 219-40.

Noll, W., Kircher, H., and Sybertz, W. (1958) Adsorptionsvermögen und spezifische Oberfläche von Silikaten mit röhrenförmig gebanten Primär-kristallen: *Kolloid-Z.,* v. 157, (1) pp. 1-11.

Nyun, M. A., and McCaleb, S. B. (1955) The reddish brown lateritic soils of the North Carolina Piedmont region, Davidson and Hiwassee series: *Soil Sci.,* v. 80, pp. 27-41.

Oberlin, A. (1957) Altération des cristaux de kaolinite. Détermination par microdiffraction électronique de la structure des produits altérés: *Compt. Rend. Acad. Sci.,* v. 244, pp. 1658-61.

Oberlin, A., and Tchoubar, C. (1958) Etude en microscopie et diffraction électroniques de l'alteration de la kaolinite par l'eau influence des sels dissous: *Silicates Industriels,* v. 24, pp. 197-202.

Oberlin, A., and Tchoubar, C. (1960) Etude en microscopie et microdiffrac-tion électroniques de l'alteration des cristaux de la kaolinite par une solu-tion acide: *Compt. Rend. Acad. Sci.,* v. 250, pp. 728-29.

O'Daniel, H., and Hahn-Weinheimer, P. (1952) Zum Faserwachstrum von Serpentin: *Neues Jb. Mineral.,* Mh. (A), v. 7, p. 213.

Palmeri, V. R. (1953) Propiedades fisicas de 49 arcillas y caolines Argen-tinos: *An. Soc. Cient. Argentina,* No. 155, p. 61.

Radczewski, O. E. (1952) Elektronenoptische Untersuchungen an nontronite: *Fortschr. Min.,* v. 31, pp. 59-60.

Roy, D. M., and Roy, R. (1954) An experimental study of the formation and properties of synthetic serpentines and related layer silicate minerals:

Am. Min., v. 39, pp. 957-75.

Sudo, T. (1956) X-ray and thermal data for clay minerals formed by the alteration of volcanic materials: *Sc. Rep. Tokyo Univ. Educ.,* No. 5 (43), pp. 39-55.

Sudo, T., and Ossaka, J. (1952) Hydrated halloysite from Japan: *Japanese J. Geol. Geog.,* v. 22, pp. 215-29.

Sudo, T., and Takahashi, H. (1956) Shapes of halloysite particles in Japanese clays: Proc. 4th Nat. Conf. *Clays and Clay Minerals,* Nat. Acad. Sci.-Nat. Res. Council Publ. 456, pp. 67-79.

Taggart, M. S., Jr., Milligan, W. O., and Struder, H. P. (1955) Electron micrographic studies of clays: Proc. 3rd Nat. Conf. *Clays and Clay Minerals,* Nat. Acad. Sci.-Nat. Res. Council Publ. 395, pp. 31-64.

Takahashi, H. (1958) Structural variations of kaolin minerals: *Bull. Chem. Soc. Japan,* v. 31, (3), pp. 275-83.

Takahashi, H. (1959) Effects of dry grinding on kaolin minerals: I-III, *Bull. Chem. Soc. Japan,* v. 32, (3), pp. 235-63.

Takahashi, H. (1959) Wet grinding on kaolin minerals: *Bull. Chem. Soc. Japan,* v. 32, (4), pp. 381-87.

Tchoukhrov, F. V., Berkhin, S. I., and Moleva, V. A. (1960) On cupreous clay minerals: *Rep'ts. Meeting Internat. Com. for the Study of Clays,* Acad. Sci. USSR, pp. 29-44.

Tsuzuki, Y. (1961) Mechanism of the 980° exotherm of kaolin minerals: *Jour. Earth Sci.,* (Nagoya Univ.), v. 9, pp. 305-44.

Visconti, V. S., Nicot, B. N. F., and deAndrade, E. G. (1955) New observations relative to tubular kaolins. *Inst. Nac. de Tecn.,* (Rio de Janeiro), pp. 1-41.

Waser, J. (1955) Fourier transforms and scattering intensities of tubular objects: *Acta Cryst.,* v. 8, pp. 142-50.

Weaver, C. E. (1953) Mineralogy and petrology of some Ordovician K-bentonites and related limestone: *Bull. Geol. Soc. Am.,* v. 64, pp. 921-43.

Weaver, C. E. (1953) A lath-shaped non-expanded dioctahedral 2:1 clay mineral: *Am. Min.,* v. 38, pp. 279-89.

Whittaker, E. J. W. (1957) The structure of chrysotile. V. Diffuse reflexions and fibre texture: *Acta Cryst.,* v. 10, pp. 149-56.

Whittaker, E. J. W. (1955) The diffraction of X-rays by a cylindrical lattice: IV: *Acta Cryst.,* v. 8, pp. 726-29.

V . . . Laboratory Techniques in the Electron Microscopy of Clay Minerals

John L. Brown

Introduction

The ease with which specimens may be examined in the light microscope is not often duplicated for the electron microscope. In the electron microscope the specimen is exposed to high vacuum conditions, heating effects from electron absorption, and charge effects from the absorption or secondary emission of electrons. Instability of the sample may affect the interpretation of its appearance. Proper operation of the electron microscope and attention to specimen preparation techniques are necessary to obtain an undistorted view of the specimen.

Most minerals are stable under the electron beam, and the problem facing the biological microscopist of preserving delicate organic structure is seldom encountered. Therefore, preparation procedures for clay minerals are among the simpler techniques in electron microscopy. The procedures described include particle dispersion, freeze drying, ultra–microtomy, shadowing, and surface replication.

Some initial preparation techniques common to electron microscopy in general will be discussed first.

Preparation of supporting substrates

For observation with the optical microscope, a powdered specimen is usually mounted on a glass slide. In the electron microscope the penetrating power of the electron beam is so slight that the sample must be supported by a very thin membrane or substrate. This membrane is in turn supported by a fine mesh metal grid about ⅛ inch in diameter. In the early days of electron microscopy actual wire mesh grids were used. The convolutions at wire intersections produced a hill–and–dale substrate, and thermal expansion caused relative motion of the wires frequently breaking the substrate. The modern grid is an electrolyti-cally–made, one–piece disc available in a wide variety of patterns and openings per inch. The usual grid is made of copper because of its high thermal and electrical conductivity, but grids of nickel, titanium, gold, silver, and other metals are available for special purposes.

The supporting membranes should satisfy a number of requirements. The following are among the most important:

1. Strength and stability in the electron beam
2. Transparency to electrons
3. A minimum of visible structure

Membranes may be made from both organic and inorganic materials. In general the organic materials show the most structure, particularly when the contrast is enhanced by shadowing. Inorganic films are more stable and have the advantage of insolubility in the various organic solvents which are sometimes used in specimen preparation. Organic films have the advantage of ease of preparation without special equip-ment.

Organic substrates

Thin membranes may be made from a number of organic materials. The two most frequently used are cellulose nitrate (Collodion, Parlodion) and polyvinyl formal (Formvar). Formvar is somewhat more stable in the electron beam than Collodion, but good Formvar films are not quite as easy to prepare as Collodion.

U.S.P. Collodion is available in solution with a mixture of alcohol and ether. This solution is diluted with 5 to 10 parts of amyl acetate for use. The exact dilution is best determined empirically and will be described later.

Formvar is obtained as a dry powder. Solvents used are ethylene dichloride, chloroform, or dioxane, depending upon the method of film preparation.

Collodion—A popular method of preparing Collodion films is as follows:

A drop of Collodion solution in amyl acetate is released from a medicine dropper held a few centimeters above a distilled water surface. The water may be conveniently contained in a 1–liter beaker or large petri dish. A watch glass is placed over the beaker to slow the evaporation of the solvent. As the solvent evaporates, colored bands due to the interference of light within the film will form and disappear. A desk lamp may be suitably arranged for viewing the liquid surface. If interference colors remain after the solvent is dry, the film is too thick. More amyl acetate is added to the solution and the process is repeated after scooping the old film from the water surface. If the film is too thin it will be patchy, irregular, and full of holes. A film of the proper thickness will have smooth areas exhibiting a silvery–gray color by reflected light. Such films of Collodion are about 200 to 300 angstroms thick.

To mount the film on grids the discs may be placed directly on the film surface using care not to break the film. If the grids have been punched from a sheet, the lip on the edge of the grid should face upwards; otherwise as the film drys it may lift from the grid surface. After 6 to 10 grids are placed in rows on the surface and spaced about ¼ inch apart, a clean glass microscope slide is lowered, vertical edge on into the film surface, in such a manner that film and grids adhere to one side of the slide. The slide is carefully removed, still vertical, and excess water drained onto a filter paper. After drying, the grids are held to the slide by the Collodion film and may be removed with jewelers' tweezers. If there is a tendency for the film to come off the grid on removal, the perimeter of each grid may be scraped with a sharp needle to break the film before lifting the grid.

There is some feeling among electron microscopists that Collodion films prepared in the foregoing manner are not the best in regard to stability and lack of holes. There is some mutual solubility between amyl acetate and water, and films cast on water may contain irregularities in structure because of this. Furthermore, rapid evaporation of ether from the Collodion solution may also cause holes.

Parlodion—An alternative method avoiding these difficulties is as follows:

Parlodion (Mallinckrodt trade name for a solid form of cellulose nitrate) is dissolved in amyl acetate to form a 0.5 per cent by weight solution. Dissolution is slow and the mixture may be left standing overnight. Three drops of this solution are placed on a clean 1 x 3 microscope slide, and the slide is rocked and tilted until the solution covers about ⅔ of the surface. The slide is then held vertically and excess solution drained onto a filter paper. Drying should take place in a location free of draft and dust. After drying, the edge of the glass slide is scraped lightly with a scalpel to sever the film, the film surface is breathed on to form a light coating of moisture, and the slide is slowly immersed at a slight angle into distilled water. The Parlodion film will float onto the water surface. Concentration of the solution may be changed to suit individual techniques and produce films of the proper thickness.

This film is best mounted on grids by bringing the grids up beneath the film as it floats on the surface. Several grids may be placed on a screen wire beneath the water surface before floating the film. A convenient apparatus for getting the film on a number of grids is shown in Fig. 1. The grids are supported on a piece of screen wire (bronze

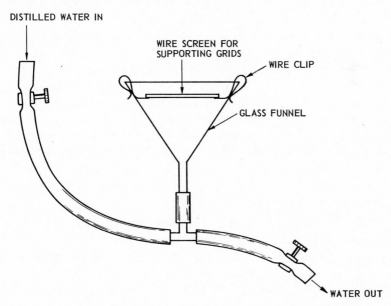

Figure 1. A convenient apparatus for preparation of grids.

paper pulp support screen is convenient, because it has been rolled flat) beneath the water surface. The film is floated onto the surface and the water level lowered in the funnel to trap the film on the grids. As the water level is lowered the film may be maneuvered with a dissecting needle. Large numbers of grids may be prepared in one operation with this device.

Formvar—Formvar films are usually prepared by dipping techniques. A wide–mouth bottle is partially filled with a 0.75 per cent solution of Formvar in chloroform or ethylene dichloride. The solvents used should be as water–free as possible and the bottle of solution should be stored in a desiccator when not in use. The slide is dipped into the solution and removed with the final draining and drying taking place within the bottle mouth in the solvent vapor. This, of course, produces a film on both sides of the slide. The slide edge is scored with a scalpel and the film floated off as is done with collodion.

If the film is breathed on lightly during drying, a network film will be produced by the small condensed water droplets. This type of support is convenient for very thin specimens where it is desirable to view portions of the specimen with no substrate in the background.

Inorganic substrates

Inorganic materials normally require a vacuum system for their preparation as substrates. An exception to this are techniques for the utilization of single crystal graphite and mica as substrates (Fernandez–Moran, 1960). A plastic solution is poured over the surface of the mica or graphite and mechanically stripped. The resulting film is floated on its solvent and releases the small crystalline lamellae which have been pulled from the surface. These are selected for thickness by their reflected light appearance (as previously described) and fished out on microscope grids. Such films are extremely flat and structureless and useful for studies of very small particles in the 50 to 100 angstroms region where organic film structure begins to appear.

Inorganic substrates made from silicon monoxide, silica, and carbon are in common use—particularly the last. These require vacuum evaporation for their formation and will be described in the discussion on shadowing.

Preparing a dispersion of clay particles

Of all the pigments examined in the electron microscope, clays are among the easiest to disperse. A number of dispersing agents for a water suspension may be used, depending upon the clay involved and its surface activity. Some companies producing kaolinite for paper coating purposes use tetra sodium pyrophosphate (TSPP) or Calgon. Ammonium hydroxide and various wetting agents may also be used.

Slurry techniques

A Waring Blendor provides a simple mechanical means of dispersing clay particles. It is preferable to use the small pint–size cup into which 100 cc. of distilled water is placed along with 3 to 5 drops of TSPP or 1 drop of Kodak Photo–Flo. The amount of powdered clay to add to the mixture is best determined empirically since it depends upon the particle size range, the type of clay, and the final use of the prepared sample. A good start may be had by adding a few cubic millimeters of powder and running the Blendor about 20 seconds. When a noticeable turbidity is produced, a trial amount of suspension may be extracted with a hypodermic syringe, glass rod, or medicine dropper, and droplets of different sizes placed on several filmed microscope grids. The different sized droplets will give a choice of population density on the substrate.

As a convenient means of holding the filmed grids to receive the droplets, two strips of double face cellulose tape are placed on a microscope slide and spaced just under 3 mm. apart. The grids are placed between the strips and are held at their edges.

If a given number of specific clay minerals are to be examined regularly, a weighed quantity of clay may be determined and added to the Blendor each time.

When a large number of samples must be examined the Blendor technique becomes time–consuming because of the necessary thorough cleaning of the Blendor cups between samples. If an ultrasonic generator is available the clay suspensions may be made up in individual test tubes and agitated in the ultrasonic field. The ultra sound frequency is not critical but extreme power levels and very high frequencies of 1 mc/s or higher might produce particle degeneration. The frequencies from 20 to 100 kc/s will produce better mechanical agitation. This is the frequency range usually encountered in ultrasonic cleaners. Bendix and Branson are two suppliers of this type of unit.

A better dispersion of particles on a substrate may be obtained by first placing a drop of water solution containing 0.1 per cent bovine albumin on the surface. The excess is blotted off and the remainder allowed to dry. This leaves a mono–layer of protein which renders the surface hydrophilic. Better wetting of the substrate by the suspension droplet will be obtained. The only drawback to this technique is an increase of background structure noticeable at high magnification on shadowed specimens.

Mulling techniques

For the occasional sample which fails to disperse properly in water, other liquid media may be tried, or techniques applying high shearing forces to agglomerates may be used. The latter methods are usually necessary on pigments other than clays. The general technique consists of placing a small quantity of pigment between two glass microscope slides along with a drop of turpentine oil, dibutyl phthalate, (Schuster and Fullam, 1946), or ethylene glycol and mulling the sample until a dispersion is obtained. The slides are separated, and if ethylene glycol was used (Chaiken, 1961) a filmed grid is placed, film side down, into the glycol–pigment layer and then lifted off. Droplets of the suspension cling to the film, and after insertion of the sample into the electron microscope vacuum the ethylene glycol sublimates. With turpentine and dibutyl phthalate better results are obtained by casting a relatively thick Parlodion film on the suspension surface and floating this off on water. If the film refuses to float off it may be dry–stripped with cellulose tape. A disc of lens paper slightly smaller than a grid is placed on the adhesive side of the tape. A grid is placed over the lens paper and is held at the edges by the tape. A condensed film of moisture is formed on the specimen by breathing on it, and tape and grid are quickly pressed onto the surface. As the tape is carefully stripped the Parlodion film will come free with the grid.

A simple and rapid dispersion for materials not requiring high shear may be achieved by mulling the sample in a drop of 0.5 per cent Parlodion in amyl acetate. As the suspension between the slides nears dryness a final wipe of one slide across the other spreads the suspension into a thin film which dries before the particles can reagglomerate.

Unfortunately the resulting dispersion cannot be shadowed since the particles are embedded in the film; for the same reason image contrast is reduced for very fine particle materials.

Freeze drying

A technique normally reserved for biological materials, freeze drying, may sometimes be advantageously applied to clay minerals. If a delicate structure contains water the structure may be distorted during drying by the surface tension of the liquid interface. Thin platy materials such as montmorillonite possess a three–dimensional structure as seen in the electron microscope when prepared by freeze–drying techniques.

For simple freeze drying a brass block is brought to a very low temperature in liquid nitrogen or dry ice and acetone. A filmed specimen grid mounted on a glass slide and containing a droplet of clay suspension is placed on the block. This assembly is immediately transferred to a vacuum system which is evacuated to about 10^{-4} Torr. The block rests on a plastic insulator in the vacuum system and can only gain heat by radiation. The frozen droplet sublimates without appreciable distortion of the particle structure, provided a very low temperature is maintained. Upon completion of sublimation the sample may be shadowed to reveal three–dimensional structure.

Ultra microtomy

Slicing materials thin enough to observe in the electron microscope is another biological technique which has thus far seen limited application in mineralogy. Recent development of diamond knives permits the sectioning of hard materials such as metals, teeth, ceramics, and minerals, provided sections of very small area (100 to 200 microns square) are cut. Nonporous solid materials may be trimmed or ground to a conical tip and sections cut from this tip. Mineral aggregates must be thoroughly impregnated with methacrylate or epoxy resins before sectioning. Fine particles may be dispersed directly in the resin before curing.

A schematic diagram of an ultra–microtome is shown in Fig. 2. The specimen is mounted on a rotating drum and is carried past the knife edge. As the knife is advanced into the specimen a section is cut with

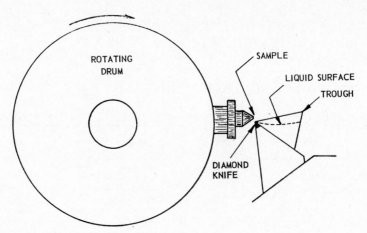

Figure 2. Schematic diagram of an ultra-microtome.

each revolution of the drum. The sections float on the surface of distilled water which is contained in a trough behind the knife edge. The liquid level is adjusted so that the meniscus contacts the knife edge. The sections may be observed through the stereomicroscope and fished out on specimen grids.

Since the section thickness is normally in the neighborhood of a few hundred angstroms, mechanical advance of the knife into the specimen is unreliable. Most ultra–microtomes utilize thermal expansion by controlled electrical heating to bring the specimen into contact with the knife. Ultra–microtomy is an art in itself and will not be dealt with in further detail here. The future will no doubt see greater application of the technique to studies in clay mineralogy. An example of its use is given in Fig. 3.

There are many other techniques for particle dispersion to be found in the literature. An excellent compilation of these techniques and others in the field of electron microscopy may be found in Hall, 1953, and Kay, 1961.

Metal vapor shadowing

The shadowing technique is one of the greatest aids to electron micrographic interpretation of surface structure. On the original negative or a reversal print the sample appears to have been illuminated

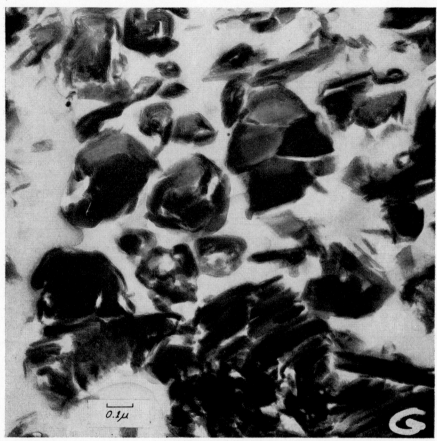

Figure 3. An ultra—microtome section of a clay sample from New Zealand. The sample was permeated with an epoxy resin and sectioned with a diamond knife. The layer structure of the particles can be seen. The sample contains halloysite and possibly allophane. Both longitudinal and cross sections of halloysite tubes are evident.   Original magnification 67,000X.

from the side by a strong light. Surface configurations may be interpreted and with a known shadow angle the thickness of particles may be determined.

Essentially the process consists of depositing a thin film of metal on the sample from a source placed at an acute angle to the surface. Varying inclinations of the sample surface to the incoming metal atoms results in a film of differential thickness. A particle projecting above the

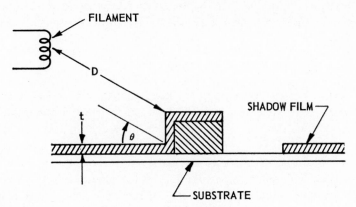

Figure 4. Geometry of the shadowing process.

substrate will shield the deposition of metal on the side opposite the metal source. A fixed shadow is cast.

When the sample is examined in the electron microscope the varying shadow film thickness causes differential scattering of electrons and reveals the gradations of the original surface.

The geometry of the shadowing process is shown in Fig. 4. The source is an electrically heated filament containing the metal. Assuming spherical propagation from the filament, if M grams of metal are evaporated, the weight w per unit area of a film deposited on a surface perpendicular to the incoming metal is

$$w = \frac{M}{4\pi D^2}$$

where D is the distance from filament to sample. When the surface is inclined at an angle Θ to the incoming metal

$$w = \frac{M}{4\pi D^2}\sin \Theta$$

Since $w = td$, where t is thickness and d is density of the metal, by substitution

$$t = \frac{M \sin \Theta}{4\pi D^2 d}$$

This equation may be used to estimate the necessary amount of metal to evaporate for a given film thickness. It serves as a starting point for empirical determinations. Inaccuracies arise from the assumption of spherical propagation; no filament is an ideal point source and the radiation pattern is a function of the filament geometry. Furthermore the densities of thin metal films may not be the same as the bulk density.

Shadowing vacuum requirements

Shadowing must be carried out under high vacuum conditions. The mean free path of the residual gases in the vacuum system should be greater than the distance from filament to specimen. This requires a pressure of 10^{-4} Torr or better. Frequently the pressure may rise during the shadowing process. This is particularly true in the evaporation of platinum. The heavy filaments and high temperatures required may cause outgassing of the chamber walls. If this occurs evaporation should be halted and the system permitted to return to the proper vacuum before continuing.

When shadowing is done under poor vacuum conditions the resulting shadows are indistinct due to scattering of the metal atoms. The effect is analogous to soft lighting in photography. The final micrograph may have a satisfactory appearance but measurement of shadow lengths will be uncertain.

Filaments

Most of the shadowing metals may be evaporated from tungsten baskets or helices. A number 6 woodscrew may be used as a mandrel for forming baskets of tungsten wire thinner than 20 mils. The wire is not very ductile and is less likely to break if wound slowly around the mandrel. Larger diameters of tungsten wire are normally used in a V shaped filament or a helix. The helix may be wound around a ¼ inch steel rod which has been preheated a little above 100°C. with a Bunsen burner. If the tungsten wire is overheated it becomes very brittle.

Shadowing metals

Metals used for shadowing should have a high atomic number in order to yield contrasty shadows from the thinnest possible films. Metals of low density require shadowing films thick enough to cause distortion of fine surface structure and are suitable only for low magnification work. Other requirements to be met by a shadowing metal are lack of granularity, stability in the electron beam, and ease of evaporation.

Chromium was one of the first metals to be used and remains a popular choice. It is available in granular form and is easy to evaporate from a tungsten basket, but its relatively low density requires a thick film. Furthermore film granularity limits its application to low and medium magnifications. Gold is dense and easily evaporated, but the crystallites in the film aggregate under an intense electron beam.

Platinum is probably the best metal for shadowing, considering all requirements. Its chief drawback is difficulty in evaporation. It alloys with tungsten at high temperatures and may destroy the filament before evaporation. This can be avoided by placing the required amount of Pt in foil or wire form on a 2 turn helix of 30 mil tungsten wire, dividing the load equally on each coil. Under normal shadowing conditions the amount of Pt on each coil is insufficient to cause parting of the filament.

Care should be taken that the two turns of the helix are close together in order to approximate a point source with respect to the specimen. A broad source yields unsharp shadows with a consequent loss of resolution.

Some shadowing metals and approximate thicknesses required for perceptible shadows are given in Table 1.

Table 1. *Approximate thicknesses of metals required for perceptible shadows.*

Metal	Specific gravity	Thickness required in Angstrom units
Platinum	21.5	10
Chromium	6.9	20–50
Uranium	18.7	5–10
Zirconium	6.4	15

Simultaneous carbon–platinum shadowing

A recently developed shadowing technique (Bradley, 1959) utilizes a metal and nonmetal. If platinum and carbon are evaporated simultaneously from the same source, a composite film is deposited on the specimen. The film has a high scattering power, comparable to a platinum film, but very low granularity. Apparently the carbon inhibits the crystallite growth of the platinum during deposition. Comparison of the film structures by electron diffraction techniques shows a much smaller crystallite size in the combination film.

This shadowing technique has been used in the carbon replication process to reveal surface structures of the order of 10 angstroms. The details of the process will be covered in the section on replication.

Shadowing for height determination

When shadowing a dispersion of particles on a substrate for the purpose of measuring particle height, care must be taken that the shadowing angle is known at each point on the substrate. If the particles are dispersed on a Parlodion–coated glass slide they may be shadowed *in situ* and the film floated off for examination. The measured angle be-

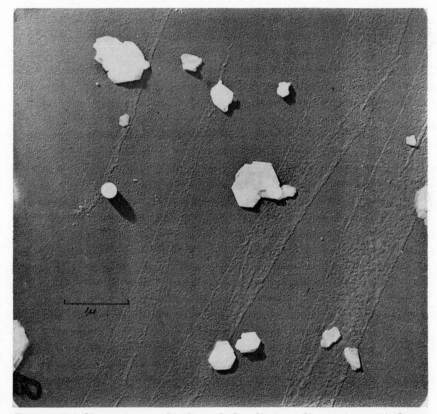

Figure 5. Chromium shadowed kaolinite dispersion. A latex sphere is included in the field for shadow angle determination. The background structure is due to serum albumin. 17,000X.

tween selected areas of the slide and the filament may be used as the shadowing angle.

If the particles are deposited on a film–coated grid, the shadow angle will vary from point to point due to wrinkles in the substrate. Two methods are available for determining shadow angle. If a small amount of polystyrene latex suspension is added to the original particle suspension before deposition on the substrate, some small latex spheres will be visible in each field of view. Measurement of sphere diameter versus shadow length (Fig. 5) will give the shadow angle for that particular field of view.

If the polystyrene latex is not available, the sample may be shadowed from two diametrically opposed sources and the height computed from the average shadow length.

Replication of surfaces

Some progress has been made in recent years in the examination of surfaces by reflected electron microscopy. The best resolution obtainable thus far is about 500 angstrom units, better than the light microscope by a factor of 4 but far short of the transmission electron microscope. Furthermore, the view presented by this technique is distorted due to the low angle of incidence of the imaging beam. At the present time the best means of observing the surface of an opaque object is by replication.

A replica is a thin film of material transparent to electrons and duplicating exactly the surface contours of a specimen. The films may be made of either organic or inorganic materials, but the latter show less visible structure.

There are two basic methods of making a replica. The single–stage replica is made by depositing the replicating material on the specimen surface, separating the film from the surface, and examining this in the electron microscope. For the two–stage replica a mold of the surface is formed with one material, a second material is deposited on the mold, the two are separated, and the film of the second material examined in the microscope. Some methods carry this process through additional stages; however, each additional stage interjects the structure of the material used and degrades the final replica. The single stage replica is the most authentic, but unless the surface is smooth the specimen is usually destroyed or modified during the removal.

Single–stage plastic replicas

Simple plastic replicas may be made without the use of a vacuum system. Relatively smooth surfaces of minerals or ceramics may be flooded with a 2 per cent solution of Parlodion in amyl acetate, the excess drained, and the dry film floated onto a water surface. In some cases a porous specimen may be soaked in water to fill the pores prior to application of the solution. This prevents the Parlodion solution from draining into the pores and mechanically anchoring the film.

A film which adheres to the surface may sometimes be removed by coating with a 25 per cent water solution of PVA (polyvinyl alcohol, Dupont "Elvanol"). The combination film is thick and may be stripped mechanically. After stripping the film is cut into ⅛ inch squares and floated PVA side down in warm water. When the PVA has completely dissolved, the Parlodion films may be fished out on specimen grids.

Plastic replicas must be thin in order to show sufficient contrast, but thin organic films are hard to strip and unstable in the electron beam. If the replicas are shadowed on the side which was in contact with the specimen surface, contrast will be enhanced and the metal film will stabilize the replica in the electron beam. However, care must be used in interpretation of the final picture. "Hills" on the specimen will look like "holes" on the replica.

Two–stage plastic replicas

A simple two–stage plastic replica of a surface may be made with two materials each insoluble in the solvent of the other (Hall, 1953, p. 342). A first impression of the surface may be made with polyvinyl alcohol (PVA) or carboxymethyl cellulose in water. This negative impression is coated with Formvar in ethylene dichloride, or Parlodion in amyl acetate. The PVA is dissolved by water flotation and the replica mounted by holding a grid in tweezers, approaching the top of the film, and scooping the film out with the grid so that the side in contact with the water is uppermost. After drying, the film is shadowed. Surface topography will appear as in the original specimen. This is known as a positive replica.

The most satisfactory material for the final replica film is carbon. Thin films of carbon may be prepared by evaporation from a carbon arc in a high vacuum. Two ⅛ inch spectrographic grade carbons are

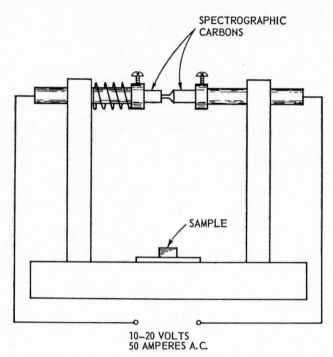

Figure 6. Holder for spectrographic carbons used in preparation of replicas.

axially aligned in a holder and butted together as shown in Fig. 6. One is fixed and the end filed flat and perpendicular to the axis. The opposing carbon is either pointed or sharpened in a commercially available device to produce a tip about 40 mils in diameter and $\frac{3}{16}$ inch long. Such devices are available from Ladd Industries. The rods are held together under light spring tension. When electrical current is passed through the rods, heating occurs at the point of contact and the carbon is vaporized. When the opposing rod is pointed, the evaporation procedure is stopped when a light tan color appears on the specimen or a test piece of white glass placed in the chamber. With the necked–down rod the amount of carbon evaporated may be controlled by the length of the tip.

Preliminary impressions made with PVA of a surface may be carbon coated instead of using plastic solutions. The final replica film is far more stable in the electron microscope.

Preshadowed platinum–carbon replicas

The platinum–carbon replica is capable of high resolution and is most suitable to clays, minerals, and ceramics (Comer and Turley, 1955). The technique described is essentially that developed by Comer and Turley.

The first step in preparing the replica is to shadow the surface with platinum. Bulk materials such as lump clays or minerals are broken to yield fresh fracture faces. Some samples may require drying in a vacuum desiccator to avoid a long pump–down time in the shadowing unit. No other treatment is applied except to blow gently any loose material from the fracture surface.

Rods formed from a mixture of powdered carbon and platinum are available from Edwards High Vacuum, Ltd. These may be used in the holder described above to produce very fine grain shadow films. This procedure may be used instead of platinum shadowing if very high resolution is required.

Fine particle materials may be dispersed by mulling in a liquid between glass slides as described in a previous section. The dry dispersion on the slide serves as the sample surface.

When the sample has a rough and uneven surface it is necessary to shadow with the platinum at two angles in directions mutually perpendicular to each other. In some areas both shadows may appear while in others only one of the evaporated films may have deposited on the specimen. The first layer is applied at an angle of incidence of about 20 degrees using enough platinum to give a film approximately 5 to 10 angstroms in thickness. A second evaporation is made at a 45 degree incidence in a direction normal to the first to deposit a film of approximately the same thickness. This will require about half the amount of metal on the second filament as used on the first.

The shadowed specimen is next coated at normal incidence with an evaporated film of carbon. Using necked–down carbons the $\frac{3}{16}$ inch tip length is a satisfactory average for most specimens when the tip–to–specimen distance is 12 to 13 cm. Small particles on a glass substrate will require only a $\frac{1}{16}$ inch tip; rough porous surfaces may require $\frac{1}{4}$ inch. The final film on a porous surface is normally uniform. Apparently there is some molecular redistribution after the film is applied, or possibly reflection from adjacent surfaces. Care must be exercised, however, to avoid unnecessarily thick films since contrast and resolving power decrease as the thickness is increased.

In order to avoid breakage of the combined platinum and carbon films during the removal of the clay, it is necessary to support these films in a plastic base. Polystyrene granules are heated and compressed between glass microscope slides to form discs approximately 2 to 3 mm. in thickness. This is done by placing the sandwich of slides and polystyrene on a hot plate heated to 160°C. to 170°C. The assembly is squeezed by pressing with a wooden dowel. When the granules have formed the proper size discs, the assembly is removed to a cool (room temperature) metal surface and pressing continued until the plastic hardens. The top slide is removed and the lower slide and discs returned to the hot plate. When the discs have softened to the point where cavities made in the surface of the plastic by a pointed object disappear as soon as the object is withdrawn, the clay is placed with the replica side in contact with the plastic and gently but firmly pushed into intimate contact with it. The slide is removed from the hot plate and the plastic allowed to harden without disturbing the clay. Inspection through the back of the plastic will determine if good contact has been achieved between the plastic and the evaporated film.

The plastic disc containing the replica and the clay may be held under running water to remove the excess clay. It is then placed replica side down in 48 per cent hydrofluoric acid for as long as necessary to remove the specimen. This will take about 1 hour. When it appears that the surface of the replica is free of all clay, the disc is placed in fresh acid for another hour. It is then washed with distilled water and allowed to dry.

In the event that a given clay is too fragile to embed successfully in polystyrene it may be possible to float it directly on the surface of the acid with the replica side up. The sides are first scraped to remove carbon from undesired areas of the specimen; otherwise they may float free and be picked up. As the replica sections come free they may be removed with a piece of fine-mesh platinum gauze and transferred to a water bath. There is usually considerable breakage when the replica is transferred to the water. It should be removed from the water on 500-mesh grids. It may be necessary to use grids with substrates to avoid further breakage of the film upon drying. Addition of a wetting agent such as Kodak Photo–Flo to the water will aid in the removal of the films. One drop of Photo–Flo to 250 cc. of water is sufficient.

Fine particle specimens on a glass surface are simply treated. The

Figure 7. Preshadowed platinum-carbon replica of an attapulgite fracture face. 21,000X.

slide is slowly lowered at an angle into the hydrofluoric acid. The replica films will float on the surface and may be treated as above.

The replica may be removed from the plastic by scoring the surface with a sharp blade to divide it into ⅛ inch squares. The polystyrene disc is then pushed to the bottom of a small petri dish filled with ethylene dichloride. With the replica side up the plastic adheres to the bottom of the dish and the sections of replica float free within a few minutes. They are then transferred to a fresh dish of solvent. An additional wash in a third dish may be necessary. The replicas are picked up using ⅛ inch specimen screens held in fine tweezers. Rapid evaporation of the solvent causes convection currents which make the films hard to trap. This effect may be reduced by using ethyl bromide with 10 per cent benzene to reduce volatility as the final dish of solvent.

An electron micrograph of a platinum–carbon replica of attapulgite is shown in Fig. 7.

Inorganic substrates produced in a vacuum

Silica and silicon monoxide

After Parlodion or Formvar substrates have been mounted on grids they may be overcoated with silica or silicon monoxide. Small chips of silica may be evaporated from a 20 mil tungsten basket. Films produced from either of these materials are resistant to solvents and stable in the electron microscope. Silicon monoxide may be preferable since it evaporates at a lower temperature.

If additional contrast is necessary the Parlodion film may be removed. The grid is clamped in tweezers and immersed for a few seconds in methyl ethyl ketone. After removal from the solvent the excess is drained onto a filter paper and the grid is ready for use.

Carbon

Carbon may be evaporated onto plastic substrates using the same techniques involved in replication. The backing film may also be removed with methyl ethyl ketone. The only disadvantage to carbon is the hydrophobic nature of the surface; it is usually necessary to apply a serum albumin mono–layer as described previously unless the sample is suspended in a liquid of low surface tension.

Almost structureless carbon films may be prepared by evaporation onto the surface of freshly cleaved mica. The carbon layer is scribed into ⅛ inch squares and the films easily floated onto a distilled water surface. A small amount of wetting agent added to the water after the films are floated off will aid in mounting them on microscopic grids.

References

1. Bradley, D. E. (1959) High resolution shadow-casting technique for the electron microscope: *Brit. Jour. of App. Phys.*, v. 10, pp. 198-203.
2. Chaiken, S. W. (1961) Simple powder dispersion method for electron microscope: *Anal. Chem.*, v. 33, p. 1808.

3. Comer, J. J. and Turley, J. W. (1955) Replica studies of bulk clays: *Jour. App. Phys.,* v. 26, pp. 346-50.
4. Fernandez-Moran, H. (1960) Electron Microscope Society of America. Conference: Milwaukee, Wisconsin.
5. Hall, C. E. (1953) *Introduction to Electron Microscopy:* McGraw-Hill Book Co., Inc.
6. Kay, Desmond (1961) *Techniques for Electron Microscopy:* Charles C. Thomas, Publisher.
7. Schuster, M. C. and Fullam, E. F. (1946) Preparation of powdered materials for electron microscopy: *Ind. Eng. Chem.,* v. 18, pp. 653-57.

VI...Infrared Analysis of Soil Minerals

R. J. P. Lyon

I Introduction

Automatically recording infrared spectrophotometers became readily available after World War II and there has been a great increase in the use of these instruments for structural analysis. There are thousands of infrared spectra of organic compounds available, but the inorganic field has been sparingly touched. Routine use of infrared analysis for mineralogical investigations has been largely neglected.

Much of this has been due to the overwhelming dominance of the X–ray analysis techniques in mineralogy, which are regarded by many as being *the* definitive tools, the final arbiter in the correct identification of a mineral.

But the whole essence of mineralogy lies in the subtle chemical substitutions which divide one mineral species from another. Thus it is often minor compositional differences on which final decisions must be based. These differences are often not discernible by the X–ray diffraction approach, with its dominantly physical observations.

X ray is also largely concerned with long–range ordering or periodicity in crystals. The fine structure, the short–range ordering of nearest–neighbor atoms is often most clearly shown by infrared analysis. The joint use of the two techniques offered, however, enables one to make much more accurate analyses of mineral compositions and structures.

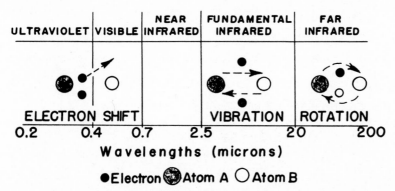

Figure 1. Diagram showing the energy levels involved in the infrared region of the electromagnetic spectrum. Only the 2.5 to 15
(or 25) micron region is utilized for most analytical studies. By
kind permission of the Perkin-Elmer Corporation (See References).

II Theory of infrared spectroscopy

Electromagnetic radiation of different energy levels has markedly
different effects upon atomic and molecular associations. The higher
energy levels of the ultraviolet and visible regions will cause electron
shifts in the outer orbitals of atoms, which will appear as absorption
bands in the resultant spectrum. If atomic configurations of molecules
are excited by the lower–energy infrared radiations, then only vibrational
and rotational modes can occur; the electronic transitional states are
not affected (see Fig. 1).

All molecules are composed of atoms connected by electromagnetic
bonds. These atoms are in continuous motion, vibrating and rotating
about their center of gravity. The atoms of each molecule vibrate at a
definite frequency with respect to each other, the frequency being specific for that molecular structure and for no other.

The atoms in polyatomic molecules vibrate not only according to the
frequencies of their bonds, but weakly also to overtones and harmonics
of these frequencies. Their frequency patterns are therefore uniquely
diagnostic.

If any single bond is considered to be like a spring, then this may
be seen to vibrate at a definite frequency. In a complex molecule with
many types of atoms with differing bond strengths and bond angles,
the vibrations can be compared to a complex spring system in continuous

motion. The pattern is governed by the vibration frequencies of the masses of the atoms present. This can also be calculated mathematically for simple molecules, in the formula:

$$f = \frac{1}{2\pi c} \left(\frac{k}{\mu}\right)^{\frac{1}{2}}$$

where f = frequency (cm^{-1})

k = force constant

c = velocity of light

μ = reduced mass of the atoms AB = $\dfrac{M_A \cdot M_B}{M_A + M_B}$

(Dachille and Roy, 1959, p. 466)

If a radiation of a given frequency (υ)[1] passes into a molecule, containing a bond of the same vibration frequency, this energy is absorbed by that bond increasing its natural vibration. If radiation of some other frequency enters, not matched by an interatomic bond, then it passes through the molecule without change. Since molecular vibrational frequencies lie in the infrared radiation region, this portion of the spectrum can be used to characterize molecular structures.

Application to study of hydrogen bonding

Infrared spectroscopy has found extensive use for study of hydrogen bonding. This bonding results in a weakening of the other bonds involved, and thus results in readily measurable shifts of their respective absorption bands. Hydrogen bonding involving O–H groups causes the largest shifts, with lesser ones observed for other groups. Infrared spectroscopy offers a simple method for distinguishing between intramolecular hydrogen bonding, intermolecular hydrogen bonding, and chelation (very strong intramolecular hydrogen bonding).

Individual factors, namely temperature and concentration, can substantially alter the position of the bonded O–H vibration absorption frequency. Standardization of operating conditions, therefore, is a critical factor in comparative studies (Cross, 1960, p. 37).

---

1. υ is defined as the reciprocal of a wavelength $(\upsilon = \frac{1}{\lambda})$ of the radiation measured in cms. The product υc, where c is the velocity of light (3×10^{10} cm/sec), gives the frequency in cycles/sec. The expression $(\upsilon$ cm$^{-1})$ for wavenumber is becoming more common in the literature, particularly in the physical journals. (Reciprocals may be found in Section VII).

Bellamy (1954, p. 96) lists the following assignments for hydroxyl peaks in the hydroxyl stretching frequency region:

Table 1: Hydroxyl stretching frequencies

Free OH . . .	$3650-3590$ cm.$^{-1}$	Sharp
Intermolecular hydrogen bonds	(1) Single–bridge compounds $3550-3450$ cm.$^{-1}$	Sharp
	(2) Polymeric association $3400-3200$ cm.$^{-1}$	Broad
Intramolecular hydrogen bonds	(1) Single–bridge compounds $3570-3450$ cm.$^{-1}$	Sharp
Chelate compounds	Strong intramolecular bonds $3200-2500$ cm.$^{-1}$	Very broad bands
Other references	Cross, 1960, p. 3 Stewart, 1962, p. 17 Clark, 1961, p. 451 Willard, *et al.*, 1960, p. 141	

For a discussion of CO_2 molecular vibrations as a type molecule, see Cross (1960, p. 50; p. 80); or Clark (1961, pp. 406-7).

III Infrared recording equipment

A. *General*

This article is not concerned with the design and operating requirements of the recording equipment, as most laboratory texts in use today will give the reader adequate descriptions. Fig. 2, however, shows a descriptive representation of a typical spectrometer.

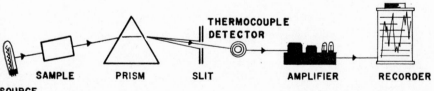

Figure 2. Diagrammatic representation of the operation of a typical spectrometer. Only a single beam is shown here, the reference beam being chopped before the sample area and recombined after the final slit. By kind permission of the Perkin-Elmer Corporation (See References).

The best general handbook of this type is that of Willard, Merritt, and Dean (1960), Chapter VI of which is devoted to the practical methodology of infrared laboratory techniques and experimentation. For a specific instrument, the reader is referred to the procedural manual normally supplied with the equipment. Two of these are listed in the references (Perkin–Elmer Corp., 1961; Beckman Instruments, 1961).

B. *Instrument settings*

Settings for an instrument will vary depending upon the type of sample and its preparation. Some of these settings are stated in Willard, *et al.,* 1960, p. 173, for the Perkin–Elmer 21 model.

The optimum settings that we have found best for mineralogical work are as follows:

Table 2: Instrument settings for mineralogical analysis

PE 21 Model

	NaCl Prism	NaCl Prism (Milkey, 1960, p. 487)
Slit schedule	960	927
Gain	4.5	5
Response	1	1
Source	0.3 amp.	0.3 amp.
Speed	4–8	2
Suppression	5	2

PE 221 Model

	NaCl Prism–grating	KBr Prism (Abscissa Contracted to 0.4)
Slit	927	945
Gain	4*	4*
Attenuation	11:00	11:00
Scan Time	16	10
Suppression	7	7
Scale	1x	1x
Source	0.32 amp.	0.32 amp.

Beckman IR 4

	Normal Scale	(X5) Abscissa Expanded Scale
Speed	2 minutes/micron	12 minutes/micron
Scale	2 inches/micron	10 inches/micron
Gain	3 per cent	3 per cent
Period	2	8
Ordinate scale	0–100	—

* Varies from 2–4 with particular unit.

IV Preparatory techniques for solid materials

A. *Preferred method*

Alkali Halide Pellets—Solid materials like minerals are generally insoluble in most solvents. The discovery that solid samples may be mixed at a low level of concentration with a powdered alkali halide, and then pressed into a clear solid disc or pellet for analysis has revolutionized the preparatory steps for these materials. The pellet technique has been shown by many to be the most satisfactory method for handling rock and mineral samples for infrared analysis (Tuddenham and Lyon, 1960b, p. 492; Farmer, 1955, p. 586; Milkey, 1958, p. 1931). Most procedures are similar to those discussed in the following statement and use potassium bromide (KBr) as the embedding medium. Other halides (KCl, KI) may be used and the grinding, blending techniques may vary in some details from one method to another.

Any concentration of sample in the KBr may be selected. It is usual to choose one with absorption of the infrared beam of almost full scale deflection results in the region of interest. For silicates in the 9 to 10 micron region, from 0.15 per cent to 0.25 per cent is a suitable level of sample dilution in the potassium bromide.

Method: A well–tested method of preparation involves grinding 10 mg. of the sample by hand with 10 drops of absolute alcohol in a 60 mm. mullite mortar until the alcohol evaporates. This amount of grinding reduces the grain size to below 5 microns (about 50 per cent minus 2 microns) so that refractive index and scattering effects are minimized. One and one–half mg. of this preground sample are added to 1.00 gm. of infrared quality KBr and blended in a dentists' amalgamator (Wig–L–Bug), using a metal vial with a glass bead. *Do not use* the plastic vial or the plastic ball, or spurious absorptions due to abraded plastic will result (Lyon, 1963). Enough of the blend is weighed out to form a disc of the desired thickness (350 mg.) and pressed in a vacuum die. About 65 tons pressure per square inch is adequate to obtain permanently clear discs. These have been redried overnight in a vacuum oven, stored and used years later.

It has been found necessary to grind the samples under alcohol because the structure of many minerals, particularly those containing OH groups, can be obliterated in a few minutes by vigorous dry grinding (see Fig. 7). Careful, consistent preparatory grinding, coupled with adequate blending, is also quite critical. If these factors are controlled, then linear calibration curves for quantitative analysis can be obtained with mineral specimens (Lyon, *et al.,* 1959, p. 1048; Tuddenham and Lyon, 1959, p. 378; Tuddenham and Lyon, 1960a, p. 1631; Nahin, 1955, p. 113).

B. *Other special applications*

1. *Deposited Films*—Hunt, Wisherd, and Bonham (1950, p. 1478), and Hunt and Turner (1953, p. 1170) described the use of films of finely divided minerals deposited from alcohol "solution" on rock salt windows. This was an advance toward a good preparatory technique for rapid infrared studies, but suffered from excessive scatter of the radiation by the particles in the shorter wavelength regions below 4.0 microns. It was a fairly quick method but suffered a further problem due to the preparation techniques of settling used to collect the fine grain sizes. In a mixture of several minerals differential settling in the water column, used for elutriation, often gave an enhanced concentration of the heavier particles, and platy and micaceous minerals were left in suspension. The window was weighed before and after depositing the film from which a rough quantitative measure could be obtained. This method is not recommended unless specific orientations are to be desired, as for O–H orientation studies.

Ulrich (1961, p. 16), in an article on uses of specular infrared reflectance, gives a good review of methods for obtaining absorption spectra by reflection off an aluminum–mirror substrate. The infrared beam impinges at a 30° incident angle onto a very thin clay coating. It passes through to the mirror, is reflected back through the clay layer again, and emerges, producing an absorption spectra of the clay. Hannah (private communication) has found this method very useful when analyzing oxide coatings, paint layers, etc., on metals.

2. *Oriented Clay "Papers"*—Serratosa and Bradley (1958, p. 1164) and Serratosa (1962, p. 486) have described the use of a "paper" of oriented, dried clay to secure spectral absorption data from the O–H vibrations of clay particles. The reader should see also the excellent recent paper by Wolfe (1963, p. 390).

3. *Nujol Mulls*—To avoid the scattering effects by finely divided materials the mineral powders were immersed or mulled in a suitable oil (Nujol). This oil is a fluor–hydrocarbon which has a minimal number of absorptions, and none occurring in the regions of interest for mineral analysis.

Miller and Wilkins (1962, p. 1254) compiled an excellent catalog of inorganic and mineral spectra, using these oil–mull techniques. The techniques suffered occasionally from interference with the absorption bands of the oil itself, but mostly from the lack of desired control for quantitative purposes.

V Differential analysis

One of the most powerful assets of modern spectrophotometers is the double–beam design. The source infrared signal is reflected down two parallel paths through the equipment and later integrated by a chopping mirror. If no sample is present, then the chopped signals are of equal strength, and the pen traces a zero line. If the sample absorbs in one beam the chopped signals differ and the pen records an absorbance.

An important corollary to this statement exists. If both beams have samples of equal absorbance at any given wavelength, then a matched signal will be sensed and a "zero" recorded. A given material (A) may be "subtracted" from a spectrum of a mixture (A and B) if it is placed at the same concentration in the reference beam. Only the spectrum of (B) will appear. If too much energy is removed from the signals by this process, however, the pen will become very sluggish. Scanning speeds must be kept very slow for this technique. The differential spectroscopy method uses two KBr discs, one in each beam. By subtraction, the spectrum of the difference between the two samples is automatically obtained. Minor components in a mixture may be identified, or a contaminant removed (e.g., quartz in a clay–soil sample). Two KBr discs are prepared: disc (a) containing the unknown sample and disc (b) containing the estimated composition of the contaminant. For example, if quartz is determined at 50 per cent in a clay, then disc (b) contains 0.075 per cent quartz in KBr.

The amount of contaminant (quartz) may be read off a calibration chart, and the differential spectrum of (a) versus (b) is run. If the absorption peaks now become slightly reversed into "reflection" peaks, then there is too much of the material (b) in the reference beam (see Clark, 1960, p. 417-20).

Quartz is by far the principal contaminant with a strong absorption spectrum in most soil and mineral specimens. This technique is extremely useful for "removing" it from a sample. It is also applicable to cation–anion–exchange (as with PO_4, NH_4), by running discs of (a) clay plus exchanged material, differentially against (b), the original clay before treatment (Eyring and Wadsworth, 1956, p. 531).

VI Quantitative analysis

The infrared spectrophotometer also lends itself readily to quantitative analytical techniques. As with all other absorption measurements the sample preparation and dilution controls are critical. Careless work in the various stages of sample weighing and grinding can give widely varying precision with repeated sampling. The alkali halide disc method gives by far the maximum over–all accuracy as long as the precision of repeated sample preparations can be kept to a high level (see Tuddenham and Lyon, 1960a, p. 1630, for a statistical analysis of this preparation method).

It is usual to express a mineralogical analysis in percentages which total 100 per cent, and regardless of the method of analysis used this encourages erroneous answers. The fact that the various components in an analysis *must total 100 per cent* introduces problems in statistical analysis of the resultant data. Instruments are sensitive to different minerals; anyone who has tried to compare X–ray diffraction and optical results is aware of this fact (see Lyon and Tuddenham, 1959, p. 1234). Infrared analysis is certainly not the final answer — one must use several approaches, each sensitive in its own particular manner, to give the total composition of a soil sample.

Presuming a requisite high degree of precision in sample preparation, one can analyze the spectrum for its components in the following manner. One assumes that the sample in an alkali halide pellet is comparable to a true solution and applies the Lambert–Beer law. The absorbancy index (or molar absorbancy index) is then determined at a selected wavelength of strong absorbance for the sample.

The spectrum for a mixture in most cases is the addition of the spectrum of each component (see Fig. 3). It is possible to determine the concentration of each component at particular wavelengths which are specific for each compound, and where absorbancies do not over-

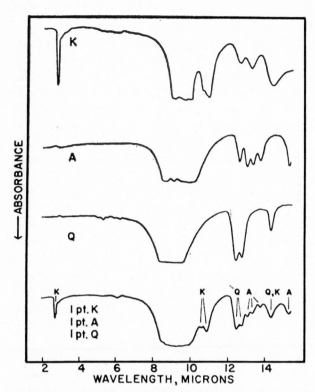

Figure 3. Mineral identification with infrared. Absorption curves of kaolinite (K), albite (A), quartz (Q), and a mixture of the three minerals. By kind permission of McGraw-Hill Publishing Co., Inc. Reproduced from Engineering & Mining Journal, Vol. 16, Fig. 1, 1960.

lap. A few such wavelengths for minerals in typical silicate matrices (soils, rocks, and clays) are as follows:

Table 3: Specific absorption wavelengths

Mineral	Specific Absorption Wavelength (microns)
Quartz	12.6 or 12.8
Plagioclase	13.48 (varies with An per cent)
Microcline	15.45
Orthoclase	15.6 (broad)
Calcite	7.0, 11.4, 14.02
Kaolinite	2.7, 2.75, 10.8, 11.0

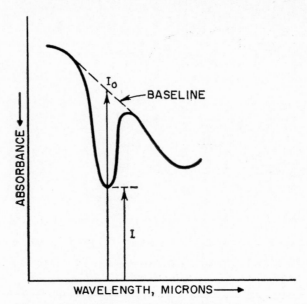

Figure 4. Method of drawing baseline for plotting composition versus log I₀/I. (After Willard, et al., 1960, Fig. 6-2). If absorbance values are used, plot against I₀-I.

The absorbancy index for each mineral in a mixture can be determined at its one or more characteristic wavelength. A series of linear equations can be set up and solved simultaneously for the desired concentrations (Willard, *et al.*, 1960, p. 146; Lyon, *et al.*, 1959, p. 1051).

A. Baseline Method

(1) If an absorption band of a mineral is chosen, the value of the incident radiation (I_o) is obtained by drawing a straight line tangential to the shoulders of the absorption band to be determined. The transmitted radiation (I) is measured at the point of maximum absorption. The value of log I_o/I is plotted against concentration in the normal manner (see Fig. 4). If absorbance readings are used the concentration is plotted directly against I_o–I.

(2) An alternative method we have used many times is shown in Fig. 5a. The baseline is drawn in the same manner, tangentially across the shoulders of the absorption band. The quantity (I_{abs}), the

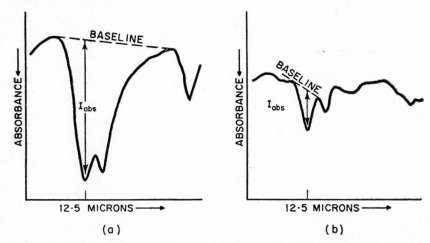

Figure 5. Methods of drawing baselines. (a) *Quartz in absence of other silicates,* (b) *Quartz in presence of other silicates.*

absorbance due to the sample, is plotted linearly against concentration. Straight line plots usually result.

(3) In the special case of minerals in soils and rocks, many silicates have broad and strong absorptions in the region 13.0 to 15.5 microns. Quartz is almost universally present in soils and its characteristic doublet will be seen riding on the flank of this area of broad absorption. It is no longer possible to draw a true baseline tangential to both the shoulders, but it is often found useful to join one shoulder (about 12.4 microns) tangentially to a mid–point about 12.7 microns (Fig. 5B). The useful calibration curves of I_{abs} versus concentration can be then used.

(4) Further use can be made of differential analysis. A mixture can be examined and its spectrum measured. Quartz and other minerals, for example, can be determined and a "synthetic" mixture prepared. This can be rerun against the original sample and differences identified by either over– or under–compensation.

(5) An alternate technique is to run the original mixture first, and then run the synthetic over the same trace. Differences of even a few per cent can be readily identified by one or the other of these methods. A clear illustration of this technique is shown by Lyon, *et al.* (1959, Fig. 4, p. 1052), using the powdered granite rock standard G–1.

VII Assignment of infrared spectral absorptions

For a polyatomic non–linear molecule of N atoms, there are a total of 3N possible degrees of freedom — 3 rotational, 3 translational, and 3N–6 vibrational motions; each with a characteristic fundamental band frequency. Since absorption only occurs where a change of dipole character takes place, total symmetry about a bond will eliminate some of these absorption bands (Cross, 1960, pp. 3-4).

Spectroscopists designate these modes as:

"υ" for stretching vibrations
"δ" for bending deformations with bond–angle changes
"τ" for twisting vibrations

Overtones and combinations of these fundamental frequencies often occur, and can be calculated at 1, 2, and 3 times the fundamental frequency.

A. *Organics*

1. *General*—The infrared spectrophotometer was developed for structural study of organics, and today probably 99.9 per cent of all units are being used for the study of these materials. To describe the assignment of infrared spectra of organics would merit a series of volumes. There are innumerable good references, including direct–reading wall charts like those prepared by Bellamy (1954) and Cross (1960, p. 50-73).

The following tabulation is taken from Cross (1960, p. 74) for organosilicon compounds, of some interest to mineralogists:

Table 4: Organo—Silicon absorption frequencies

Si–C Vibrations	cm.$^{-1}$	Microns	Strength	Assignment
Si–CH$_3$	1,260	7·94	vs.	sym.CH$_3$def.
	ca. 800	ca. 12·50	vs.	Si–CH$_3$str.
Si(CH$_3$)$_2$	1,260	7·94	vs.	sym.CH$_3$def.
	815–800	12·27–12·50	vs.	Si–CH$_3$str.
Si(CH$_3$)$_3$	1,250	8·00	vs.	sym.CH$_3$def.
	840	11·90	vs.	Si–CH$_3$str.
	755	13·25	vs.	Si–CH$_3$str.
Si–phenyl	1,430–1,425	6·99–7·02	vs.	
	1,135–1,090	8·81–9·17	vs.	

Table 4. Continued

Si–H Stretching Vibrations

Si–H	2,280–2,080	4·39–4·81	vs.	

Si–O Stretching Vibrations

| Si–O–Si and Si–O–C | 1,090–1,020 | 9·17–9·80 | vs. | Si–O str. |

2. *Organics adsorbed on Clays*—This new field of study is concerned with the modifications of the infrared spectra of organics induced by their adsorption onto clay and other mineral surfaces. Changes in bond lengths, bond angles, and strengths are noticeable, and may be used diagnostically both for the organic and for the clay. Differential analysis techniques are usually used and the clay matrix cancelled out.

Recent studies have shown that oriented clay (as "slips" or "papers") can induce orientations in the adsorbed organics, detectable in the same manner as orientation in the stretching of O–H bonds. References are:

Brindley and Rustom, 1958, p. 627
Hoffman and Brindley, 1961, p. 446
Serratosa, 1962, p. 486

B. *Inorganics*

1. *General*—Several workers have prepared tabulations for the inorganic functional groups. The list below is taken from Cross (1960, pp. 74-75) and forms a very useful tabulation of the inorganic spectral frequencies. Other references are listed below. It is recommended that the reader collect spectra into an "atlas," for as yet no complete compilation for mineralogical use has been prepared.

Table 5: Inorganic group absorption frequencies (after Cross, 1960, pp. 74-75)

	cm.$^{-1}$	microns		
$AsO_4{}^{3-}$	ca. 800	ca. 12·50	s.	
$AsF_6{}^-$	705– 690	14·18–14·49	vs.	
$BH_4{}^-$	2,400–2,200	4·17– 4·55	s.	1 or more bands
	1,130–1,040	8·85– 9·62	s.	
$BF_4{}^-$	ca. 1,060	ca. 9·43	vs.	
	ca. 1,030	ca. 9·71	vs.	

Table 5. Continued

BrO_3^-	810– 790	12·35–12·66	vs.	
CO_3^{2-}	1,450–1,410	6·90– 7·09	vs.	
	880– 800	11·36–12·50	m.	
HCO_3^-	1,420–1,400	7·04– 7·14	s.	
	1,000– 990	10·00–10·10	s.	
	840– 830	11·90–12·05	s.	
	705– 695	14·18–14·39	s.	
ClO_3^-	980– 930	10·20–10·75	vs.	
ClO_4^-	1,140–1,060	8·77– 9·43	vs.	broad absorption
CrO_4^{2-}	950– 800	10·53–12·50	s.	complex strong bands
$Cr_2O_7^{2-}$	950– 900	10·35–11·11	s.	
CN^-, CNO^-, and CNS^-	2,200–2,000	4·55– 5·00	s.	
CO	2,100–2,000	4·76– 5·00	s.	normal carbonyls
	ca. 1,830	ca. 5·46	s.	bridged carbonyls
HF_2^-	ca. 1,450	ca. 6·90	s.	
	ca. 1,230	ca. 8·13	s.	
IO_3^-	800– 700	12·50–14·29	s.	complex strong bands
MnO_4^-	920– 890	10·87–11·24	vs.	
	850– 840	11·76–11·90	m.	
NH_4^+	3,335–3,030	3·00– 3·30	vs.	
	1,485–1,390	6·73– 7·19	s.	
N_3^-	2,170–2,080	4·61– 4·81	s.	
	1,375–1,175	7·27– 8·51	w.	
NO_2^-	1,400–1,300	7·14– 7·69	s.	2 bands in complex nitrites
	1,250–1,230	8·00– 8·13	vs.	
	840– 800	11·90–12·50	w.	
NO_3^-	1,410–1,340	7·09– 7·46	vs.	
	860– 800	11·63–12·50	m.	
NO_2^+	1,410–1,370	7·09– 7·30	s.	
NO^+	2,370–2,230	4·22– 4·48	s.	
NO^+ (coordination comps.)	1,940–1,630	5·16– 6·14	s.	
NO^- (coordination comps.)	1,170–1,045	8·55– 9·57	s.	
NO (nitrosyl halides)	1,850–1,790	5·41– 5·59	s.	
PF_6^-	850– 840	11·76–11·90	vs.	
PO_4^{3-}, HPO_4^{2-}, and $H_2PO_4^-$	1,100– 950	9·09–10·53	s.	
$S_2O_3^{2-}$	1,660–1,620	6·02– 6·17	w.	
	1,000– 990	10·00–10·10	s.	
SO_4^{2-}	1,130–1,080	8·85– 9·26	vs.	
	680– 610	14·71–16·40	m.	
HSO_4^-	1,180–1,160	8·84– 8·62	s.	
	1,080–1,000	9·26–10·00	s.	
	880– 840	11·36–11·90	s.	
SO_3^{2-}	ca. 1,100	ca. 9·09	v.	l.v.
SeO_4^{2-}	ca. 830	ca. 12·05	s.	
SiF_6^{2-}	ca. 725	ca. 13·79	s.	
all silicates	1,100– 900	9·09–11·11	s.	
UO_2^{2+}	940– 900	10·64–11·11	s.	

The following are useful references:

Grim, 1953, p. 303
Adler, 1950, pp. 1-73
Hunt, *et. al.,* 1950, pp. 1478-97
Hunt and Turner, 1953, pp. 1169-74
Keller, 1952, pp. 453-71
Launer, 1952, pp. 764-84
Miller and Wilkins, 1952, pp. 1253-94

It is possible to predict from the symmetry of simple molecules (usually gases) the fundamental vibrational frequencies to be expected. For most solids this is extremely difficult, and essentially impossible for minerals such as the silicates. An empirical approach is then used. Isostructural materials such as minerals are selected and the patterns of the Si–O functional configurations determined for each major group. Launer (1952, p. 774) describes an excellent study of this type, and there have been several more recent attempts to refine these associations (Nahin, 1955, p. 115; Stubican and Roy, 1961b, p. 625; Lyon and Tuddenham, 1960a, p. 374).

The ensuing discussion will cover applications of this basic technique — to prepare absorption spectra of isostructural minerals and then compare and contrast their patterns.

Stubican and Roy (1961b, p. 625) have successfully used synthetic clays of known composition to assign peak absorptions (Fig. 6). It should be clearly noted, however, that even when this degree of knowledge exists about a sample, assignments made for one structural group do not always apply to another. Stubican and Roy (1961a, p. 202) elsewhere emphasize this difficulty and describe the effect that atoms in the "secondary" sphere of coordination of an atomic configuration have upon the spectra. These two papers should be carefully read, before advancing too far into the problems of assigning absorption peaks (see Farmer, 1958, pp. 834-39; Lyon and Tuddenham, 1960a, p. 374; Tuddenham and Lyon, 1959, p. 377).

2. *Free– and Bonded–Hydroxyl*—A certain amount of confusion has arisen in clay literature with the terms "free (OH)" and "bonded (OH)." This can usually be resolved if one considers which particular point of view is assumed — that of the clay particle or that of the solution surrounding the particle. "Free OH" then means "free from hydrogen bonding." The absorption for this bond is at higher

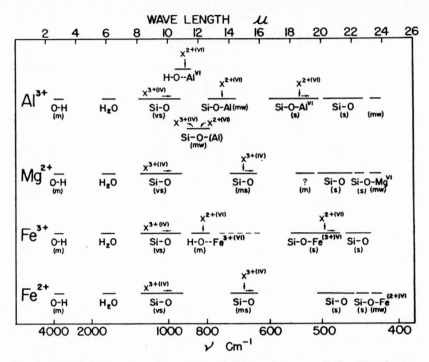

Figure 6. Schematic summary of assignments of the IR absorption bands in layer lattice silicates containing basically Al³⁺, Mg²⁺, Fe³⁺, or Fe²⁺ in the octahedral sites. The relative intensities of bands are described as vs=very strong, s=strong, m= medium, w=weak. From Stubican and Roy, 1961b, by kind permission of the American Ceramic Society.

frequencies (3700 cm.⁻¹; 2.7 microns), than that of "hydrogen—bonded" hydroxyl (3510 cm.⁻¹; 2.85 microns). From the *mineralogical* point of view, one can assign the 2.7 micron peak to "bonded OH" (i.e., OH *essential* to the structure), and the 2.85 micron peak to "free H₂O" (*adsorbed* onto the structure) (See Lyon and Tuddenham, 1960b, p. 835). One may further distinguish "inner" and "outer" bonded hydroxyls as in the 2– and 3–layer clays (like kaolinite, and the micas and chlorites). These both have absorption peaks at higher frequencies (3700, 3625 cm.⁻¹; 2.7, 2.76 microns) than "free H₂O" (3510 cm.⁻¹; 2.85 microns).

Deuteration of the (OH) sites causes a predictable change in the wavelength position to (OD) sites, and allows their assignment, even

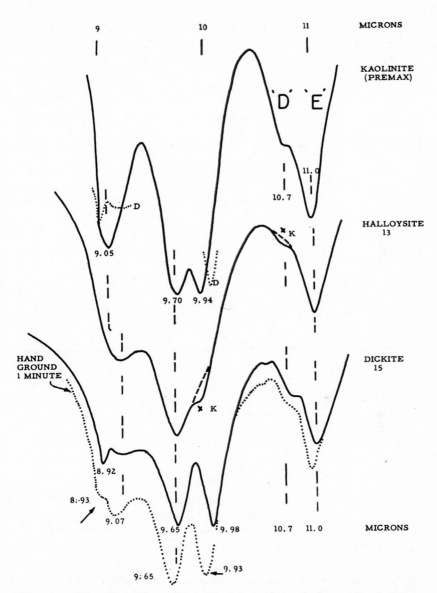

Figure 7. Details of 8- to 11-micron section of absorption spectra of the kaolin group minerals. Note the effect of hand grinding dickite (dry), and the similarity to kaolinite after this treatment.

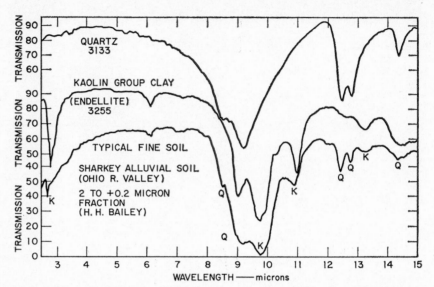

Figure 8. Comparison spectra of quartz and kaolin clay, as used to analyze the spectrum of the Sharkey Alluvial soil. Original soil spectrum by H. H. Bailey.

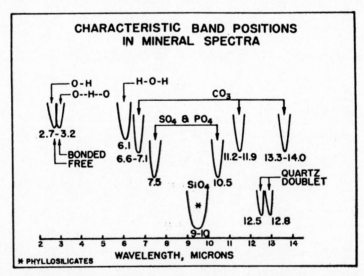

Figure 9. Diagram showing characteristic positions for the absorption bands of typical functional groups in mineral spectra. From Nahin (1955) by kind permission of the California State Division of Mines.

Table 6. Mineralogically Important Studies*

A. CARBONATES
  Huang (1960), Adler (1961)
B. CLAYS AND CLAY MINERALS
  1. Clay Structures
    Stubican (1956, 1957, 1959, 1960, 1961a,b,c), Beutelspacher (1956a,b)
  2. Cations in Clays
    Tettenhorst (1962)
C. FELDSPARS
  Hafner (1957), Laves (1956, 1960)
D. MICAS AND CHLORITES
  1. Mica Structures
    Stubican (1956, 1957, 1959, 1960, 1961a), Lyon (1960a), Tuddenham
    (1959), Marel (1958, 1960, 1961)
  2. Hydroxyl Orientation
    Bassett (1960), Serratosa (1958, 1962), Wolfe (1963)
E. PREPARATORY TECHNIQUES FOR MINERALS
  1. KBr Pelleting
    Nahin (1955), Tuddenham (1960a), Hunt (1950, 1953), Farmer (1955)
  2. Grinding
    Farmer (1957), Milkey (1958)
  3. Particle Size
    Duyckaerts (1959)
F. QUARTZ–COORDINATION AND ASSIGNMENTS
  Saksena (1940, 1958), Lippincott (1958), Dachille (1959)
G. PHOSPHATES
  Omori (1960), Posner (1954, 1960, 1961)
H. SILICATE STRUCTURAL GROUPING
  Launer (1952), Lazarev (1957, 1958, 1960a,b, 1960, 1961, 1961a,b,
  1962), Moenke (1961), Saksena (1940, 1958, 1961), Milkey (1960a,b)
I. SUBSTITUTIONS IN SILICATE MINERALS
  1. Aluminum Effects
    Lyon (1960a), Tuddenham (1959), Kolesova (1954, 1959, 1959)
  2. Gallium Effects
    Roy (1960)
  3. Germanium Effects
    Tarte (1960a, 1962), Lazarev (1961a, 1962)
  4. Titanium Effects
    Tarte (1960b,c, 1961)
J. SERPENTINES—STRUCTURAL STUDIES
  Brindley (1959)
K. SOILS AND COLLOIDS
  Beutelspacher (1956a,b), Fieldes (1955, 1956), Marel (1961)
L. SULFATES
  Omori (1962)

* Only senior authors listed.

Table 7. Reciprocals—Conversion of Microns to Cm. $^{-1}$

	0	1	2	3	4	5	6	7	8	9	1	2	3	4	5	6	7	8	9
														SUBTRACT					
1·0	1·0000	·9901	·9804	·9709	·9615	·9524	·9434	·9346	·9259	·9174	9	18	27	36	45	55	64	73	82
1·1	·9091	·9009	·8929	·8850	·8772	·8696	·8621	·8547	·8475	·8403	8	15	23	30	38	45	53	61	68
1·2	·8333	·8264	·8197	·8130	·8065	·8000	·7937	·7874	·7813	·7752	6	13	19	26	32	38	45	51	58
1·3	·7692	·7634	·7576	·7519	·7463	·7407	·7353	·7299	·7246	·7194	5	11	16	22	27	33	38	44	49
1·4	·7143	·7092	·7042	·6993	·6944	·6897	·6849	·6803	·6757	·6711	5	10	14	19	24	29	33	38	43
1·5	·6667	·6623	·6579	·6536	·6494	·6452	·6410	·6369	·6329	·6289	4	8	13	17	21	25	29	33	38
1·6	·6250	·6211	·6173	·6135	·6098	·6061	·6024	·5988	·5952	·5917	4	7	11	15	18	22	26	29	33
1·7	·5882	·5848	·5814	·5780	·5747	·5714	·5682	·5650	·5618	·5587	3	7	10	13	16	20	23	26	30
1·8	·5556	·5525	·5495	·5464	·5435	·5405	·5376	·5348	·5319	·5291	3	6	9	12	15	18	20	23	26
1·9	·5263	·5236	·5208	·5181	·5155	·5128	·5102	·5076	·5051	·5025	3	5	8	11	13	16	18	21	24
2·0	·5000	·4975	·4950	·4926	·4902	·4878	·4854	·4831	·4808	·4785	2	5	7	10	12	14	17	19	21
2·1	·4762	·4739	·4717	·4695	·4673	·4651	·4630	·4608	·4587	·4566	2	4	7	9	11	13	15	17	20
2·2	·4545	·4525	·4505	·4484	·4464	·4444	·4425	·4405	·4386	·4367	2	4	6	8	10	12	14	16	18
2·3	·4348	·4329	·4310	·4292	·4274	·4255	·4237	·4219	·4202	·4184	2	4	5	7	9	11	13	14	16
2·4	·4167	·4149	·4132	·4115	·4098	·4082	·4065	·4049	·4032	·4016	2	3	5	7	8	10	12	13	15
2·5	·4000	·3984	·3968	·3953	·3937	·3922	·3906	·3891	·3876	·3861	2	3	5	6	8	9	11	12	14
2·6	·3846	·3831	·3817	·3802	·3788	·3774	·3759	·3745	·3731	·3717	1	3	4	6	7	8	10	11	13
2·7	·3704	·3690	·3676	·3663	·3650	·3636	·3623	·3610	·3597	·3584	1	3	4	5	7	8	9	11	12
2·8	·3571	·3559	·3546	·3534	·3521	·3509	·3497	·3484	·3472	·3460	1	2	4	5	6	7	9	10	11
2·9	·3448	·3436	·3425	·3413	·3401	·3390	·3378	·3367	·3356	·3344	1	2	3	5	6	7	8	9	10
3·0	·3333	·3322	·3311	·3300	·3289	·3279	·3268	·3257	·3247	·3236	1	2	3	4	5	6	7	9	10
3·1	·3226	·3215	·3205	·3195	·3185	·3175	·3165	·3155	·3145	·3135	1	2	3	4	5	6	7	8	9
3·2	·3125	·3115	·3106	·3096	·3086	·3077	·3067	·3058	·3049	·3040	1	2	3	4	5	6	7	8	9
3·3	·3030	·3021	·3012	·3003	·2994	·2985	·2976	·2967	·2959	·2950	1	2	3	4	4	5	6	7	8
3·4	·2941	·2933	·2924	·2915	·2907	·2899	·2890	·2882	·2874	·2865	1	2	3	3	4	5	6	7	8
3·5	·2857	·2849	·2841	·2833	·2825	·2817	·2809	·2801	·2793	·2786	1	2	2	3	4	5	6	6	7
3·6	·2778	·2770	·2762	·2755	·2747	·2740	·2732	·2725	·2717	·2710	1	2	2	3	4	5	5	6	7
3·7	·2703	·2695	·2688	·2681	·2674	·2667	·2660	·2653	·2646	·2639	1	1	2	3	4	4	5	6	6
3·8	·2632	·2625	·2618	·2611	·2604	·2597	·2591	·2584	·2577	·2571	1	1	2	3	3	4	5	5	6
3·9	·2564	·2558	·2551	·2545	·2538	·2532	·2525	·2519	·2513	·2506	1	1	2	3	3	4	4	5	6
4·0	·2500	·2494	·2488	·2481	·2475	·2469	·2463	·2457	·2451	·2445	1	1	2	2	3	4	4	5	5
4·1	·2439	·2433	·2427	·2421	·2415	·2410	·2404	·2398	·2392	·2387	1	1	2	2	3	3	4	5	5
4·2	·2381	·2375	·2370	·2364	·2358	·2353	·2347	·2342	·2336	·2331	1	1	2	2	3	3	4	4	5
4·3	·2326	·2320	·2315	·2309	·2304	·2299	·2294	·2288	·2283	·2278	1	1	2	2	3	3	4	4	5
4·4	·2273	·2268	·2262	·2257	·2252	·2247	·2242	·2237	·2232	·2227	1	1	2	2	3	3	4	4	5
4·5	·2222	·2217	·2212	·2208	·2203	·2198	·2193	·2188	·2183	·2179	0	1	1	2	2	3	3	4	4
4·6	·2174	·2169	·2165	·2160	·2155	·2151	·2146	·2141	·2137	·2132	0	1	1	2	2	3	3	4	4
4·7	·2128	·2123	·2119	·2114	·2110	·2105	·2101	·2096	·2092	·2088	0	1	1	2	2	3	3	4	4
4·8	·2083	·2079	·2075	·2070	·2066	·2062	·2058	·2053	·2049	·2045	0	1	1	2	2	3	3	3	4
4·9	·2041	·2037	·2033	·2028	·2024	·2020	·2016	·2012	·2008	·2004	0	1	1	2	2	2	3	3	4
5·0	·2000	·1996	·1992	·1988	·1984	·1980	·1976	·1972	·1969	·1965	0	1	1	2	2	2	3	3	4
5·1	·1961	·1957	·1953	·1949	·1946	·1942	·1938	·1934	·1931	·1927	0	1	1	2	2	2	3	3	3
5·2	·1923	·1919	·1916	·1912	·1908	·1905	·1901	·1898	·1894	·1890	0	1	1	2	2	3	3	3	3
5·3	·1887	·1883	·1880	·1876	·1873	·1869	·1866	·1862	·1859	·1855	0	1	1	1	2	2	3	3	3
5·4	·1852	·1848	·1845	·1842	·1838	·1835	·1832	·1828	·1825	·1821	0	1	1	1	2	2	2	3	3
	0	1	2	3	4	5	6	7	8	9	1	2	3	4	5	6	7	8	9

	0	1	2	3	4	5	6	7	8	9	1	2	3	4	5	6	7	8	9
															SUBTRACT				
5·5	·1818	·1815	·1812	·1808	·1805	·1802	·1799	·1795	·1792	·1789	0	1	1	1	2	2	2	3	3
5·6	·1786	·1783	·1779	·1776	·1773	·1770	·1767	·1764	·1761	·1757	0	1	1	1	2	2	2	3	3
5·7	·1754	·1751	·1748	·1745	·1742	·1739	·1736	·1733	·1730	·1727	0	1	1	1	2	2	2	2	3
5·8	·1724	·1721	·1718	·1715	·1712	·1709	·1706	·1704	·1701	·1698	0	1	1	1	1	2	2	2	3
5·9	·1695	·1692	·1689	·1686	·1684	·1681	·1678	·1675	·1672	·1669	0	1	1	1	1	2	2	2	3
6·0	·1667	·1664	·1661	·1658	·1656	·1653	·1650	·1647	·1645	·1642	0	1	1	1	1	2	2	2	3
6·1	·1639	·1637	·1634	·1631	·1629	·1626	·1623	·1621	·1618	·1616	0	1	1	1	1	2	2	2	2
6·2	·1613	·1610	·1608	·1605	·1603	·1600	·1597	·1595	·1592	·1590	0	1	1	1	1	2	2	2	2
6·3	·1587	·1585	·1582	·1580	·1577	·1575	·1572	·1570	·1567	·1565	0	0	1	1	1	1	2	2	2
6·4	·1563	·1560	·1558	·1555	·1553	·1550	·1548	·1546	·1543	·1541	0	0	1	1	1	1	2	2	2
6·5	·1538	·1536	·1534	·1531	·1529	·1527	·1524	·1522	·1520	·1517	0	0	1	1	1	1	2	2	2
6·6	·1515	·1513	·1511	·1508	·1506	·1504	·1502	·1499	·1497	·1495	0	0	1	1	1	1	2	2	2
6·7	·1493	·1490	·1488	·1486	·1484	·1481	·1479	·1477	·1475	·1473	0	0	1	1	1	1	2	2	2
6·8	·1471	·1468	·1466	·1464	·1462	·1460	·1458	·1456	·1453	·1451	0	0	1	1	1	1	2	2	2
6·9	·1449	·1447	·1445	·1443	·1441	·1439	·1437	·1435	·1433	·1431	0	0	1	1	1	1	1	2	2
7·0	·1429	·1427	·1425	·1422	·1420	·1418	·1416	·1414	·1412	·1410	0	0	1	1	1	1	1	2	2
7·1	·1408	·1406	·1404	·1403	·1401	·1399	·1397	·1395	·1393	·1391	0	0	1	1	1	1	1	2	2
7·2	·1389	·1387	·1385	·1383	·1381	·1379	·1377	·1376	·1374	·1372	0	0	1	1	1	1	1	2	2
7·3	·1370	·1368	·1366	·1364	·1362	·1361	·1359	·1357	·1355	·1353	0	0	1	1	1	1	1	2	2
7·4	·1351	·1350	·1348	·1346	·1344	·1342	·1340	·1339	·1337	·1335	0	0	1	1	1	1	1	1	2
7·5	·1333	·1332	·1330	·1328	·1326	·1325	·1323	·1321	·1319	·1318	0	0	1	1	1	1	1	1	2
7·6	·1310	·1314	·1312	·1311	·1309	·1307	·1305	·1304	·1302	·1300	0	0	1	1	1	1	1	1	2
7·7	·1299	·1297	·1295	·1294	·1292	·1290	·1289	·1287	·1285	·1284	0	0	0	1	1	1	1	1	1
7·8	·1282	·1280	·1279	·1277	·1276	·1274	·1272	·1271	·1269	·1267	0	0	0	1	1	1	1	1	1
7·9	·1266	·1264	·1263	·1261	·1259	·1258	·1256	·1255	·1253	·1252	0	0	0	1	1	1	1	1	1
8·0	·1250	·1248	·1247	·1245	·1244	·1242	·1241	·1239	·1238	·1236	0	0	0	1	1	1	1	1	1
8·1	·1235	·1233	·1232	·1230	·1229	·1227	·1225	·1224	·1222	·1221	0	0	0	1	1	1	1	1	1
8·2	·1220	·1218	·1217	·1215	·1214	·1212	·1211	·1209	·1208	·1206	0	0	0	1	1	1	1	1	1
8·3	·1205	·1203	·1202	·1200	·1199	·1198	·1196	·1195	·1193	·1192	0	0	0	1	1	1	1	1	1
8·4	·1190	·1189	·1188	·1186	·1185	·1183	·1182	·1181	·1179	·1178	0	0	0	1	1	1	1	1	1
8·5	·1176	·1175	·1174	·1172	·1171	·1170	·1168	·1167	·1166	·1164	0	0	0	1	1	1	1	1	1
8·6	·1163	·1161	·1160	·1159	·1157	·1156	·1155	·1153	·1152	·1151	0	0	0	1	1	1	1	1	1
8·7	·1149	·1148	·1147	·1145	·1144	·1143	·1142	·1140	·1139	·1138	0	0	0	1	1	1	1	1	1
8·8	·1136	·1135	·1134	·1133	·1131	·1130	·1129	·1127	·1126	·1125	0	0	0	1	1	1	1	1	1
8·9	·1124	·1122	·1121	·1120	·1119	·1117	·1116	·1115	·1114	·1112	0	0	0	1	1	1	1	1	1
9·0	·1111	·1110	·1109	·1107	·1106	·1105	·1104	·1103	·1101	·1100	0	0	0	1	1	1	1	1	1
9·1	·1099	·1098	·1096	·1095	·1094	·1093	·1092	·1091	·1089	·1088	0	0	0	0	1	1	1	1	1
9·2	·1087	·1086	·1085	·1083	·1082	·1081	·1080	·1079	·1078	·1076	0	0	0	0	1	1	1	1	1
9·3	·1075	·1074	·1073	·1072	·1071	·1070	·1068	·1067	·1066	·1065	0	0	0	0	1	1	1	1	1
9·4	·1064	·1063	·1062	·1060	·1059	·1058	·1057	·1056	·1055	·1054	0	0	0	0	1	1	1	1	1
9·5	·1053	·1052	·1050	·1049	·1048	·1047	·1046	·1045	·1044	·1043	0	0	0	0	1	1	1	1	1
9·6	·1042	·1041	·1040	·1038	·1037	·1036	·1035	·1034	·1033	·1032	0	0	0	0	1	1	1	1	1
9·7	·1031	·1030	·1029	·1028	·1027	·1026	·1025	·1024	·1022	·1021	0	0	0	0	1	1	1	1	1
9·8	·1020	·1019	·1018	·1017	·1016	·1015	·1014	·1013	·1012	·1011	0	0	0	0	1	1	1	1	1
9·9	·1010	·1009	·1008	·1007	·1006	·1005	·1004	·1003	·1002	·1001	0	0	0	0	0	1	1	1	1
	0	1	2	3	4	5	6	7	8	9	1	2	3	4	5	6	7	8	9

Copyright: Cambridge University Press

out to 11.5 microns (see Roy and Roy, 1957, p. 72)). Intensities of the OH peaks will also vary with the character of the interlayer cation, as in DTA studies (Nahin, 1955, p. 114).

3. *Hydroxyl Orientation*—By the use of thin plates of mica (0.1 mm. thick), transmission spectra of the hydroxyl–stretching region (2.7–2.9 microns) can be obtained. When these plates are inclined to the infrared beam it is possible to produce changes in the relative intensities of the several OH absorption peaks, for all micas except the truly dioctahedral muscovites. These changes can be related to the orientation of the proton–oxygen linkages. Because of variations in octahedral layer deficiencies, the O–H bands are not in parallel orientation. In phlogopite, with a filled octahedral layer, they are all vertical. Oriented "papers" of clays may be analyzed in a similar manner (Serratosa and Bradley, 1958, p. 1166; Serratosa, *et al.,* 1962, p. 486; Wolfe, 1963, p. 390).

4. *Minerals*—Infrared analyses have been performed on a great variety of inorganic mineralogical specimens. For a longer exposition the reader is referred to an article by Milkey (1960, pp. 488-89) from which this section has been abstracted. In a recent bibliographical compilation (Lyon, 1963) it was possible to list 452 mineral spectral curves from a total of 440 references in mineral–related literature. But few compilations or atlases of curves exist. One is forced to prepare one's own suite of curves for reference purposes and correlate their absorption characteristics for personal use. Fig. 7 shows a set of high resolution spectra of the kaolin group minerals as used for diagnostic studies. Fig. 8 shows spectra for quartz, halloysite, and a typical fine soil clay. An excellent recent reference is that of Marel (1961, pp. 23-82).

Spectra exist for the simple sulfate, carbonate, phosphate, and oxide minerals in the wavelength range of 2 to 15 microns (4000–667 cm.$^{-1}$), the range of the commonly available NaCl prism–equipped units (Fig. 9). They show fewer and more broadened absorptions than one finds with the organic materials, and the oxides and sulfides show even more diffuse absorptions.

With those minerals which possess more complex anions, the absorption spectra are dominated by these structural effects, and reflect the covalent character of the anionic bonding. A series of carbonates with different metal ratios show comparable spectra, but are displaced in wavelength as a function of the mass of the metal cation. In a similar manner, wavelength shifts in spectra of sulfates and phosphates, nitrates and borates may be predicted, determined, and assigned.

In the past decade silicate mineralogists have been developing an understanding of silicate absorption spectra. "Standardized spectra" have been obtained of silicates of every structural class, ranging from the tight, framework–bonded tektosilicates to the least tightly–bonded and individual SiO_4 tetrahedra.

In Table 6 (taken from Lyon, 1962, pp. 10-11) are presented the mineralogically important studies appearing in the literature to the end of 1962.

VIII Conclusion

It should be obvious by now to the reader that a considerable body of published material is available on the infrared analysis of minerals which occur in soils. It is not within the scope of this paper to review completely the structural groups of minerals one by one, but it has been hoped that this discussion would introduce the student to the possible techniques, and to applications in which the method has been used.

References

A. *General Texts*

Bellamy, L. J. (1954) *The Infrared Spectra of Complex Molecules:* John Wiley, New York.

Brown, C. R., Ayton, M. W., Goodwin, T. C., and Derby, T. J. (1951) *Infrared–Bibliography:* Off. Tech. Serv., U.S. Dept. of Commerce (PB111643).

Clark, G. L. (editor) (1961) *The Encyclopedia of Spectroscopy:* Reinhold, New York, pp. 450-53, 487-94.

Cross, A. D. (1960) *An Introduction to Practical Infrared Spectroscopy:* Butterworth Scientific Publications, London (or Butterworth, Inc., 7235 Wisconsin Avenue, Washington 14, D. C.).

Grim, R. E. (1953) *Clay Mineralogy:* McGraw-Hill, New York, Chapter 12b.

Kruse, P. W., McGlauchlin, L. D., and McQuistan, R. B. (1962) *Elements of Infrared Technology — Generation, Transmission Detection:* John Wiley, New York.

Neuringer, L. J. (1960) *Infrared, Fundamentals and Techniques: Electrical Manufacturing,* pp. 101-28. (Excellent summary of infrared radiation sources, uses, in theory and practice), Electrical Manufacturing (Basic Science and Engineering series), 205 East 42nd St., New York 17, N. Y.

Stewart, H. S. (1962) The New Optics: *International Sci. and Tech.,* v. 1, pp. 15-26.

Ulrich, W. F. (1961) Bibliography of Infrared Applications: Bull. 754, Beckman Inc.

Willard, H. H., Merritt, L. L., Jr., and Dean, J. A. (1960) *Instrumental Methods of Analysis* (3rd ed.); Van Nostrand, New York, Chapter 6.

B. *Individual Papers* (With Chem. Abstract listings).

Adler, H. H. (1950) Infrared investigations of clay and related minerals: Preliminary Report No. 8 (Infrared spectra of reference clay minerals). *American Petroleum Institute, Project 49,* Columbia University, pp. 1-72.

Adler, H. H. and Kerr, P. F. (1961) Infrared study of aragonite and calcite: *Am. Min.,* v. 47, pp. 700-17.

Bassett, W. A. (1960) Role of hydroxyl orientation in mica alteration: *Bull. Geol. Soc. Am.,* v. 71, pp. 449-56.   C.A. 54-11871 d.

Beutelspacher, H. (1956a) Infrared studies on soil colloids: *Sixieme Congress de la Science du Sol,* Paris, v. 1, 47, pp. 329-36.

Beutelspacher, H. (1956b) Beitrage zur Ultrarotspektroskopie von Boden-Kolloiden: *Landwirtschaftiche Forschung.,* v. 7, pp. 74-80.

Brindley, G. W. and Rustom, M. (1958) Adsorption and retention of an organic material by montmorillonite in the presence of water: *Am. Min.,* v. 43, pp. 627-40.

Brindley, G. W. and Zussman, J. (1959) Infrared absorption data for serpentine minerals: *Am. Min.,* v. 44, pp. 185-88.   C.A. 53-8808 d.

Chayes, F. (1950) Composition of the granites of Westerly and Bradford, Rhode Island: *Am. Jour. Sci.,* v. 248, pp. 378-407.

Chayes, F. (1951) Modal analysis of the granite and diabase test rocks: Part 5 of a cooperative investigation of precision and accuracy in chemical, spectrochemical, and modal analysis of silicate rocks: *U.S. Geol. Survey Bull.,* v. 980, pp. 59-68.

Dachille, F. and Roy, R. (1959) The use of infrared absorption and molar refractivities to check coordination: *Zeitsch. Krist.,* v. 111, pp. 462-70.   C.A. 54-11697 g.

Duyckaerts, G. (1959) The infrared analysis of solid substances: *Analyst,* v. 84, pp. 201-14.

Eyring, E. M. and Wadsworth, M. E. (1956) Differential spectra of adsorbed monolayers of n–hexanethiol on zinc minerals: *Min. Eng.,* v. 8, pp. 531-36.

Farmer, V. C. (1955) Pressed-disk technique in infrared spectroscopy: *Chem. Ind.* (London), pp. 586-87.   C.A. 49-12966 g.

Farmer, V. C. (1957) Effects of grinding during the preparation of alkali halide disks on the infrared spectra of hydroxylic compounds: *Spectrochim Acta,* v. 8, pp. 374-89.   C.A. 51-11069 a.

Farmer, V. C. (1958) The infrared spectra of talc, saponite and hectorite: *Mineral. Mag.,* v. 31, pp. 829-45.

Fieldes, M. and Williamson, K. I. (1955) Clay mineralogy of New Zealand soils: (1) Electron micrography: *New Zealand J. Sci. Technol.,*

v. 37B, pp. 314-35. (II) Allophane and related mineral colloids: *Ibid.,* pp. 336-50.

Fieldes, M., Walker, I. K., and Williams, P. P. (1956) Clay mineralogy of New Zealand soils. III. Infrared absorption spectra of clay soils: *New Zealand J. Sci. Technol.,* v. 38B, pp. 31-43.   C.A. 51-1514 b.

Hafner, St. and Laves, F. (1957) Order/disorder and infrared absorption II: Variation of the position and intensity of some absorptions of feldspars; the structure of orthoclase and adularia: *Zeitsch. Krist.,* v. 109, pp. 204-25.

Heller, L., Farmer, V. C., MacKenzie, R. C., Mitchell, B. D., and Taylor, H. F. W. (1963) The dehydroxylation and rehydroxylation of tri-phormic dioctahedral clay minerals: *Mineral. Mag.,* v. 34, pp. 56-72.

Hoffman, R. W. and Brindley, G. W. (1961) Infrared extinction coefficients of ketones adsorbed on Ca–montmorillonite in relation to surface coverage. Clay-organic studies, Part IV: *J. Phys. Chem.,* v. 65, pp. 443-48.

Huang, C. K. and Kerr, P. F. (1960) Infrared study of the carbonate minerals: *Am. Min.,* v. 45, pp. 311-24.   C.A. 54-14943 d.

Hunt, J. M., Wisherd, P., and Bonham, L. C. (1950) Infrared absorption spectra of minerals and other inorganic compounds: *Anal. Chem.,* v. 22, pp. 1478-97.

Hunt, J. M. and Turner, D. C. (1953) Determination of mineral constituents of rocks by infrared spectroscopy: *Anal. Chem.,* v. 25, pp. 1169-74.

Keller, W. D., Spotts, J. H., and Biggs, D. L. (1952) Infrared spectra of some rock-forming minerals: *Am. Jour. Sci.,* v. 250, pp. 453-71.

Kerr, P. F. and Adler, H. H. (1950) Infrared spectra of reference clay minerals: *American Petroleum Institute, Project 49,* Columbia University, pp. 141-46.

Kolesova, V. A. (1954) Problem of the interpretation of vibration spectra of the silicates and the silicate glasses: *Zhur Eksptl. i. Teoret. Fiz.,* v. 26, pp. 124-27.   C.A. 50-59 f.

Kolesova, V. A. (1959) Infrared absorption spectra of the silicates containing aluminum and of certain crystalline aluminates: *Optics and Spectroscopy* (USSR), v. 6, p. 20.   C.A. 53-8820 g.

Kolesova, V. A. and Ryskin, Ya. I. (1959) Infrared absorption spectrum of hydrargillite $Al(OH)_3$: *Optics and Spectroscopy* (USSR), v. 7, pp. 165-66.   C.A. 54-8299 i.

Launer, P. J. (1952) Regularities in the infrared absorption spectra of silicate minerals: *Am. Min.,* v. 37, pp. 764-84.   C.A. 48-7501 e.

Laves, F. and Hafner, St. (1956) Order/disorder and infrared absorption I. (Aluminum, silicon) — Distribution in feldspars: *Zeitsch. Krist.,* v. 108, pp. 52-63.   C.A. 51-3291 e.

Laves, F. (1960) Al/Si distributions, phase transformations, and names of alkali feldspars: *Zeitsch. Krist.,* v. 113, pp. 265-96.

C.A. 54-17161 f.

Lazarev, A. N. (1957) Absorption spectrum of KH₂PO₄ in the region of
hydroxyl valence vibration: *Soviet Tech. Phys.*, v. 2, pp. 385-86.
                                                                C.A. 53-4902 d.

Lazarev, A. N. and Voronkov, M. G. (1958) Vibrational spectra of
alkoxysilane and silioxanes. I. Infrared spectra of esters of orthosilic
acid: *Optics and Spectroscopy* (USSR), v. 4, pp. 180-88.
                                                                C.A. 52-9764 f.

Lazarev, A. N. (1960a) Vibrational spectra of silicates. I. Infrared spectra
of silicates containing an anion of the type $(Si_2O_7)^{6-}$: *Optics and
Spectroscopy* (USSR), v. 9, pp. 195-202.   C.A. 56-1067 i.

Lazarev, A. N. (1960b) Vibrational spectra of alkoxysilane and silioxanes.
II. Vibrations of the SiO₄ groups in the spectra of tetraalkoxysilanes:
Optics and Spectroscopy (USSR), v. 8, pp. 511-15.   C.A. 56-15063 c.

Lazarev, A. N. and Voronkov, M. G. (1960) Vibrational spectra of
alkoxysilane and siloxanes. III. Vibrations of silicon and oxygen
chains in the spectra of polyalkoxysiloxanes: *Optics and Spectroscopy* (USSR), v. 8, pp. 614-22.   C.A. 55-2274 e.

Lazarev, A. N. (1961) Spectroscopic identification of Si₂O₇ groups in
silicates: *Kristallografiya*, v. 6, No. 1, pp. 124-27.

Lazarev, A. N. and Tenisheva, T. F. (1961a) Vibrational spectra of the
silicates. II. Infrared absorption spectra of silicates and germanates
with chain anions: *Optics and Spectroscopy* (USSR), v. 10, pp. 79-85.
                                                                C.A. 55-13055 a.

Lazarev, A. N. and Tenisheva, T. F. (1961b) Vibration spectra of silicates. III. Infrared spectra of the pyroxenoids and other chain meta-
silicates: *Optics and Spectroscopy* (USSR), v. 11, pp. 584-87.
                                                                C.A. 56-8181 h.

Lazarev, A. N. (1962) Vibrational spectra of silicates. IV. Interpretation of the spectra of silicates and germanates with ring anions:
Optics and Spectroscopy (USSR), v. 12, pp. 28-30.   C.A. 57-292 e.

Lippincott, E. R., Van Valkenberg, A., Weir, C. R., and Bunting, E. N.
(1958) Infrared studies on polymorphs of silicon dioxide and germanium dioxide: *J. Res. Nat. Bur. Std.*, v. 61, pp. 61-70.
                                                                C.A. 53-5876 g.

Lyon, R. J. P. and Tuddenham, W. M. (1959) Quantitative mineralogy
as a guide in exploration: *Min. Eng.*, v. 11, pp. 1233-37.

Lyon, R. J. P., Tuddenham, W. M., and Thompson, C. S. (1959) Quantitative mineralogy in 30 minutes: *Econ. Geol.*, v. 54, pp. 1047-55.

Lyon, R. J. P. and Tuddenham, W. M. (1960a) Direct determination of
aluminum in mica by infrared absorption analysis: *Nature*, v. 185,
pp. 374-75.

Lyon, R. J. P. and Tuddenham, W. M. (1960b) Infrared determination of
the kaolin group minerals: *Nature*, v. 185, pp. 835-36.

Lyon, R. J. P. (1962) *Minerals in the Infrared:* Stanford Research Institute, 88 pp.

Lyon, R. J. P. (1963) Sample container contamination in the infrared
spectra of minerals: *Am. Min.*, v. 48, pp. 1170-72.

Marel, H. W., van der and Zwiers, J. H. L. (1958) O-H stretching bands of the kaolin minerals: Journees Int. d'etude des Argilles, de l'Association belge pour favoriser l'etude des Verres et des Composes siliceus., 1-11, also (1960) *Silicates Industrials*, v. 14, pp. 359-68.

Marel, H. W., van der (1960) Quantitative analysis of kaolinite: *Silicates Industrials*, v. 25, pp. 23-31.

Marel, H. W., van der (1961) Quantitative analysis of the clay separate of soils: *Acta. Universitatis Carolinae — Geologica Supplementum,* v. 1, pp. 23-82.

Milkey, R. G. (1958) Potassium bromide method of infrared sampling: *Anal. Chem.,* v. 30, No. 12, pp. 1931-32.

Milkey, R. G. (1960a) Infrared spectra of some tectosilicates: *Am. Min.,* v. 45, p. 990.   C.A. 55-4260 f.

Milkey, R. G. (1960b) Mineral compositions and structures: in the *Encyclopedia of Spectroscopy,* ed. G. L. Clark, Reinhold Pub., New York, pp. 487-91.

Miller, F. and Wilkins, C. H. (1952) Infrared spectra and characteristic frequencies of inorganic ions: *Anal. Chem.,* v. 24, pp. 1253-94.
                                                        C.A. 46-10892 i.

Miller, F. A., Carlson, G. L., Bentley, F. F., and Jones, R. H. (1960) Infrared spectra of inorganic ions in the cesium bromide region (700-300 cm.$^{-1}$): *Spectrochim. Acta.,* v. 16, pp. 135-235.
                                                        C.A. 54-13858 a.

Mitchell, B. D. and Farmer, V. C. (1961) Amorphous clay minerals in some Scottish soil profiles: *Mineral. Mag.,* v. 32, pp. 128-44.

Moenke, H. (1961) Ultrarot absorption spektralphotometrie and silikatforschung: *Silikattechnik,* v. 12, pp. 323-27.   C.A. 55-26877 i.

Nakamoto, K., Margoshes, M., and Rundle, R. E. (1955) Stretching frequencies as a function of distances in hydrogen bonds: *J. Am. Chem. Soc.,* v. 77, pp. 6480-86.

Nahin, P. G. (1955) Infrared analysis of clays and related minerals: *Calif. Bur. Mines Bull.,* v. 169, pp. 112-18.

Newham, R. E. (1961) A refinement of the dickite structure and some remarks on polymorphism in kaolin minerals: *Mineral. Mag.,* v. 32, pp. 683-704.

Omori, K., and Seki, T. (1960) Infrared study of some phosphate minerals: *Japanese Assn. of Mineralogists, Petrologists and Economic Geologists Jour.,* v. 44, pp. 13-17.   C.A. 54-13995 a.

Omori, K. (1961) Infrared absorption spectra of some essential minerals: *Sendai, Japan Tohoku Univ. Science Reports,* Serial 3, v. 1, No. 1, pp. 101-31.

Omori, K. and Kerr, P. F. (1962) Infrared study of sulfate minerals, Abstr.: *Am. Min.,* v. 47, pp. 198-99.

Perkin-Elmer Corp. (1960) *Selective instruments to solve your analytical problems:* Perkin-Elmer Corp., Norwalk, Conn., p. 23 (Amp-3595).

Posner, A. S. and Duyckaerts, G. (1954) Infrared study of the carbonate in bone, teeth, and francolite: *Experimentia,* v. 10, No. 10, pp. 424-25.
C.A. 49-6407 f.

Posner, A. S., Stutman, J. M., and Lippincott, E. R. (1960) Hydrogen-bonding in calcium-deficient hydroxyapatites: *Nature,* v. 188 (4749) pp. 486-87.   C.A. 55-6152 d.

Posner, A. S., Stutman, J. M., and Lippincott, E. R. (1961) Hydrogen bonding in calcium deficient hydroxyapatite: *Society for Analytical Chemists, Pittsburg Spectroscopy Soc.,* 1961 meeting, paper 213.

Roy, D. and Roy, R. (1957) Hydrogen-deuterium exchange in clays and problems in assignment of infrared frequencies in the hydroxyl region: *Geochem. et Cosmochem. Acta.,* v. 11, pp. 72-85.

Roy, R. (1960) High pressure—a new chemical tool: *Min. Industries, Penn. State Coll. of Min. Ind.,* v. 29, No. 5.

Saksena, B. D. (1940) Analysis of the Raman and infrared spectra of α–quartz: *Proc. Indian Acad. Sci.,* Sec. A, v. 12, pp. 93-139.
C.A. 35-30-8.

Saksena, B. D. (1958) Infrared absorption spectra of α–quartz between 4 and 15 microns: *Proc. Phys. Soc.* (London), v. 72, pp. 9-16.
C.A. 54-23731 c.

Saksena, B. D. (1961) Infrared absorption studies of some silicate structures: *Trans. Faraday Soc.,* v. 57, (2), pp. 242-55.   C.A. 55-17213 e.

Serratosa, J. M. and Bradley, W. F. (1958) Determination of the orientation of OH bond axes in layer silicates by infrared absorption: *J. Phys. Chem.,* v. 62, No. 10, pp. 1164-67.

Serratosa, J. M., Hidalgo, A., and Vinas, J. M. (1962) Orientation of OH bonds in kaolinite: *Nature,* v. 195, pp. 486-87.

Stubican, V., Lisenko, N., and Wrischer, M. (1956) Bentonites. II. The morphology of montmorillonite particles and the crystal form of free silica in some bentonites: *Yugoslav, Akad., Zagreb: Croat. Chem. Acta,* v. 28, pp. 239-48.   C.A. 51-17634 c.

Stubican, V. (1957) Infrared spectra of high-temperature phases of kaolinite and halloysite: *Nature,* v. 179, p. 542.   C.A. 51-12657 b.

Stubican, V. (1959) Residual hydroxyl groups in the metakaolin range: *Mineral. Mag.,* v. 32, pp. 38-52.   C.A. 53-15875 e.

Stubican, V. and Roy, R. (1960) Proton retention in heated 1:1 clays; studies by infrared spectroscopy, weight loss and deuterium uptake: *American Petroleum Institute,* Rept. 55, Annual Report 1959-60.
C.A. 55-26393 g.

Stubican, V. and Roy, R. (1961a) A new approach to assignment of infrared absorption bands in layer-lattice silicates: *Zeitsch. Krist.,* v. 115, p. 200-14.   C.A. 55-25468 e.

Stubican, V. and Roy, R. (1961b) Infrared spectra of layer lattice silicates: *J. Am. Ceram. Soc.,* v. 44, p. 625-27.

Stubican, V. and Roy, R. (1961c) Isomorphous substitution and infrared spectra of the layer lattice silicates: *Am. Min.,* v. 46, pp. 32-52.
C.A. 55-13186 i.

Simon, J. and McMahon, H. O. (1953) Study of the structure of quartz, cristobalite, and vitreous silica by reflection in infrared: *Jour. Chem. Phys.*, v. 21, pp. 23-30.

Tarte, P. (1959a) La distinction mullite-sillimanite par spectrometrie infrarouge: *Silicates, Inds.*, v. 24, No. 1.   C.A. 54-16294 g.

Tarte, P. (1959b) Hydrogen bonding and the infrared spectra of alkali metal bicarbonates: *Hydrogen Bonding*, ed. by D. Hadzi, Pergamon Press, New York, pp. 115-20.   C.A. 54-18071 g.

Tarte, P. (1960a) The infrared spectra of some silicate. Behavior of the anti-symmetrical valence vibrations of solid solutions of orthosilicates in orthogermanates: *Bull. Classe Sci., Acad. Roy. Belg.*, v. 46, pp. 169-79.   C.A. 55-8039 b.

Tarte, P. (1960b) Infrared spectrum of garnets: *Nature*, v. 186, p. 234.   C.A. 54-17049 a.

Tarte, P. (1960c) Infrared spectra of silicates. II. Determination of the structural role of Ti in certain silicates: *Silicates Inds.*, v. 25, pp. 171-75.   C.A. 54-16294 g.

Tarte, P. (1961) Infrared spectroscopic evidence of four-fold coordination of titanium in barium orthotitanate: *Nature*, v. 191, pp. 1002-3.   C.A. 56-5476 c.

Tarte, P. and Ringwood, A. E. (1962) Infrared spectrum of the spinels Ni_2SiO_4, Ni_2GeO_4 and their solid solutions: *Nature*, v. 193, pp. 971-72.   C.A. 57-1762 b.

Tettenhorst, R. (1962) Cation migration in montmorillonites: *Am. Min.*, v. 47, pp. 769-73.

Thompson, C. S. and Wadsworth, M. E. (1957) Determination of the composition of plagioclase feldspars by means of infrared spectroscopy: *Am. Min.*, v. 42, pp. 334-41.

Tuddenham, W. M. and Lyon, R. J. P. (1959) Relation of infrared spectra and chemical analysis for some chlorites and related minerals: *Anal. Chem.*, v. 31, pp. 377-80.

Tuddenham, W. M. and Lyon, R. J. P. (1960a) Infrared techniques in the identification and measurement of minerals: *Anal. Chem.*, v. 32, pp. 1630-34.

Tuddenham, W. M. and Lyon, R. J. P. (1960b) Infrared analysis of min. erals and rocks: in the *Encyclopedia of Spectroscopy*, ed. G. L. Clark, Reinhold Pub., New York, pp. 491-94.

Uhlrich, W. F. (1961) Applications of specular infrared reflectance: *The Analyzer* (Beckman Inc. house journal), pp. 14-16.

White, J. L., Bailey, G. W., Brown, C. B., Alrichs, J. L. (1961) Infrared investigation of the migration of lithium ions into empty octohedral sites in muscovite and montmorillonite: *Nature*, v. 190, p. 342.

White, J. L. and Burns, A. F. (1963) Infrared spectra of hydronium ion in micaceous minerals: *Science*, v. 141, pp. 800-1.

Wolfe, R. G. (1963) Structural aspects of kaolinite using infrared absorption: *Am. Min.*, v. 48, pp. 390-99.

VII... The Thermal Investigation of Soil Clays

R. C. Mackenzie

While not so diagnostic as X–ray diffraction techniques, thermal methods nevertheless find a very considerable application in the field of clay mineralogy. There are many reasons for this, the main one probably being that the group of minerals known as the clay minerals consists of secondary minerals containing different amounts of hydroxyl groups which are liberated with an absorption of energy and loss in weight at moderate temperature. Several of these minerals also undergo marked lattice transformations below 100°C. and these also are reflected as energy changes. Before proceeding further it seems desirable to define the types of curves most frequently encountered in thermal investigations.

a) *Heating curves* are temperature/time curves for the sample heated in an environment of uniformly increasing temperature.

b) *Differential thermal curves* are curves for the difference in temperature between the sample and a thermally inert material (ΔT) plotted against either time (t) or temperature (T), the two samples being heated in an environment of uniformly increasing temperature; they are thus not strictly *differential* curves but merely temperature difference curves.

c) *Thermogravimetric curves* are weight/time curves for the material heated in an environment of uniformly increasing temperature.

d) Differential thermogravimetric curves are obtained from thermo-gravimetric curves by plotting the difference in weight per unit time against temperature; they are in fact true differential curves.

Heating curves are not generally so useful as the other three types, since small energy changes can easily be overlooked. Therefore, the remainder of this article will deal with differential thermal, thermo-gravimetric, and differential thermogravimetric curves. It is important to note at this point that differential thermal curves show all changes occurring in the sample, as long as these are associated with evolution

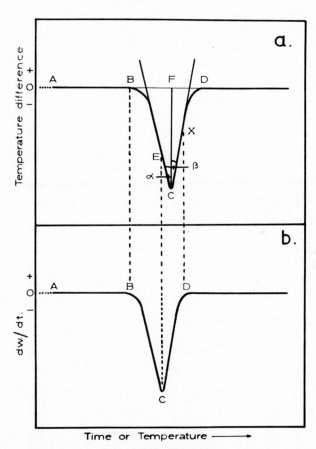

Figure 1. Comparison of formalized differential thermal (a) and differential thermogravimetric (b) curves for the same hypothet-cal material at identical heating rates, showing the various attributes of the peaks: for explanation, see text.

or absorption of energy, whereas thermogravimetric and differential thermogravimetric curves show only reactions associated with loss or gain in weight of the sample. Comparison of, for instance, a differential thermal curve and a differential thermogravimetric curve for the same sample can therefore show immediately which energy changes are due to loss or gain of material and which are due to lattice rearrangements or other factors.

A typical differential thermal curve is represented diagramatically in Fig. 1a. When no reaction occurs in the specimen this curve takes the form of a straight line, AB (the base–line), but as soon as a reaction commences the curve departs from the base–line along BC, reaches a maximum, or peak, C, and then returns to the base–line at D. Point B, where the curve departs from the base–line, represents the commencement of the reaction, and point C represents the point at which the rate of heat inflow into the sample is equal to the amount of heat absorbed by the reaction. Point D does not represent the end of the reaction, which in fact occurs at some indeterminate point X along the line CD. The maximum rate of reaction occurs at the point of maximum slope E along the line BD. It will be clear, therefore, that the only characteristic point of the peak with a strict physical significance is B. However, this is usually extremely difficult to determine because the curve departs very gradually from the base–line, and in differential thermal investigations it is customary to quote the temperature at point C, which is termed the peak temperature. This, it will be appreciated, because of its definition, can vary depending on various external conditions such as rate of heating, size of sample, etc. The area enclosed by BECXDF is usually termed the peak area, the height CF is called the peak height or amplitude, and the length BD the peak width. The angle enclosed by BCD is known as the peak angle. One other parameter which should be defined at this point is the "slope ratio" (Bramão, et al., 1952) which is a measure of the asymmetry of the peak. This "slope ratio" is $\tan \alpha / \tan \beta$ where α and β have the significance shown in Fig. 1a.

The characteristics of a peak on a differential thermogravimetric curve are somewhat different (Fig. 1b). Along the base–line there is no change in weight of the material, but the material starts to decompose at point B where the curve departs from the base–line. In this instance, however, point C (the peak temperature) represents the point of maximum rate, and point D, where the curve returns to the base–line, the end of the reaction. It must therefore be remembered that the points

B, C, and *D* on a differential thermogravimetric curve all have a precise physical significance and that the peak temperature always represents the point of maximum rate. The peak area here represents the weight loss over the period of the peak.

Historical

Differential thermal analysis

The differential thermal technique originated in the metallurgical studies of Roberts–Austen (1899), who found that with normal heating curves transformations involving small energy changes could easily be overlooked. The recording arrangements used in such early work were rather cumbersome, but considerable advances were made in 1904 when Kurnakov invented the photographic recording drum and Le Chatelier developed the method of Saladin using a flat photographic plate. In the former apparatus the light spot from a mirror galvanometer fell on a cylindrical lens in a longitudinal slit in the light–tight box surrounding the drum (which was coated with photographic paper and rotated by a clock mechanism), thus giving a direct plot of galvanometer deflection against time. In the Le Chatelier–Saladin system the light spot from the galvanometer indicating temperature difference was further reflected from the mirror of the galvanometer recording temperature, and by suitable arrangement of these galvanometers the trace for temperature difference against temperature was displayed on a flat plate. The latter technique has largely fallen into disuse, but the photographic recording drum still finds considerable use, although it has now to a large extent been displaced by accurate microvolt pen–and–ink recorders. These have the advantages that the trace can be followed continuously and that no photographic darkroom facilities are necessary.

Most early work was on metallurgy, but in 1913 Wallach applied the method to clays, and in the same year Fenner used it to examine the silica minerals. A considerable advance in technique was seen in 1915, when Hollings and Cobb developed a controlled–atmosphere apparatus for investigating carbonaceous materials. By using an inert gas or oxygen they could either suppress or enhance combustion reactions.

About 1930 the classical research of Orcel and Caillère (see Orcel, 1927; Orcel and Caillère, 1933) showed the value of the method in mineralogical studies with particular reference to the chlorites; the same authors were also the first to appreciate quantitative application. Although Agafonoff (1935) examined the possibility of applying the technique to the investigation of soil clays, little work on clays was in fact performed before the late 1930's. The investigations of Norton and of Hendricks and Alexander in 1939, however, led to widespread use of the technique in this application. By this time the basic structures of most of the clay minerals were known and the growth of the method has since then been quite spectacular. The first book largely devoted to the subject was published in 1944 by Berg, Nikolaev, and Rode, and in 1945 Speil developed the first theoretical study.

Although the period since 1945 is perhaps too recent to develop a proper perspective, nevertheless some advances are worthy of note. In 1950 Berg and Rassonskaya described a rapid method of differential thermal analysis using a linear heating rate of approximately 100°C/min, i.e., about 10 times that normally employed. Such a technique can be extremely useful and time–saving in examining large numbers of samples. In 1951, Stone developed the controlled–atmosphere technique in such a manner that the atmosphere inside the specimen itself could be rigidly controlled; this has proved to be of considerable advantage in very accurate work. Grimshaw and Roberts in 1953 and Sabatier in 1954 pointed out the necessity for diluting the sample with inert material in order to obtain accurate quantitative results, and the same year Teitelbaum and Berg developed an apparatus which enabled automatic registration of gas evolution under constant volume conditions during differential thermal analysis. In 1957 Yagfarov and Berg (1957a) described a novel device for temperature control which has since been considerably developed (Berg, 1961a). Recently, Brewer and Zavitsanos (1957) and Nedumov (1960) have extended the temperature range up to about 3000°C., and Mazières (1959) has constructed an apparatus using only 10 µg of material (i.e., near the theoretical point sample).

It is interesting to note that in the period up to 1939 the technique was more widely used in Russia than in any other country and that its major applications were in the fields of metallurgy and inorganic salts. An excellent review of this earlier work has been given by Berg, Nikolaev, and Rode (1944). In recent years, several books (Berg, 1955; Eliáš, Štovick, and Zahradník, 1957; Mackenzie, 1957a; Smothers and Chiang, 1958; Ramachandran and Garg, 1959; Berg, 1961a, 1961b), review articles (Lehmann, Das, and Paetsch, 1954; Murphy, 1958, 1960, 1962; Földvári–Vogl, 1958; Mackenzie and Mitchell, 1962), and a punched card data index (Mackenzie, 1962) have appeared. The reader is referred to these for additional information on the various aspects mentioned in this article.

Thermogravimetry and differential thermogravimetry

The history of thermogravimetry is not so well established and the originator of the technique is not known. It would appear, however, that the word "thermobalance" was coined by Honda in 1915. Honda's thermobalance differed from a conventional balance in having a quartz beam, from one end of which the sample was suspended in an electrically heated furnace. The other end of the beam was fixed to a spring immersed in oil in a Dewar flask and also had another damping system attached. Guichard (1925) employed a more conventional balance, one pan of which was replaced by a wire suspending the specimen holder in a furnace below the balance, and the other pan of which was replaced by a hydrostatic device which enabled the balance always to be maintained at zero deflection. Guichard (1925, 1935) was the first to introduce techniques enabling linear heating rates to be obtained, originally with gas and later with electric heating.

Since that time many thermobalances have been constructed by replacing one of the pans of a conventional balance by a crucible holding the sample suspended in a furnace below the balance (see Merveille and Boureiville, 1950; Duval, 1953). Agate bearing surfaces are, however, insufficiently hard for continuous use, and in 1944 Chevenard developed a specialized thermobalance in which the use of knife edges was avoided (Chevenard, Waché, and de la Tullaye, 1944). Although this thermobalance is still fairly widely used, particularly in France, the development of harder materials than agate for bearing surfaces has enabled the commercial production of accurate and reliable thermobalances based on conventional types. All modern types of thermobalance have the furnace situated above the balance in order to avoid convection effects. In 1953 Duval published the first book dealing entirely with thermogravimetry, which has recently appeared in a second edition (Duval, 1963).

Differential thermogravimetry originated in the work of De Keyser (1953). He and Erdey, Paulik, and Paulik (1954, 1956) independently developed different systems of direct registration of the derivative of the thermogravimetric curve and the apparatus of the latter workers has for several years been in commercial production.

Theory

Differential thermal analysis

Originally, differential thermal analysis was a purely empirical method, and although, as mentioned above, its quantitative applications were appreciated in the late 1930's, it was not until 1945 that even a simplified theory was produced (Speil, 1945). This theory was later slightly modified by Kerr and Kulp (1948) who pointed out some errors in the original but in whose paper several typographical errors make the theory rather difficult to follow. It would be impossible to detail the various theories here, but the final equations obtained with different premises are interesting and correlations of these brings out certain fundamental relationships. The final equation obtained from the Speil–Kerr–Kulp theory is:

$$M = \frac{g\lambda}{\Delta H} \int_{t_1}^{t_2} \Delta T dt \quad \ldots\ldots\ldots\ldots (1)$$

where M is the mass of reactant, g is a geometrical constant, λ is the thermal conductivity of the specimen, ΔH is the difference in heat content of 1 g specimen before and after reaction, and $\int_{t_1}^{t_2} \Delta T dt$ is the peak area on a $\Delta T/t$ curve. This equation indicates that the mass of reactant is proportional to the peak area on a $\Delta T/t$ curve, and also that the peak area is independent of heating rate, if the differential thermal curve is plotted against time. Using the more common plot of ΔT against temperature, the relationship between the mass of reactant and peak area would only hold if heating rate (i.e., the T/t curve) were identical for all traces.

In 1957, Yagfarov and Berg (1957b) independently developed a very similar theory, leading to the equation:

$$Q = \frac{2\pi l \lambda}{\ln(d_2/d_1)} \int_{t_1}^{t_2} \Delta T dt \quad \ldots\ldots\ldots\ldots (2)$$

where Q is the heat of reaction; l, d_2 and d_1 are the length, the external, and the internal diameters of the cylindrical specimen, and the other symbols are as in equation (1) above. Still later, Proks (1961) in a rather more intensive study arrived at a somewhat similar equation, namely:

$$U \cdot \Delta_R H = k P_T \qquad \dots \dots \dots \dots \dots \quad (3)$$

where U is the heating rate, $\Delta_R H$ is the reaction enthalpy, k is a constant, and P_T is the peak area on a $\Delta T/T$ trace.

Since $Q = \Delta_R H = M$ x ΔH, equations (1), (2), and (3), for a constant heating rate, all reduce to the form:

$$M = k P_T,$$

indicating that the mass of reactant is proportional to the peak area. A corollary of equation (3) is that if the heating rate varies, then with a given mass of reactant the peak area on a $\Delta T/T$ trace is proportional to the heating rate. It may also be noted that equations (1) and (2) are identical except that $\dfrac{2\pi l}{\ln(d_2/d_1)}$ in equation (2) replaces, for a cylindrical specimen, the rather vague "geometrical constant" in equation (1).

It should be stressed, however, that equations (1), (2), and (3) are based essentially on an oversimplified system and that several variables or parameters are not taken into account. The deriviation of a rigorous theory is extremely difficult, not only because of the dynamic system involved, but also because of the nature of the specimen, which is normally a powder packed into a suitable receptacle. Of the more rigorous theories so far proposed (Soulé, 1952; Eriksson, 1953-54; Sewell, 1952-56) that of Sewell is probably the most highly developed. It leads to the equation:

$$\int_{t_0}^{t_2} \underbrace{[(\Delta T)_o - (\Delta T)]\, dt}_{A} = \underbrace{W(P_1)}_{B} - \underbrace{W(P_2)}_{C}$$

where term A represents the peak area and terms B and C are peak area functions involving both heating rate and time.

From consideration of the theories then available, Sewell and Honeyborne in 1957 made the following deductions:

1. It is easiest to reduce base-line drift and keep the displacement of the base-line at a minimum when metal blocks are used and probably nearly as easy with ceramic blocks in virtual contact with the furnace wall; it is most difficult when separated platinum crucibles are used.

2. The area of a peak is proportional to the heat of reaction associated with it. This relationship is independent of the heating rate, of the rate at which the reaction takes place (and thus of the peak shape), and of the specific heats of the test material and the other materials within the furnace.

3. *The peak area/heat of reaction* relationship does, however, involve the thermal conductivities of some, or all, of these materials, and particularly the thermal conductivity of the test sample. The assumption on which most quantitative work is based, namely that for differential thermal curves obtained with different mixtures containing a common component the peak area due to this component is proportional solely to its concentration in the mixture, is thus not valid if the conductivities of the mixtures are appreciably different. Because of this, the dilution procedure suggested by Grimshaw and Roberts (1953) and by Sabatier (1954) is advocated.

4. Because the thermal conductivity of a powder is much influenced by the composition of the gas that fills its voids it seems likely that quantitative analysis of materials which undergo reactions involving the release of gases can be satisfactorily achieved only if the furnace atmosphere is controlled [see Stone, 1951]. This applies particularly to dehydrations and dehydroxylations.

5. Small displacements of the thermocouple junction from the central position in either the test or the reference sample have a negligible effect on base-line drift and peak area when a metal block assembly is used; such displacements are of greater importance for ceramic blocks.

6. In any given apparatus the area of a peak depends on the *shape*, as well as on the mass of the test sample.

7. In some forms of apparatus, thermal conduction along the thermocouple wires considerably affects the areas of peaks.

8. Use of the cosecant of the peak angle for estimating the size of a peak (Dean, 1947) may be applied approximately to reactions following a first-order law, but not to phase changes.

An additional conclusion from the theoretical work of Eriksson (1953-54) is that when the depth of a cylindrical sample is more than twice its diameter it reacts as an infinite cylinder, and when the diameter is more than four times its depth it acts as an infinite slab; the dimensions of the sample wells should therefore not approach either of these two extremes.

All these conclusions have an obvious bearing upon apparatus and technique, and the extent to which they are observed gives some indication of the validity of the results obtained.

Thermogravimetry and differential thermogravimetry

The theory of thermogravimetry is extremely simple and is expressed by the equation:

$$w = f(t),$$

where w is the weight of the sample and t is time. For differential thermo-gravimetry this equation becomes:

$$\frac{dw}{dt} = f'(t),$$

and it is on this latter equation that the methods of De Keyser and Erdey (1953), Paulik, and Paulik (1954, 1956) are based. For both techniques, as for differential thermal analysis, it is necessary to employ a linear and reproducible heating rate.

Differential thermal apparatus

It has already been noted that the validity of differential thermal results depends upon suitability of apparatus and technique. It is fitting, therefore, that some more detailed consideration be given to these aspects here.

Until very recently there has been little commercial development of suitable apparatus and most laboratories have constructed their own. Although such a procedure has the advantage of cheapness, it is doubt-ful whether this is sufficient compensation for the grave disadvantage that those constructing the apparatus are probably unfamiliar with the precautions necessary to enable best results to be obtained. The last few years, however, have seen a marked development of commercial types of apparatus. Some of these have been mentioned in a recent review (Mackenzie and Mitchell, 1962) and several others are now known to the author[1].

Irrespective of whether an apparatus is home–built or commercial, it should incorporate a number of features desirable on theoretical or practical grounds. Lack of attention to such detail, or the saving of expense by using too primitive an apparatus, can lead to most unfor-tunate results (Markowitz and Boryta, 1960). Much of the criticism

1. E. I. Du Pont de Nemours and Co., Wilmington, Delaware, U.S.A. (designed primarily for organic materials; atmosphere control; high sensitivity; controlled heating and cooling rates over wide range; extremely compact).

Harrop Precision Furnace Co., Columbus, Ohio, U.S.A. (many types of furnace and specimen holders available; atmosphere control; large range of heating rates).

Linseis K G, Selb/Bayern, Germany (basically similar to Netzsch apparatus; furnaces suitable for use up to 2800° C.).

Tem-Pres Research Inc., State College, Pennsylvania, U.S.A. (two basic units; atmosphere control; many optional extras).

Perkin-Elmer Corporation, Norwalk, Connecticut, U.S.A. (rapid heating rate; very small sample).

of the technique has in fact originated with those who have attempted to perform precision work with inadequate apparatus — or with those who have been unfamiliar with the limitations of the technique. It would be impossible to review here even a cross–section of the types of apparatus described in the literature; those interested in "do–it–yourself" construction can find details of the more common and successful types in the various books and reviews listed above.

The minimum functional units required in any apparatus are a heat source, a temperature control system, a specimen holder, and a temperature measuring and recording system. Brief consideration should therefore be given to the fundamental precautions which must be observed with regard to each of these units. Only a few of the more important or recent literature references will be given as basic reference lists are incorporated in the various textbooks.

Heat source

The usual heat source employed is an electric furnace, although liquid baths and other arrangements have occasionally been employed. Several types of electric furnace have been used, but by far the most common is the conventional tube type arranged either horizontally or vertically. Vertical forms probably insure more homogeneous temperature distribution but have the disadvantage that, should a sample melt and flow down the tubes carrying the thermocouples, the specimen holder and block have to be replaced, thus necessitating recalibration. There are, therefore, certain practical advantages in using the horizontal type unless, as in the vertical arrangement of Stone (1960), the thermocouples can be arranged to enter the specimen holder wells from the side rather than from the base. Other suitable furnaces are the tube type with internal longitudinal rod elements (McConnell and Earley, 1951), the tube type with longitudinally disposed coiled elements (Gérard–Hirne and Lamy, 1951), the split vertical type with similar elements (Yarembash, 1955), and the pot type with internal heating element (Butterworth and Honeyborne, 1952). Irrespective of the type of furnace, it is essential: (*a*) that it have sufficient heat output to raise the temperature of the contents at a more rapid rate than that desired over the whole temperature range, and (*b*) that the specimen holder be heated evenly.

For the conventional tube furnace used at temperatures up to 1000°C., the usual winding is nichrome or kanthal. For temperatures above 1000°C. the choice of winding naturally depends upon the maximum temperature. Thus, platinum or its alloys can be used up to 1750°C., and molybdenum, which requires a hydrogen atmosphere around the winding, to at least 2000°C. Induction heating can be used up to about 2500°C. (Brewer and Zavitsanos, 1957), and recently Nedumov (1960) has used a tungsten winding to perform differential thermal analysis up to 2800°C.

Whichever type of furnace is used, it is desirable that the uniform temperature zone be as large as possible. In conventionally wound furnaces a fairly heavy winding insures a long life, but the actual gauge of wire employed will depend upon the current capacity of the supply. The winding should be as even as possible, as any unevenness can show up in the results (Oades, 1962). With conventionally wound furnaces it is essential to avoid any appreciable current surges in the winding since these may lead to spurious e.m.f.'s in the thermocouple system. All furnaces should be provided with an earthed metal sheath inserted between the winding and the block to suppress such e.m.f.'s (Mitchell, 1961).

Temperature control system

As already mentioned, it is essential that the heating rate be reproducible and, for quantitative work particularly, that it be linear. Manual control of temperature increase is therefore most undesirable, since not only can the unevenness of manual control lead to spurious effects, despite an earthed shield, but the furnace windings gradually age and reproducibility is consequently affected. Motorized systems supplying a constantly increasing voltage or current to the furnaces are also inadequate because such systems cannot take into account such factors as changes in mains voltage or ageing of the furnace windings. They may, however, be the only practicable arrangement for very high temperatures (Nedumov, 1960) and are certainly preferable to manual control, since large surges are avoided. However, the only entirely satisfactory method of temperature control is one based upon the actual temperature conditions inside the furnace. Many home–constructed automatic temperature–control devices have been described (see, e.g., Theron, 1952; Teitelbaum, 1955; Kaurkovskii, 1955), but a large range of suitable commercial temperature controllers are now available, and, with the advent of transistorized circuits, are relatively cheap.

To avoid surges in the furnace winding, proportional control using a saturable reactor is undoubtedly the best technique (Hodgson, 1963; see also descriptive brochure on the R. L. Stone apparatus), but other satisfactory systems are based on the use of either a motorized auto-transformer with a reversible motor operated from the temperature controller (Wilburn, 1958), or a motorized two–point autotransformer with a voltage difference of about 50 V between the two contacts (Mitchell and Mackenzie, 1959). An interesting recent development is the ingenious system of Yagfarov and Berg (1957a), whereby a constant temperature difference is maintained between the winding and the inner wall of the furnace core and heat losses at higher temperatures are compensated for by using a shunt across the differential thermocouple employed for control (Berg and Yagfarov, 1958). Originally a high–low resistance arrangement was used to control the heating rate, but recently a system using a motorized autotransformer has been developed (Berg, 1961a).

Although the conditions required are that the specimen should be heated at a constant rate, it is generally not practicable to use the thermocouple in the specimen or inert material for temperature control because of the large difference in temperature between this point and the furnace winding, and the consequent lag in response. It is generally preferable, therefore, to use a thermocouple outside the specimen holder and close to the winding. Positioning the control thermocouple too close to the furnace winding may lead to irregular heating (Steg-müller, 1953), so a compromise between distance and sensitivity of control must be obtained. Separation of the control thermocouple from that inside the specimen leads to some difficulties in providing an absolutely linear heating rate in the sample, but this may be readily overcome by a trial–and–error method of calibration (Mackenzie and Mitchell, 1957). In platinum–wound furnaces it is sometimes possible to use part of the winding as a platinum resistance thermometer.

Another method of temperature control which has been used is that provided by moving the specimen holder steadily into the heated zone (Siške and Proks, 1958). Provided the movement is suitably arranged, the heating rate can be made both linear and reproducible.

Specimen holder

Most conventional types of apparatus employ a specimen holder of circular or rectangular cross section which may or may not be integral with the larger specimen holder block; if not integral the holder and block may or may not be of the same material. Some apparatus, however, use platinum crucibles (Gruver, 1948), porcelain or refractory crucibles (Berg, 1961a), or sleeves of platinum fitted on the end of the ceramic tubes carrying the thermocouple wires (e.g., the Netzsch apparatus). The design of the specimen holder depends upon the sample size employed. Ideally, an infinitely small amount of material around the thermocouple junction should give an infinitely sharp deflection at the moment of reaction; specimen holders should therefore be designed to give the maximum thermal effect from the minimum amount of material.

Specimen holders may be metal or ceramic. The more common metals used are nickel and inconel with platinum or platinum–rhodium for higher temperatures. The more common ceramic specimen holders are constructed of sintered alumina or fireclay. Both types have their advantages and disadvantages. For example, metal specimen holders are easier to construct, can be more accurately machined, are nonporous, and minimize base–line drift. There is a tendency for the peak to be small because of rapid heat transfer throughout the specimen holder and between it and the sample, but this can be overcome by the use of more sensitive recording equipment. Ceramic holders tend to give larger peaks for the same amount of material because of the slow rate of heat transfer. In addition, no insulation of the thermocouple leads is necessary. Their main disadvantages are that the positioning in the furnace is critical, that their porous nature may influence the shape of the peak (Webb, 1954), and that base–line drift may be more serious because of inhomogeneity of the ceramic. Both types, however, have their uses. For example, Mitchell and Mackenzie (1959) found that in a controlled–atmosphere apparatus under inert atmosphere conditions, a metal holder was preferable, but in the same apparatus under oxidizing conditions, where one wishes the atmosphere inside the sample to be maintained at a high oxygen content, a porous ceramic holder had definite advantages. Special refractory holders are of course necessary for very high temperatures (see Nedumov, 1960).

Most specimen holders have only two wells, one for the sample and one for the inert material, but designs using up to twelve wells (Kulp and Kerr, 1949), enabling six samples to be examined simultaneously, have been described. A few specimen holders are shown diagrammatically in Fig. 2. The most common shape of well is cylindrical and, as mentioned above, the dimensions of the well should be such that the depth is less than twice the diameter and the diameter less than four times the

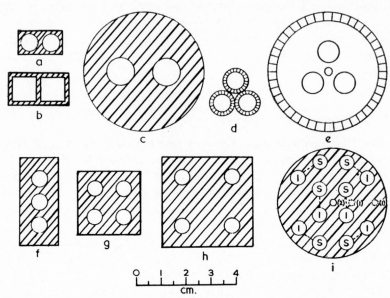

Figure 2. Various examples of specimen holders in plan. For details, see Mackenzie and Mitchell (1957, Fig. 11. 2).

depth (Eriksson, 1953). In practice a well with a depth: diameter ratio of 1 to 1.5 gives good results. The septum between the two wells should be sufficiently thick to minimize heat transfer from the sample to the inert material, but on the other hand the wells must be sufficiently close together to insure that heat transfer into each be the same. The effect of varying well dimensions on the resultant curve has been investigated in detail by Stegmüller (1953), and Dilaktorskii and Arkhangelskaya (1958). It is clear that results from two different specimen holders can only be compared if they are machined to within extremely close limits of tolerance.

The provision of close–fitting lids on specimen holders influences the ingress and egress of gases and vapors appreciably and can therefore modify or even suppress reactions. On the other hand, the provision of a loose–fitting lid gives rise to a more stable thermal environment. It has recently been shown by Cole and Rowland (1961) that spurious peaks can be obtained in the absence of a lid with certain thermocouple arrangements.

In general, when metallic specimen holders are used, the specimen holder and block are integral, but when ceramic holders are used the specimen holder is usually separate from the block. The same arguments apply in choice of block materials as in choice of specimen holder materials and need not be repeated. Information on specialized specimen holders may be obtained from the various books and reviews available.

Temperature measuring and recording system

The most common temperature measuring system is undoubtedly a thermocouple arrangement, but in choosing suitable thermocouples various factors must be considered. Thus, the thermocouples used should not be affected chemically either by the materials being investigated or by their decomposition products, and they should give an easily measurable e.m.f. for the smallest amount of material it is desired to detect. Rare–metal thermocouples, despite their initial expense, are robust and generally have a longer life than base–metal thermocouples; for temperatures in the 1000–1500°C. range, they are more or less essential. On the other hand, in the presence of certain carbonates and sulphides they may easily become contaminated, and they require a more sensitive recording arrangement because of the small e.m.f. generated. Base–metal thermocouples, besides their cheapness, are easily constructed and replaced, and give a fairly large e.m.f. They are, however, more readily attacked than rare–metal couples and their life is shorter, but the recent introduction of very fine sheathed mineral–insulated thermocouples may overcome these disadvantages. The most common rare–metal thermocouples used are platinum–platinum/rhodium and the most common base–metal couples, chromel–alumel.

For temperatures above 1500°C. special thermocouples are necessary. Thus Greenaway, Johnstone, and McQuillan (1951) have used tungsten–molybdenum thermocouples up to 2000°C., and Brewer and Zazitsanos (1957) claim that tantalum carbide–graphite couples may be used up to 3000°C. Alternatives to thermocouples for high temperature work are resistance thermometers. For example, Nedumov (1960) has used tungsten resistance thermometers up to 2800°C. In order to minimize heat conduction into or away from the specimen and to maintain a low heat capacity in the thermocouple system, very thin wires should be used and their path through the sample should be as long as possible. Thin wires, however, have a very short life and a compromise is necessary. For base–metal thermocouples wire diameters of 0.2–0.4 mm. are suitable, but for rare–metal couples thinner wires,

< 0.2 mm., can well be used. To minimize base–line drift, the heat capacity of the thermocouple system in the sample and in the inert material should be identical; therefore, two thermocouples should not be located in one sample unless a compensating dummy thermocouple is introduced in the other (Lehmann, Das, and Paetsch, 1954). In addition, the resistance of each limb should be the same and should be constant. Stegmüller (1953) and McLaughlin (1954) consider the size of the thermocouple bead to be of importance, but Webb (1958) found no appreciable effect over a considerable size range. In view of this uncertainty, which may of course be associated with the materials investigated, a general precaution should be taken to maintain the bead size within relatively small limits.

The thermocouple junctions should be centrally positioned in the sample and inert material. Sewell and Honeyborne (1957) claim that a small departure from centrality is not serious, but Berg (1961a), while confirming this for horizontal displacement, finds that the vertical positioning is more critical. Cold junctions are unnecessary for the temperature–difference thermocouple since it is a complete system; nevertheless, some form of temperature equalization is required where the wires connect with those leading to the recording system. This may be obtained through mercury troughs in a thermally stable environment or by providing a fairly large metal block around the junctions.

Two criteria have to be recorded — T and ΔT. The former creates no difficulty. If the heating rate is reproducible and linear, a check every five minutes or so is all that is necessary, or alternatively a continuous record may be obtained using a conventional recorder. For ΔT the system employed must be sufficiently sensitive to give reasonably sized peaks for the types of material and sample sizes employed, and instances are known where it is difficult to assess the validity of peaks because of too low sensitivity. The recording system should be more sensitive than is essential, so that accurate measurement of smaller reactions than customary may be made by simple alteration of a series resistance or potential divider. The range of sensitivity desirable can be assessed from the curves for quartz and gibbsite on the same scale (Fig. 3), which represent the minimum and maximum heat energy changes likely to be encountered from pure materials in normal work. For quantitative determination of quartz a 20–fold increase in sensitivity is obviously desirable.

Despite the fact that visual readings of galvanometer deflections with subsequent manual plotting of the curve requires continuous attention

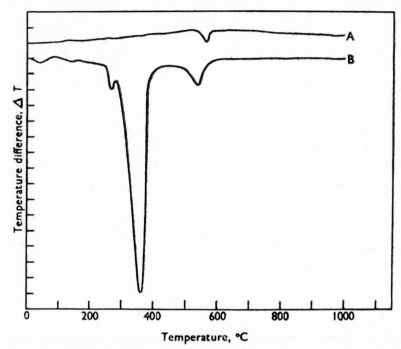

Figure 3. Differential thermal curves for: **A** - *quartz and* **B** -
gibbsite, on the same scale. Each division on the T *axis is equivalent to 2°C., sample weights 0.20 g and 0.35 g, respectively; heating rate 10° C/min.*

and is time consuming, this method is very cheap and may be quite useful in laboratories where few samples are being investigated. It is customary, however, to record the differential temperature and the temperature
at the center of the sample or inert material either photographically or
by a pen–and–ink recorder. Photographic recording is most readily performed using a photographic recording drum. It has the advantage of
high sensitivity, requires little attention during the run, and, by using
different galvanometers, enables several traces for different parameters
to be simultaneously recorded on the same chart. It is still very widely
used in the U.S.S.R. (Berg, 1961a), although, as with all photographic
methods, it has the disadvantage that one cannot directly follow the
course of a determination and that darkroom facilities are necessary.
The alternative photographic method using the Le Chatelier–Saladin
technique is relatively rarely used except in France.

The most convenient, and by far the most widely used, recording system in western countries is the commercial pen–and–ink automatic recorder, operating on a mechanical or electronic basis. This system has the advantage that the curve may be observed directly during the whole course of the determination, so that corrections for sensitivity, etc., may be made at any point necessary. In addition, it requires no development or darkroom facilities. It has, however, the disadvantage over photographic recording that the equipment is more expensive. Two alternative arrangements are possible to obtain the necessary sensitivity: one is to use a relatively insensitive recorder with a d.c. amplifier in circuit (Wilburn, 1958); the other, to use a highly sensitive microvolt recorder (Mitchell, 1961). Either method is satisfactory and the final decision on this point may depend upon the equipment available or the relative cost of the two arrangements.

Most commercial recorders give a record against time. In differential thermal analysis, however, it is customary to plot the ΔT curve against temperature. This can be performed manually from two curves, $\Delta T/t$ and $T/t,$ obtained on different recorders or on the same recorder if a two–point instrument is used. On the other hand, it is possible to

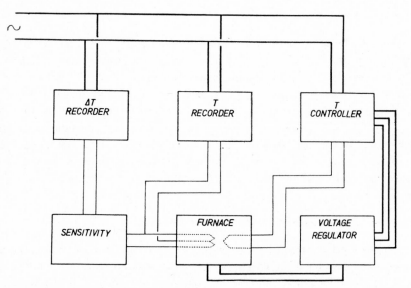

Figure 4. Diagrammatic sketch of a suitable system for a differential thermal apparatus; thin lines indicate thermocouple circuit, thick lines, power supply.

employ "X–Y" recorders to plot the difference curve directly against temperature. It has already been noted that the Le Chatelier–Saladin photographic technique gives such a curve, and conventional recorders can often be adapted for this purpose by the use of servo motors (Mackenzie and Mitchell, 1957). However, X–Y pen–and–ink recorders are also on the market, and, provided the heating rate is absolutely reproducible, may conveniently be used (Wilburn, 1958).

When a common lead is used in the temperature–difference and temperature circuits with a galvanometric recording system, the current must be alternately switched into two galvanometers, or into the same galvanometer with two sensitivity ranges, in order to avoid a sloping base–line (Lehmann, Das, and Paetsch, 1954). Insertion of a very high resistance into the temperature circuit as compared to that in the temperature–difference circuit (Berg, Nikolaev, and Rode, 1944) reduces drift almost to zero, and use of continuously self–balancing potentiometric instruments also obviates drift, since no current flows in the temperature circuit and thus the temperature–difference trace is not affected. Commercial X–Y recorders of the potentiometric type can therefore be used with a common–lead thermocouple arrangement.

General conclusions

A system suitable for a differential thermal apparatus is shown diagrammatically in Fig. 4. In any such system the components should be chosen to conform with the criteria mentioned above. A much more flexible system is obtained if the atmosphere in the furnace is controllable, since peaks can be enhanced or suppressed by introduction of appropriate gases, and most recently described types of apparatus have provision for this. An additional advantage of such a system is that superimposed peaks may be resolved by varying the pressure of a gaseous product of reaction (Stone, 1960).

Differential thermal technique

The earliest attempt at international standardization of technique was that made by the Differential Thermal Analysis Sub–Committee of C.I.P.E.A. (Mackenzie and Farquharson, 1953) and the recommendations made then still generally hold. It is desirable here, however, to consider technique, in the light of recent studies, from four aspects —

namely, the characteristics of the sample, the characteristics of the inert material, the position of the temperature thermocouple, and the heating rate.

Sample

It has been mentioned above that theoretically the sample should be infinitely small. Although this is unattainable in practice, it has been approached by Mazières (1959), who used only 10–100 μg. of material. Very small samples raise problems of temperature control and recording (Mitchell, 1961) and the sample size employed in most conventional types of apparatus is in the range 200–500 mg. Smaller sample sizes give better resolution of double peak systems (Dilaktorskii and Arkhangelskaya, 1958), but as regards peak temperature, sample weight in the range 0.2–1.0 gm. does not seem to have as great an influence upon results as might be expected (Mackenzie and Farquharson, 1953). In practice, the sample size may have to be determined by the sensitivity of the recording arrangement and the magnitude of the effects given by the minerals investigated, but consideration should be given to reducing sample size to the minimum consistent with these factors. The smaller the sample the greater the sensitivity required and the more rigorous must be the control of experimental conditions (Mitchell, 1961).

In considering the effect of particle size of the sample, one must distinguish between actual particle size, or micelle size, and sieve size, or aggregate size. When macro crystals are triturated, particle size and sieve size are synonymous. For some minerals, such as chlorites (Sabatier, 1950; Martin, 1955; Caillère and Hénin, 1957), particle size has a considerable effect on the curve, but for others such as gibbsite (Mackenzie, 1957a) it seems to be less important. Care must be taken here to distinguish effects due to particle size from those due to disruption of the lattice on grinding (Mackenzie, Meldau, and Farmer, 1956), and trituration must be performed in the least destructive manner. For clays, however, the micelle size is generally very much less than the sieve size, and the sieve size is then not particularly important. Below 2μ equivalent spherical diameter, particle size does not seem to have any effect on the peak area, although it may affect the symmetry of the peak and the peak temperature (Carthew, 1955).

Many clay samples, particularly soil clays, contain organic matter which has an appreciably disturbing effect on the differential thermal curve. The standard procedure for removal of such organic matter is treatment with hydrogen peroxide, but it has recently been shown by Farmer and Mitchell (1963) that this reagent may affect the inorganic portion of the clay. Consequently, for soil clays it is preferable to suppress the oxidation reactions by using the controlled–atmosphere technique with nitrogen or argon as an inert gas. Clays, too, are very sensitive to environmental conditions and it is desirable that all samples be saturated with the same cation, since this influences the nature of the low–temperature endothermic peak system and the amount of hygroscopic moisture retained. Very suitable cations to use in this connection are Ca^{2+} or Mg^{2+}. The size of the low–temperature peak system is, however, also dependent upon humidity conditions, particularly for swelling minerals such as smectites. Drying of samples at, say, 100°C. prior to examination is not to be recommended, since it renders the low temperature peak systems useless for determinative purposes. The most satisfactory pretreatment in this respect is equilibration over a saturated solution of $Mg(NO_3)_2 \cdot 6H_2O$, since the relative humidity over this particular salt, 55 per cent at 65°F., is little affected by temperature changes.

The desirability of dilution of the sample with about three times its weight of inert material (Grimshaw and Roberts, 1953; Sabatier, 1954) has already been mentioned. The fact that the thermal conductivities and diffusivities of the sample and the inert material are then similar enables more accurate quantitative results to be obtained and reduces base–line drift. Dilution has other practical advantages; with carbonates and other materials evolving large amounts of gas it prevents ejection of material during the decomposition process, and it also minimizes shrinkage, which can cause undesirable changes in the thermal properties of the specimen holder system during a determination. It is therefore strongly recommended. The inert diluent should be of approximately the same particle size as the sample (Sabatier, 1954) and the two materials should be very intimately mixed. The disadvantage of smaller peak size may be overcome by increasing the sample size or, preferably, the sensitivity of recording.

Certain materials, such as those undergoing oxidation, are particularly sensitive to differences in packing (Rowland and Jonas, 1949). Several techniques for insuring reproducibility of packing have been described (Whitehead and Breger, 1950; Webb, 1958), but these do not seem to be absolutely essential, since McConnell and Earley (1951) showed that reproducibility in packing to within 1 per cent may be obtained by careful tamping. Hard–packing or tamping is certainly the most common procedure, although it may give rise to some subjective errors; in comparative work these can be avoided by one operator performing the whole series of tests.

Inert material

The inert material must be chosen with care. Grimshaw and Roberts (1953) and Sabatier (1954) have considered inert materials in some detail and it would appear that optimum results are obtained if the inert material has approximately the same particle size distribution as the sample and similar thermal properties to those of the sample. For soil clays, calcined alumina, calcined kaolinite, or part of the sample precalcined to 1000°C. (Mackenzie and Mitchell, 1957) are all satisfactory, but care must be taken with the last mentioned, since materials (such as quartz) giving a reversible peak will not be destroyed on such treatment and consequently will not be observed in the sample. Arens (1951) showed that the specific heat and thermal conductivity of calcined kaolinite are quite different from those of the raw material, but if one assumes identical bulk densities then the thermal diffusivities of the two materials, calculated from Arens' results, are almost identical. Materials other than clays may require special inert materials (Mackenzie and Mitchell, 1957), and glass beads have recently been used satisfactorily for low temperature work (Murphy, Hill, and Schacher, 1960). Quartz may not seem a satisfactory inert material because of the 573°C. $\alpha \rightleftharpoons \beta$ inversion, but in specific instances it may be useful because this particular inversion provides a useful temperature calibration point (Dunne and Kerr, 1961). In general, therefore, the choice of inert material is governed by the materials being investigated but, except with very high dilution, the particle size grading should be very similar to that of the specimen.

Position of the temperature thermocouple

Various positions have in the past been used for the temperature thermocouple (Mackenzie and Mitchell, 1957), but positioning in either the sample or inert material is undoubtedly the most common. It has been pointed out (Grimshaw, Heaton, and Roberts, 1945; Földvári–Vogl and Kliburszky, 1954) that the peak temperature as measured at the center of the sample is less markedly affected by the amount of reacting material than is the peak temperature as measured at the center of the inert material. It is, therefore, preferable to use the former as a reference basis for all differential thermal curves. If the temperature is actually measured at the center of the inert material, it can readily be converted to that at the center of the sample provided the temperature difference at the peak is known.

Heating rate

Because of the dynamic nature of the method, differential thermal curves are markedly affected by heating rate, and every effort should be made to insure that the heating rate is both linear and reproducible. It has already been mentioned when discussing theory that only if the heating rate is absolutely reproducible over the particular interval in question can peak areas (on the usual $\Delta T/T$ basis) be used to assess quantitatively the amount of reacting material present. While slow heating rates minimize base–line drift (Gérard–Hirne and Lamy, 1951) and give peak temperatures nearer the true reaction temperature, they necessitate the use of more sensitive instruments to record the ΔT curve. With rapid heating rates neighboring peaks tend to coalesce, but this can to a certain extent be offset by reduction in sample size. The optimum heating rate for any investigation must therefore be a compromise depending upon the size and thermal characteristics of the sample, the inert material, the furnace, the specimen holder, and the sensitivity of the recording arrangement. The most generally used rate is $10°\pm$ $1°C/min$ (Mackenzie and Farquharson, 1953), but, particularly in the U.S.S.R., considerable use is at present being made of rates as high as $100°C/min$ (Berg and Rassonskaya, 1950; Földvári–Vogl and Kliburszky, 1957; Ivanova, 1961) with a smaller sample. This considerably expedites the obtaining of a curve and enables more materials to be investigated in a given time, but does tend to displace the peak to a somewhat higher temperature. The effect of heating rate on the resolution of neighboring peaks is well demonstrated in the results obtained by Dilaktorskii and Arkhangelskaya (1958) for gypsum; at $16°C/min$ the two peaks were barely resolved, but at $2°C/min$ they were almost completely so.

General considerations regarding differential thermal apparatus and technique

Selection of both apparatus and technique is to a large extent in the hands of the operator. Thus, one can choose either the most suitable commercial apparatus for the investigation in hand, or construct one with the most desirable qualities, and technique can be so modified as to bring out the features which are of interest. It should be noted that certain modifications may be desirable for specialized work. Thus, an apparatus can be modified to allow measurement of gas or moisture evolution from the sample during heating (Berg, 1961a), or a gas analysis of the decomposition products can be carried out (Kulbicki and Grim, 1959; Murphy, Hill and Schacher, 1960; Ayres and Bens, 1961). Such techniques are equivalent to simultaneous differential thermal analysis and thermogravimetry — apparatus for which has also been described (Powell, 1957; Reisman, 1960; Hodgson, 1963) — and are probably simpler to operate. Other types of apparatus enable simultaneous determination of several thermal characteristics (Keler, 1955). The technique of Stone (1951, 1960) of controlling the atmosphere inside the specimen is

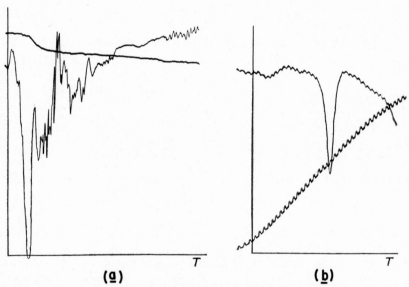

(**a**)   (**b**)

Figure 5. The effects on the differential thermal curve of: (a) a bad contact; (b) induction pickup (after Berg, 1961a).

extremely important and by introduction of a suitable decomposition product may permit resolution of two neighboring or coalescing peaks.

In his recent book, Berg (1961a) has given examples of the effects that different faults in the apparatus have on the differential thermal curve, referring particularly to galvanometric traces; the effects of two of these faults are shown in Fig. 5.

Apparatus for thermogravimetry and differential thermogravimetry

Despite the fact that these techniques are also dynamic, in neither are the demands so strict as in differential thermal analysis. Most older types of apparatus were constructed very simply by replacing the balance pan of a conventional balance with a small crucible suspended in a furnace below the balance. Baffles were inserted above the furnace to minimize the effect of heat on the balance mechanism, and some arrangements for raising the temperature of the furnace at a steady rate and for recording the loss–in–weight curve were incorporated (Guichard, 1925, 1935). An excellent balance of this type is shown in Fig. 6 (Merveille and Boureille, 1950).

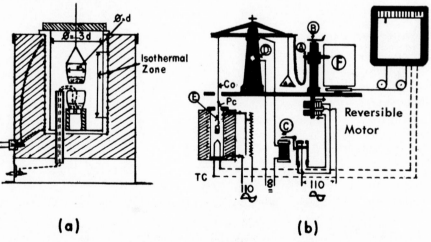

(a)   **(b)**

Figure 6. The automatic thermobalance of Merveille and Bou–reille (1950): (a) furnace arrangement; (b) general layout. A–attachment of chain to guide; B - guide column; C - relay for reversing electric motor; D - contact operating relay; E - crucible for sample; F - recording drum driven from temperature recorder.

Assuming that a smooth heating rate is provided, the main disturbing factors in thermogravimetry and differential thermogravimetry are (Lukaszewski, 1962):

(*a*) Decreasing air buoyancy with increasing temperature.
(*b*) Increasing convection with increasing temperature.
(*c*) Effect of heat on the balance mechanism.
(*d*) Thermal turbulence in the hot zone of the furnace.
(*e*) Random fluctuations in the recording mechanisms.
(*f*) Furnace induction effects.
(*g*) Electrostatic effects.
(*h*) The environment of the thermobalance.

Factors, (*c*), (*f*), and (*g*) can be eliminated by good design of the balance (e.g., factor (*c*) by placing the furnace above the balance), and factor (*h*) by the operator, so the main errors arise from factors (*a*), (*b*), and (*d*). These factors vary with the individual instrument, but may be reduced to negligible amounts by suitable design of the specimen holder (Lukaszewski, 1962). Passage of gas through the apparatus during a determination to provide limited atmosphere control also tends to reduce the buoyancy effect (*a*).

Two main types of commercial apparatus are now on the market — the Chevenard type and types based on a conventional balance. The Chevenard thermobalance bears little resemblance to a conventional balance (Chevenard, Waché, and de la Tullaye, 1944), and the principle on which it is based will be clear from Fig. 7. The conventional balance type is well exemplified by the Stanton thermobalance of which two distinct models are available. Both have the furnace situated above the balance, but one can be operated in vacuum while the other has provision only for limited atmosphere control. Both the Chevenard and Stanton types pay due regard to elimination of the disturbing factors listed above.

Two distinct types of differential thermogravimetry arrangements are in use. De Keyser (1953) employs a conventional balance with both pans replaced by identical crucibles suspended in identical furnaces below the balance. He places identical weights of sample into each crucible and heats up the furnaces at identical rates but with a constant temperature difference between them. The "Derivatograph" (Erdey, Paulik, and Paulik, 1956) is a simpler arrangement, being a conventional thermobalance with the furnace situated above the balance. The balance beam has attached to it a small coil which moves in a fixed magnetic

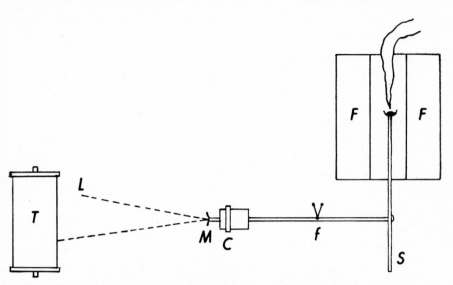

Figure 7. Principle of the Chevenard thermobalance: C - counter-weight; F - furnace; f - fulcrum; L - light source; M - mirror; S - crucible support; T - photographic recording drum.

field in such a way that the current generated in the coil is proportional to the change in weight. This system enables the thermogravimetric and differential thermogravimetric curves to be recorded simultaneously and should be easier to manipulate than the De Keyser apparatus, which has rather demanding requirements.

Significance of peaks and their use in quantitative estimation

On differential thermal curves two types of peaks are observed — namely, endothermic and exothermic. Each of these may be due to one of several reasons which are briefly discussed below.

Endothermic peaks, which indicate that the reaction proceeds with an absorption of energy, may be caused by:

(*a*) Decomposition. The loss of water, carbon dioxide, etc., is always an endothermic reaction and in clay studies this is the most common cause of an endothermic peak.

(*b*) Phase changes. This covers both changes in state (e.g., solid

→ liquid → vapor), and polymorphic transformations. The latter may be reversible on cooling (e.g., quartz), or irreversible (e.g., aragonite → calcite).

(*c*) Solid–phase reactions. Most of these are exothermic, but there is no fundamental reason why some should not be endothermic. The reaction of calcite with metakaolinite to give gehlenite has been claimed by Grim (1962) to be of this type.

(*d*) Entropy changes not covered by (*a*), (*b*), and (*c*). These include changes due to minor rearrangements in amorphous or highly defective structures not revealed by crystallographic examination; the small endothermic peak before the 900°C. exothermic peak of montmorillonite is one possible example.

Exothermic peaks indicate that the reaction occurs with an evolution of heat, and can arise from:

(*a*) Nucleation, crystallization, or recrystallization. These are the most usual causes of an exothermic peak and as examples may be quoted the 1000°C. exothermic peak of kaolinite (nucleation), the exothermic peaks of oxide gels (crystallization), and the 900°C. exothermic peak of chlorites (recrystallization).

(*b*) Reaction with the enveloping atmosphere. This is particularly noticeable with compounds containing ferrous iron, e.g., chalybite, and organic materials in an oxidizing atmosphere.

(*c*) Solid–phase reactions. A striking example of this is the reaction between various metals and sulphur to give sulphides (Bollin and Kerr, 1961).

On differential thermogravimetric curves two types of peaks are also observable, but these are due to loss or gain in weight. Loss–in–weight peaks are, of course, due to evolution of some constituent, such as water or carbon dioxide, at a specific temperature whereas gain–in–weight peaks are due to reaction of the material with the enveloping atmosphere. Phase changes, entropy changes, or solid–phase reactions give no peak.

It is clear, therefore, that comparison of a differential thermal with a differential thermogravimetric curve for the same material distinguishes immediately an endothermic peak due to decomposition from one due to any of the other causes (Fig. 8), and an exothermic peak due to reaction with the enveloping atmosphere from the others. If a peak is not due to either of these factors, then structural methods of study, such as X–ray examination, are necessary to elucidate its significance.

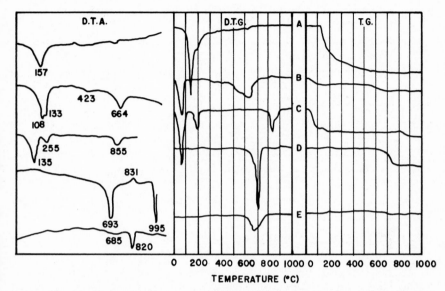

Figure 8. Comparison of differential thermal, differential thermogravimetric, and thermogravimetric curves for some minerals: A - allophane; B - montmorillonite; C - saponite; D - crocidolite; E - amèsite.

Both differential thermal analysis and differential thermogravimetry are quantitative, but the results obtained with the latter are absolute whereas those obtained by the former are very subject to the accuracy of control of experimental conditions. With reasonable experimental control, however, the order of accuracy obtainable from estimations made on the basis of peak area measurements on differential thermal curves is about ±5 per cent, or better (Mackenzie and Robertson, 1961), and this is adequate for most routine soil–clay determinations. Estimations made from peaks caused by entropy or phase changes are necessarily less accurate than those from peaks due to decomposition, polymorphic changes, or solid–phase reactions, because they are controlled by the energy conditions in the starting material and these may not always be identical. Peaks caused by reaction with the enveloping atmosphere may also be subject to some variation depending on how well the atmosphere in the specimen is maintained. Peaks due to decomposition are, therefore, the most reliable to use in quantitative studies.

Applications of differential thermal analysis in pedology

The wide range in peak size given by different materials has been referred to above and illustrated in Fig. 3. In soil–clay work a wide range of sensitivities is, therefore, obviously desirable and is essential if full information is to be extracted from the curve. Assuming, however, that sensitivity is satisfactory and that one has obtained a differential thermal curve for an unknown soil clay, let us consider the information about the clay contained therein. Since more qualitative information is contained in a differential thermal curve than in a differential thermogravimetric curve, only the former will be considered here; the latter is more useful in quantitative applications.

Information from a normal curve

While differential thermal analysis is not so diagnostic as X–ray diffraction examination, it nevertheless yields some information upon the mineralogy of a clay. Thus, for tropical or sub–tropical soil clays, which usually contain minerals giving well–defined curves, it may be possible to identify all the components, but for the less highly weathered soils of temperate regions the curves obtained give only a partial mineralogical analysis. For the colder Arctic regions the curves are usually poorly defined and yield little mineralogical information of value (Fig. 9).

The types of curves given by the more common clay minerals and some accessory minerals likely to be encountered in soil clays are shown in Figs. 10 and 11. More detailed information will be found in the books mentioned earlier, and in the data index (Mackenzie, 1962), which, while not perhaps enabling positive identification, permits one to tie a curve down to a limited number of materials which may then be tested for individually.

One of the major problems in identification of minerals from their differential thermal curves is the variability which is encountered with even one mineral. For example, montmorillonites are known which give endothermic peaks at about 700°C., at about 550°C. and 650°C., and at about 550°C. (Mackenzie, 1957b), and illites present rather a similar picture (Mackenzie, 1957a). Yet X–ray examination shows no apparent difference between the "normal" and "abnormal" types. An interesting recent observation is that despite the difference in energy

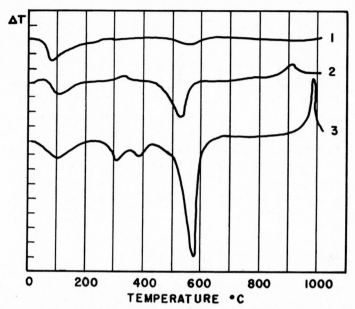

Figure 9. *Typical differential thermal curves for soil clays from:*
1 - Sweden; 2 - Scotland; 3 - West Africa.

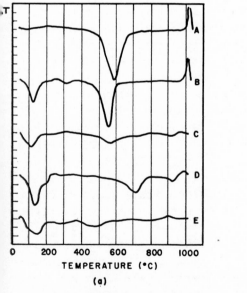

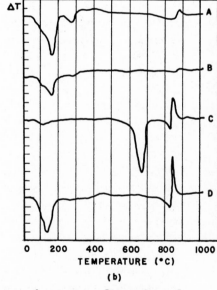

Figure 10. *Differential thermal curves for some clay minerals:*
(a) A - *kaolinite,* B - *halloysite (peak at 320° C. due to gibbsite),*
C - *illite,* D - *montmorillonite,* E - *palygorskite; (b)* A - *vermic-*
ulite, B - *hydrobiotite,* C - *pennine,* D - *sepiolite.*

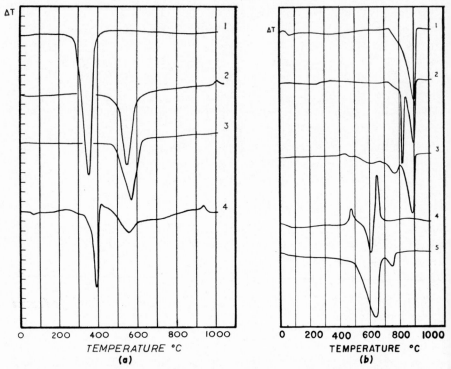

Figure 11. Differential thermal curves for some accessory minerals: (a) *aluminum and manganese oxides 1 - gibbsite, 2 - boehmite (with very slight kaolinite contamination), 3 -diaspore, 4 - manganite;* (b) *carbonates 1 - calcite, 2 - and 3 - dolomite, 4 - chalybite in air, 5 - chalybite in nitrogen.*

required to initiate dehydroxylation of montmorillonite (as assessed from the peak temperature), the actual energy involved in the dehydroxylation (as assessed from peak area) is the same for both "normal" and "abnormal" types (Mackenzie, 1961). The dehydroxylation process for both must therefore proceed by the same mechanism although the structure of one type must be such as to require a lower activation energy. Although the reason for such differences is not yet known (see Heller, *et al.,* 1962), the fact that they exist may lead to difficulty in interpretation of the curve. On the other hand, they do show that there are fundamental (even if small) differences between different specimens of the same mineral—differences which may be reflected in physical or chemical properties, and which would have gone unsuspected had not differential thermal analysis been employed.

Apart from direct mineral identification, differential thermal analysis has several other functions in soil–clay mineralogy. Thus, if the minerals in one horizon of a profile are known, either from X–ray or differential thermal identification, then a rapid qualitative and quantitative assessment of the trends up or down the profile may be made from examination of the differential thermal curves for each horizon (Mackenzie, 1956). Similarly variation within different particle–size cuts of the clay fraction may be rapidly estimated. Such estimations are much less time–consuming than quantitative X–ray examination.

The "slope ratio" of the peak (tan α/tan β), which has already been referred to in connection with Fig. 1, is a parameter which is particularly useful in diagnosis of the type of kandite present in a clay (Bramão, *et al.*, 1952). Thus, for a symmetrical peak like that of highly crystalline kaolinite the slope ratio is near unity, whereas for an asymmetrical one like that of halloysite it is high. Difficulties arise, however, in distinguishing a finely particulate, highly crystalline kaolinite from a disordered kaolinite since the values overlap (Robertson, Brindley, and Mackenzie, 1954). Actual values vary, of course, with apparatus and technique, and each apparatus has to be calibrated with known materials.

Since differential thermal analysis is particularly sensitive for such minerals as hydroxides and carbonates, these can readily be detected in soil clays in amounts which would not be observed on normal X–ray examination (Mackenzie, 1956). Recently, too, Mitchell and Farmer (1962) have shown the technique to be useful in detecting and determining amorphous inorganic material (allophane) in soil clays.

Information using special techniques

By using special techniques it is sometimes possible to make the method more diagnostic. Thus, controlled atmosphere can be of particular assistance in soil–clay examination, since determination of the curve in an inert (nitrogen or argon) atmosphere suppresses all effects due to organic matter and permits the mineral peaks to be clearly seen (Mitchell and Mackenzie, 1959). This procedure is in fact preferable to destroying the organic matter with hydrogen peroxide, since this may have a destructive effect on the inorganic material present (Farmer and Mitchell, 1963). Using as an enveloping atmosphere a gas evolved during a reaction can also displace the peak to a higher temperature (Stone, 1951, 1960) and serve to resolve overlapping peaks.

Even more diagnostic is the use of chemical pretreatment to modify one of the components without affecting the others. As an example of this may be quoted the technique of Mackenzie and Robertson (1961) for the detection and determination of gibbsite, goethite, and halloysite in tropical soil clays. Here the goethite was extracted by sodium dithionite and the gibbsite by sodium hydroxide, the curves after each treatment yielding more information upon the mineralogical composition of the original clay than could have been obtained from one curve alone. Less drastic pretreatment, but just as valuable, is the use of piperidine to distinguish montmorillonite or allophane (Allaway, 1949; Sudo, 1954; Oades, 1962), or the use of glycol to distinguish halloysite (Sand and Bates, 1953).

Disturbing factors

In the interpretation of any differential thermal curve, certain disturbing factors must be allowed for. Thus, the fact that a mineral is not of the "normal" type may lead to difficulties in diagnosis although association of several features of the curve can often lead to a valid interpretation. For example, an "abnormal" montmorillonite having a peak at 550°C., if saturated with Ca^{2+}, Mg^{2+}, or Na^+, would still have a large hygroscopic moisture peak — although it could, of course, be confused with a mixture of illite and allophane.

Many minerals, too, are particularly susceptible to grinding, as has been shown for the micas (Mackenzie, Meldau, and Farmer, 1956). Consequently, no sample should be ground for long periods, and light rubbing rather than grinding should be used for disaggregation.

The exchangeable ion has a pronounced effect upon the nature and size of the low–temperature endothermic peak, particularly for smectites and vermiculites (Mackenzie, 1957a), and can even influence the dehydroxylation peak (Mackenzie and Bishui, 1958). It is therefore preferable to saturate all samples with a standard cation such as Ca^{2+} or Mg^{2+}. However, since acetate ions can apparently exert a disturbing effect on the curves of certain minerals (Rich, 1962), it would seem desirable to avoid a pretreatment involving this anion unless it is definitely known that it is not sorbed on the minerals present.

When discussing apparatus it was pointed out that different types of specimen holders may be useful in different conditions (e.g., metal for inert gas, porous ceramic for an active atmosphere), but it must not be forgotten that the specimen holder itself and particularly its porosity may have a significant effect on the curve and on the symmetry of the peak (Webb, 1954; Mackenzie, 1954). The arrangement of the thermocouples in the sample wells may also be critical. For example, Cole and Rowland (1961) showed that in the absence of a lid certain thermocouple arrangements could give rise to false peaks on curves for vermiculite.

The fact that the combustion of organic matter may give peaks occluding mineral peaks has been referred to above. The simplest procedure for avoiding this effect is to perform the differential thermal analysis in an inert atmosphere such as nitrogen (Mitchell and Mackenzie, 1959), when the combustion peaks are completely suppressed.

Spurious effects on differential thermal curves may sometimes arise from solid phase reactions occurring in the sample. Such reactions were found by Martin (1958) with natural soils containing carbonates and soluble salts in addition to the usual clay minerals. Apparently both soluble salts and micaceous clay minerals have an appreciable effect upon the carbonate decomposition and may lead to an underestimate of the amount of carbonate present. Sometimes, too, small amounts of Na^+ in a soil clay may act as a flux and cause fusion of the sample at relatively low temperatures (Mackenzie, unpublished). For this reason, it is best to avoid sodium hydroxide as a dispersing agent in separation of the clay fraction unless the sample can subsequently be saturated with ammonium.

All these factors (and others referred to earlier) must therefore be kept in mind and their effects assessed before any curve can be adequately interpreted.

Quantitative studies with special reference to water determination

In the theoretical section much emphasis has been laid on the relationship between the peak area on a differential thermal curve and the amount of reacting material. In general, this is usually regarded as a linear relationship, but certain disturbing factors often lead to a smooth relationship which is not linear (e.g., differences in thermal conductivity and diffusivity arising from failure to dilute the sample). This again depends on how well the thermal characteristics of the inert material match those of the sample, and one may find that as he uses a more and more concentrated sample a linear relationship degenerates into a curvilinear one. The same appears to apply to reactions involving large energy changes. For example, Mitchell (1960) found a curvilinear relationship between peak area and calorific value for a series of peat samples, and Mackenzie (1961) later showed that the initial part of this curve must have been linear, or very nearly so. Since the sample here was diluted 20 times with inert material it would seem that in practice there is some energy transfer out of or into the sample for intense peaks occurring over a fair time period, despite the theoretical conclusions to the contrary (Sewell and Honeyborne, 1957). As distinct from this, differential thermogravimetry is, of course, absolute.

Some workers (Dean, 1947; Gallitelli, Cola, and Alietti, 1954; Carthew, 1955) have found better relationships between some parameter other than the area of the peak and the amount of reacting material, but this may be a function of the apparatus used or of the types of materials investigated. There is no doubt that peak area is the most universally applicable, and Ellis and Mortland (1962) have shown that good agreement is obtained between measurements of heats of reaction from peak area and from application of the Clausius–Clapeyron equation to the curve.

Recently, there has been some interest in the determination of water vapor from the differential thermal curve, and several methods have been evolved. For hygroscopic moisture, peak–area measurements were used by Tykachinskii and Afanasaev (1952). Work along these lines has also been carried out at the Macaulay Institute on halloysite and montmorillonite. It was found that the calibration curves for these materials were somewhat different (Fig. 12), but, surprisingly, that the exchangeable cation did not appreciably affect the montmorillonite curve (Mackenzie, 1963). The accuracy in such a determination depends upon the accuracy of temperature control over the initial stages of heating. The method of Teitelbaum and Berg (1953; Berg, 1961a), whereby the differential thermal curve is determined in a sealed apparatus attached to a suitable manometric system, also enables direct measurement of water evolution over the whole temperature range, if calcium hydride is inserted into the system; the water reacts quantitatively with it to give off hydrogen. Kulbicki and Grim (1959) also used calcium hydride to determine water vapor, but they inserted one junction of a difference

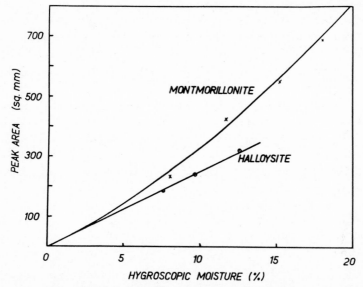

Figure 12. The relationship between area of the low-temperature peak system on differential thermal curves and moisture content for montmorillonite and halloysite.

thermocouple into the hydride and placed the other close to the hydride but in the gas stream from the differential thermal apparatus. The heat evolved during reaction of the hydride with moisture gave peaks indicating the periods during which water was evolved. The authors did not attempt any quantitative determinations, but there seems to be no valid reason why this arrangement could not be made quantitative.

General conclusions

The above discussion has been compiled with a view to giving a reasonable background in differential thermal analysis, thermogravimetry, and differential thermogravimetry to those interested in the applications of the methods, particularly to soil clays. The intention has been to emphasize fundamental aspects and, therefore, little illustrative matter has been selected from actual pedological studies. However, if the fundamental basis is understood, then interpretation of soil–clay curves to extract maximum information, without committing serious errors, should be relatively simple. It has, of course, been impossible to cover

all the finer points in this brief outline, but study of the books and reviews mentioned earlier should fill in most of the omissions. It will be
clear that, whereas most information is contained in a differential
thermal curve, quantitative measurements are only absolute on thermogravimetric and differential thermogravimetric curves.

References

Agafonoff, V. (1935) Etude minéralogique du sol: *Trans. III Int. Congr.
Soil. Sci.*, v. 3, pp. 74-78.
Allaway, W. H. (1949) Differential thermal analyses of clays treated with
organic cations as an aid in the study of soil colloids: *Proc. Soil Sci. Soc.
Amer.*, v. 13, pp. 183-88.
Arens, P. L. (1951) A study on the differential thermal analysis of clays
and clay minerals: Thesis, Wageningen, Holland.
Ayres, W. M. and Bens, E. M. (1961) Differential thermal studies with
simultaneous gas evolution profiles: *Analyt. Chem.*, v. 33, pp. 568-72.
Berg, L. G. (editor) (1955) *Transactions of the First Conference on
Thermography* [*Trudy pervogo Soveshchaniya po Thermografii*]: Izdat.
Akad. Nauk SSSR, Moscow-Leningrad.
Berg, L. G. (1961a) *Introduction to Thermography* [*Vvedenie v Termo-
grafiyu*]: Izdat. Akad. Nauk SSSR, Moscow.
Berg, L. G. (editor) (1961b) *Transactions of the Second Conference on
Thermography* [*Trudy vtorogo Soveshchaniya po Termografii*]: Kazan
Fil. Akad. Nauk SSSR, Kazan.
Berg, L. G., Nikolaev, A. V., and Rode, E. Ya. (1944) *Thermography*
[*Termografiya*]: Izdat. Akad. Nauk SSSR, Moscow.
Berg, L. G. and Rassonskaya, I. S. (1950) Rapid thermal analysis: *Doklady
Akad. Nauk SSSR*, v. 73, pp. 113-15.
Berg, L. G. and Yagfarov, M. Sh. (1958) A new precision thermographic
method for the determination of thermal constants and heat effects:
in *Transactions of the Fifth Conference on Experimental and Technical
Mineralogy and Petrology* [*Trudy pyatogo Soveshchaniya po Eksperi-
mentalnoi i Tekhnicheskoi Mineralogii i Petrografii**] (A. I. Tsvetkov,
editor): Izdat. Akad, Nauk SSSR, Moscow, pp. 63-71.
Bollin, E. M. and Kerr, P. F. (1961) Differential thermal pyrosynthesis:
Amer. Min., v. 46, pp. 823-58.
Bramão, L., Cady, J. G., Hendricks, S. B., and Swerdlow, M. (1952) Criteria
for the characterization of kaolinite, halloysite, and a related mineral in
clays and soils: *Soil Sci.*, v. 73, pp. 273-87.
Brewer, L. and Zavitsanos, P. (1957) A study of the Ge-GeO$_2$ system by an
inductively heated DTA apparatus: *J. Phys. Chem. Solids*, v. 2, pp. 284-
85.

---

* This volume is at present being translated into English and will be published
by Pergamon Press, London.

Butterworth, B. and Honeyborne, D. B. (1952) Bricks and clays of the Hastings Beds: *Trans. Brit. Ceram. Soc.,* v. 51, pp. 211-59.

Caillère, S. and Hénin, S. (1957) The chlorite and serpentine minerals: in *The Differential Thermal Investigation of Clays* (R. C. Mackenzie, editor): Mineralogical Society, London, chapter VIII, pp. 207-30.

Carthew, A. R. (1955) The quantitative determination of kaolinite by differential thermal analysis: *Amer. Min.,* v. 40, pp. 107-17.

Chevenard, P., Waché, X., and de la Tullaye, R. (1944) Étude de la corrosion seché des métaux au moyen d'une thermobalance: *Bull. Soc. Chim. Fr. (Mem.),* v. 10, p. 41-47.

Cole, W. F. and Rowland, N. M. (1961) An abnormal effect in differential thermal analysis of clay minerals: *Amer. Min.,* v. 46, pp. 304-12.

Dean, L. A. (1947) Differential thermal analysis of Hawaiian soils: *Soil Sci.,* v. 63, pp. 95-105.

De Keyser, W. L. (1953) Differential thermobalance: a new research tool: *Nature, Lond.,* v. 172, pp. 364-65.

Dilaktorskii, N. L. and Arkhangelskaya, L. S. (1958) Some problems associated with the thermal analysis technique: in *Transactions of the Fifth Conference on Experimental and Technical Mineralogy and Petrology* [*Trudy pyatogo Soveshchaniya po Eksperimentalnoi i Tekhnicheskoi Mineralogii i Petrografii*] (A. I. Tsvetkov, editor): Izdat. Akad. Nauk SSSR, Moscow, pp. 88-96.

Dunne, J. A. and Kerr, P. F. (1961) Differential thermal analysis of galena and clausthalite: *Amer. Min.,* v. 46, pp. 1-11.

Duval, C. (1953) *Inorganic Thermogravimetric Analysis:* Elsevier, Amsterdam.

Duval, C. (1963) *Inorganic Thermogravimetric Analysis* (2nd edition): Elsevier, Amsterdam.

Eliáš, M., Štovick, M., and Zahradník, L. (1957) *Chemické Rozbory Nerostuých Surovin. Sešit 12 — Diferenčni Thermická Analysa:* Naklad. Česk. Akad. Věd, Prague.

Ellis, B. G. and Mortland, M. M. (1962) A comparison of two methods of determining heats of reaction by differential thermal analysis: *Amer. Min.,* v. 47, pp. 371-78.

Erdey, L., Paulik, F., and Paulik, J. (1954) Differential thermogravimetry: *Nature, Lond.,* v. 174, pp. 885-86.

Erdey, L., Paulik, F., and Paulik, J. (1956) Ein neues thermisches Verfahren: die Derivationsthermogravimetrie: *Acta chim. hung.,* v. 10, pp. 61-97.

Eriksson, E. (1953-54) Problems of heat flow in differential thermal analysis. I, II and III: *LantbrHögsk. Ann.,* v. 19, pp. 127-43; v. 20, pp. 117-23; v. 21, pp. 189-96.

Farmer, V. C. and Mitchell, B. D. (1963) The occurrence of oxalates in soil clays following hydrogen peroxide treatment: *Soil Sci.,* v. 96, pp. 221-29.

Fenner, C. N. (1913) Stability relations of the silica minerals: *Amer. J. Sci.,* v. 36, pp. 331-84.

Földvári-Vogl, M. (1958) The role of differential thermal analysis in mineralogy and geological prospecting: *Acta geol. hung.,* v. 5, pp. 3-102.

Földvári-Vogl,, M. and Kliburszky, B. (1957) Gerät zur thermischen Differential-Schnellanalyse: *Geologie*, v. 6, pp. 542-48.

Gallitelli, P., Cola, M., and Alietti, A. (1954) Su alcuni problemi legati alla tecnica dell'analisi termica differenziale: *Mem. Accad. Lincei*, v. 4, pp. 49-60.

Gérard-Hirne and Lamy, C. (1951) Aperçu d'ensemble sur les argiles céramiques. IV — Identification des argiles par l'analyse thermique différentielle: *Bull. Soc. Franç. Céram.*, no. 10, pp. 26-40.

Greenaway, H. T., Johnstone, S. T. M., and McQuillan, M. K. (1951) High-temperature thermal analysis using the tungsten/molybdenum thermocouple: *J. Inst. Met.*, v. 80, pp. 109-14.

Grim, R. E. (1962) *Applied Clay Mineralogy:* McGraw-Hill, New York, p. 342.

Grimshaw, R. W., Heaton, E., and Roberts, A. L. (1945) The constitution of refractory clays. II: *Trans. Brit. Ceram. Soc.*, v. 44, pp. 76-92.

Grimshaw, R. W. and Roberts, A. L. (1953) The quantitative determination of some minerals in ceramic materials by thermal means: *Trans. Brit. Ceram. Soc.*, v. 52, pp. 50-67.

Gruver, R. M. (1948) Precision method of thermal analysis: *J. Amer. Ceram. Soc.*, v. 31, pp. 323-28.

Guichard, M. (1925) Étude cinématique de la déshydratation à l'aide d'une balance à compensation hydrostatique: *Bull. Soc. Chim. Fr.*, v. 37, pp. 251-53.

Guichard, M. (1935) Sur la méthode d'étude des systèmes chimiques par mesure des variations de poids, en temperature regulièrement variable: *Bull. Soc. chim. Fr. (Mem.)*, v. 2, pp. 539-45.

Heller, L., Farmer, V. C., Mackenzie, R. C., Mitchell, B. D., and Taylor, H. F. W. (1962) The dehydroxylation and rehydroxylation of triphormic dioctahedral clay minerals: *Clay Min. Bull.*, v. 5, pp. 56-72.

Hendricks, S. B. and Alexander, L. T. (1939) Minerals present in soil colloids. I — Description and methods for identification: *Soil Sci.*, v. 48, pp. 257-71.

Hodgson, A. A. (1963) A comprehensive thermal analysis apparatus: *J. Sci. Instr.*, v. 40, pp. 61-65.

Hollings, H. and Cobb, J. W. (1915) A thermal study of the carbonisation process. *J. Chem. Soc. (Trans.)*, v. 107, pp. 1106-15.

Honda, K. (1915) On a thermobalance: *Sci. Rep. Tohoku Imp. Univ.*, v. 4, pp. 97-103.

Ivanova, V. P. (1961) Thermograms of minerals: *Zap. Vsesoyuz. Miner. Obshch.*, v. 90, pp. 50-90.

Kaurkovskii, V. I. (1955) An automatic thermoregulator with thermal control element: in *Transactions of the First Conference on Thermography* [*Trudy pervogo Soveshchaniya po Termografii*] (L. G. Berg, editor): Izdat. Akad. Nauk SSSR, Moscow-Leningrad, pp. 36-41.

Keler, E. K. (1955) Complex thermal analysis of silicates: in *Transactions of the First Conference on Thermography* [*Trudy pervogo Soveshchaniya po Termografii*] (L. G. Berg, editor): Izdat. Akad. Nauk SSSR, Moscow-Leningrad, pp. 239-49.

Kerr, P. F. and Kulp, J. L. (1948) Multiple differential thermal analysis: *Amer. Min.,* v. 33, pp. 387-419.

Kulbicki, G. and Grim, R. E. (1959) A new method for thermal dehydration studies of clay minerals: *Miner. Mag.,* v. 32, pp. 53-62.

Kulp, J. L. and Kerr, P. F. (1949) Improved differential thermal analysis apparatus: *Amer. Min.,* v. 34, pp. 839-45.

Kurnakov, N. S. (1904) A new form of recording pyrometer: *Zhur. Russ. Fiz.-Khim. Obshch.,* v. 36, pp. 841-56.

Le Chatelier, H. (1904) Nouveau dispositif expérimental de la méthode de M. Saladin pour l'enregistrement des points critiques: *Rev. Métall.,* v. 1, pp. 134-40.

Lehmann, H., Das, S. S., and Paetsch, H. H. (1954) Die Differentialthermoanalyse: *TonindustrZtg,* Beiheft 1.

Lukaszewski, G. M. (1962) Accuracy in thermogravimetric analysis: *Nature, Lond.,* v. 194, pp. 959-61.

McConnell, D. and Earley, J. W. (1951) Apparatus for differential thermal analysis: *J. Amer. Ceram. Soc.,* v. 34, pp. 183-87.

Mackenzie, R. C. (1954) Comparative performance of nickel and porous alumina sample holders for differential thermal analysis: *Nature, Lond.,* v. 174, pp. 688-89.

Mackenzie, R. C. (1956) Differential thermal analysis and its use in soil-clay mineralogy: *Geol. Fören. Stockh. Förh.,* v. 78, pp. 508-25.

Mackenzie, R. C. (editor) (1957a) *The Differential Thermal Investigation of Clays:* Mineralogical Society, London.

Mackenzie, R. C. (1957b) The montmorillonite differential thermal curve. I — General variability in the dehydroxylation region: *Bull. Groupe franç Argiles,* v. 9, pp. 7-15.

Mackenzie, R. C. (1961) The quantitative determination of minerals in clays: *Acta Univ. Carol. Geol.,* Suppl. 1, pp. 11-21.

Mackenzie, R. C. (compiler) (1962) Scifax Differential Thermal Analysis Data Index: Cleaver-Hume Press, London.

Mackenzie, R. C. (1963) Retention of exchangeable ions by montmorillonite: *Trans. 1963 Int. Clay Conf., Stockholm,* pp. 183-93.

Mackenzie, R. C. and Bishui, B. M. (1958) The montmorillonite differential thermal curve. II — Effect of exchangeable cations on the dehydroxylation of normal montmorillonite: *Clay Min. Bull.,* v. 3, pp. 276-86.

Mackenzie, R. C. and Farquharson, K. R. (1953) Standardization of differential thermal analysis technique: *C.R. XIX Congr. géol. Int., Alger, 1952,* v. 18, pp. 183-200.

Mackenzie, R. C., Meldau, R., and Farmer, V. C. (1956) Einfluss der Feinstmahlung auf die Kristallstruktur von Glimmern: *Ber. dtsch. keram. Ges.,* v. 33, pp. 222-29.

Mackenzie, R. C. and Mitchell, B. D. (1957) Apparatus and technique for differential thermal analysis: in *The Differential Thermal Investigation of*

Clays (R. C. Mackenzie, editor): Mineralogical Society, London, pp. 23-64.

Mackenzie, R. C. and Mitchell, B. D. (1962) Differential thermal analysis — a review: *Analyst*, v. 87, pp. 420-34.

Mackenzie, R. C. and Robertson, R. H. S. (1961) The quantitative determination of halloysite, goethite and gibbsite: *Acta Univ. Carol. Geol.*, Suppl. no. 1, pp. 139-49.

McLaughlin, R. J. W. (1954) Quantitative differential thermal analysis of soil clays and silts: *Amer. J. Sci.*, v. 252, pp. 555-66.

Markowitz, M. M. and Boryta, D. A. (1960) A convenient system of thermogravimetric analysis and of differential thermal analysis: *Analyt. Chem.*, v. 32, pp. 1588-92.

Martin, R. T. (1955) Reference chlorite characterization for chlorite identification in soil clays: in *Clays and Clay Minerals*, Natl. Acad. Sci. — Natl. Res. Council, pub. 395, pp. 117-45.

Martin, R. T. (1958) Clay-carbonate-soluble salt interaction during differential thermal analysis: *Amer. Min.*, v. 43, pp. 649-55.

Mazières, C. (1959) Dispositif de microanalyse thermique différentielle: *C. R. Acad. Sci. Paris*, v. 248, pp. 2990-92.

Merveille, J. and Boureille, A. (1950) Identification des argiles céramiques par la thermo-balance: *Bull. Soc. franç. Céram.*, no. 7, pp. 18-27.

Mitchell, B. D. (1960) The differential thermal analysis of humic substances and related materials: *Sci. Proc. R. Dublin Soc.*, v. A1, pp. 105-14.

Mitchell, B. D. (1961) Problems associated with high sensitivity of recording in differential thermal analysis: *Clay Min. Bull.*, v. 4, pp. 246-48.

Mitchell, B. D. and Farmer, V. C. (1962) Amorphous clay minerals in some Scottish soil profiles: *Clay Min. Bull.*, v. 5, pp. 128-44.

Mitchell, B. D. and Mackenzie, R. C. (1959) An apparatus for differential thermal analysis under controlled-atmosphere conditions. *Clay Min. Bull.*, v. 4, pp. 31-43.

Murphy, C. B. (1958) Differential thermal analysis: *Analyt. Chem.*, v. 30, pp. 867-72.

Murphy, C. B. (1960) Differential thermal analysis: *Analyt. Chem.*, v. 32, pp. 168R-171R.

Murphy, C. B. (1962) Differential thermal analysis: *Analyt. Chem.* v. 34, pp. 298R-301R.

Murphy, C. B., Hill, J. A., and Schacher, G. P. (1960) Differential thermal analysis and simultaneous gas analysis: *Analyt. Chem.*, v. 32, pp. 1374-75.

Nedumov, N. A. (1960) A high-temperature method for contactless differential thermal analysis: *Zhur. Fiz. Khim.*, v. 34, pp. 184-91.

Norton, F. H. (1939) Critical study of differential thermal analysis for identification of clay minerals: *J. Amer. Ceram. Soc.*, v. 22, pp. 54-63.

Oades, J. M. (1962) An investigation of the nature of iron compounds in various soil types: Ph.D. Thesis, University of Leeds, England.

Orcel, J. (1927) Recherches sur la composition chimique des chlorites: *Bull. Soc. franç. Minér.*, v. 50, pp. 75-456.

Orcel, J. and Caillère, S. (1933) L'analyse thermique différentielle des argiles à montmorillonite (bentonites): *C.R. Acad. Sci. Paris,* v. 197, pp. 774-77.

Powell, D. A. (1957) An apparatus giving thermogravimetric and differential thermal curves simultaneously from one sample: *J. Sci. Instr.,* v. 34, pp. 225-27.

Proks, I. (1961) Vliv rychlosti záhřevu na veličiny, duležité při vyhodnocování krivek DTA: *Silikáty,* v. 5, pp. 114-26.

Ramachandran, V. S. and Garg, S. P. (1959) *Differential Thermal Analysis as Applied to Building Science:* Central Building Research Institute, Roorkee, India.

Reisman, A. (1960) Isobaric dissociation studies of alkali metal carbonate hydrates using simultaneous differential thermal analysis — thermogravimetric analysis: *Analyt. Chem.,* v. 32, pp. 1566-74.

Rich, C. I. (1962) Removal of excess salt in cation-exchange-capacity determinations: *Soil Sci.,* v. 93, pp. 87-94.

Roberts-Austen, W. C. (1899) Fifth report to Alloys Research Committee: *Proc. Instn. Mech. Engrs.,* pp. 35-102.

Robertson, R. H. S., Brindley, G. W., and Mackenzie, R. C. (1954) Mineralology of kaolin clays from Pugu, Tanganyika: *Amer. Min.,* v. 39, pp. 118-38.

Rowland, R. A. and Jonas, E. C. (1949) Variations in the differential thermal analysis curves of siderite: *Amer. Min.,* v. 34, pp. 550-58.

Sabatier, G. (1950) Sur l'influence de la dimension des cristaux de chlorites sur les courbes d'analyse thermique différentielle: *Bull. Soc. franç Minér.,* v. 73, pp. 43-48.

Sabatier, G. (1954) La mesure des chaleurs des transformations a l'aide de l'analyse thermique différentielle: *Bull. Soc. franç. Minér.,* v. 77, pp. 953-68, 1077-83.

Sand, L. B. and Bates, T. F. (1953) Quantitative analysis of endellite, halloysite and kaolinite by differential thermal analysis: *Amer. Min.,* v. 38, pp. 271-78.

Sewell, E. C. (1952-1956) Theory of differential thermal analysis: *Research Notes,* Building Research Station, Watford, Herts.

Sewell, E. C. and Honeyborne, D. B. (1957) Theory and quantitative use: in *The Differential Thermal Investigation of Clays* (R. C. Mackenzie, editor): Mineralogical Society, London, pp. 65-97.

Šiške, and Proks, I. (1958) New arrangement for differential thermal analysis: *Chem. zvesti,* v. 12, pp. 185-89.

Smothers, W. J. and Chiang, Y. (1958) *Differential Thermal Analysis:* Chemical Publishing Co., New York.

Soulé, J. L. (1952) Quantitative interpretation of differential thermal analysis: *J. Phys. Radium,* v. 13, pp. 516-20.

Speil, S. (1945) Applications of thermal analysis to clays and aluminous materials: *Tech. Pap. Bur. Min., Wash.,* no. 664, pp. 1-37.

Stegmüller, L. (1953) Ein bewährtes, im Handel beziehbares Gerät für die Differentialthermoanalyse in keramischen Betrieb: *Sprechsaal,* v. 86, pp. 1-8.

Stone, R. L. (1951) Differential thermal analysis of clay minerals under controlled thermodynamic conditions: *Bull. Ohio Engng. Exp. Sta.*, no. 146.

Stone, R. L. (1960) Differential thermal analysis by the dynamic gas technique: *Analyt. Chem.*, v. 32, pp. 1582-88.

Sudo, T. (1954) Clay mineralogical aspects of the alteration of volcanic glass in Japan: *Clay Min. Bull.*, v. 2, pp. 96-106.

Teitelbaum, B. Ya. (1955) Arrangement for the programme control of furnace heating in thermal analysis using the Kurnakov pyrometer: in *Transactions of the First Conference on Thermography [Trudy pervogo Soveshchaniya po Termografii]* (L. G. Berg, editor), Izdat. Akad. Nauk SSSR, Moscow-Leningrad, pp. 31-35.

Teitelbaum, B. Ya. and Berg, L. G. (1953) Thermal analysis with registration of the volume of gases evolved: *Zhur. Anal. Khim.*, v. 8, pp. 152-57.

Theron, J. J. (1952) An improved apparatus for the differential thermal analysis of minerals: *Brit. J. Appl. Phys.*, v. 3, pp. 216-20.

Tykachinskii, I. D. and Afanasaev, A. N. (1952) Rapid determination of moisture in raw materials and glass mixes by thermal analysis: *Steklo i Keramika*, v. 9, no. 3, pp. 6-8.

Wallach, R. (1913) Analyse thermique des argiles: *C. R. Acad. Sci. Paris,* v. 157, pp. 48-50.

Webb, T. L. (1954) Comparative performance of nickel and porous alumina sample holders for differential thermal analysis: *Nature, Lond.,* v. 174, pp. 686-88.

Webb, T. L. (1958) Contributions to the technique and apparatus for qualitative and quantitative differential thermal analysis with particular reference to carbonates and hydroxides of calcium and magnesium: D.Sci. Thesis, University of Pretoria, South Africa.

Whitehead, W. L. and Breger, I. A. (1950) Vacuum differential thermal analysis: *Science,* v. 111, pp. 279-81.

Wilburn, F. W. (1958) A differential thermal analysis apparatus: *J. Sci. Instr.,* v. 35, pp. 403-7.

Yagfarov, M. Sh. and Berg, L. G. (1957a) A new method for obtaining a linear heating rate: *Izv. Kazan. Fil. Akad. Nauk SSSR, Ser. Khim.,* no. 3, pp. 27-29.

Yagfarov, M. Sh. and Berg, L. G. (1957b) The basis of the method for determining thermal constants by thermography: *Izv. Kazan, Fil. Akad. Nauk SSSR, Ser. Khim.,* no. 3, p. 31-36.

Yarembash, E. I. (1955) Photorecording pyrometer PK-52: in *Transactions of the First Conference on Thermography [Trudy pervogo Soveshchaniya po Termografii]* (L. G. Berg, editor), Izdat. Akad. Nauk SSSR, Moscow-Leningrad, pp. 23-27.

VIII ... Soil Clay Mineralogical Analysis

M. L. Jackson

Soil clay mineralogical analysis concerns the separation of the clay fraction, qualitative identification of the components, and quantitative evaluation of the amounts present of each component. Each five–year period at least since 1925 has led to major new discoveries concerning the qualitative nature of soil clay minerals, and it is therefore not surprising that quantitative analysis methods are as yet incompletely developed. Nonetheless, substantial progress over the nearly forty–year period has been sufficient to permit a general outline of criteria and methods for the qualitative and quantitative analysis of soil clays.

Origin of soil clay minerals has frequently been through the weathering of silt and sand size minerals. Interpretation of soil clay mineralogy therefore frequently requires analytical attention to the silt and sand minerals. Moreover, the layer silicate mineral species commonly identified as "clay minerals" frequently occur in the silt, sand, or even gravel size fractions. Methods applicable to analysis of clays are frequently equally applicable for analysis of the coarser fractions. However, quartz and feldspar analysis for coarser fractions, as well as for coarse clay, are conveniently carried out by the pyrosulfate fusion method, and this method is included in this lecture series.

Clay preparation for analysis

The clay fraction of soils and sediments is the fraction containing particles less than 2 microns in equivalent settling velocity diameter, as defined by long custom and agreement among earth scientists. First, we ask ourselves the question, "Why is the clay fraction separated from soil for analysis?" To answer this we recall that many of the most important chemical and physical properties of soil and other earth materials arise in the clay fraction. Also, the soil frequently inherits coarser particles which are related primarily to the composition of the *parent rock* and not to the other factors of soil formation. In contrast, the finer particles of the clay fraction frequently reflect influences of *climate, organisms, topography,* and *time* of soil formation.

Although defining the soil clay fraction as particles less than 2 microns in diameter solves many of the problems, there is one practical problem. Some coarser particles have internal surface, as for example sand or silt–size vermiculite. These crystals give clay–like properties to the soil. The most reactive part of the soil might be termed a "colloidal electrolyte," having high specific reactive surface. Fortunately the major portion of the highly reactive fraction of the soil separates with the clay fraction.

The clay must be separated because methods are not essentially specific enough and sensitive enough to determine small components of clay when mixed with large amounts of other coarser materials in the soil. X–ray diffraction analysis comes close to "separating" the mineralogical species since each crystal reflects its own structure, but does not come "close enough" to provide quantitative analysis without the separation. For example, if one had 20 per cent of clay in the soil of which 15 per cent consisted of kaolinite, then the whole soil would contain only 3 per cent of kaolinite. It is typical that a given clay species may make up less than 5 per cent of the soil. There are exceptional soils in which a given clay species may make up much over 5 per cent—for example, 20 per cent or 50 per cent or more of the soil, but these are not usual. In the X–ray diffraction analysis, coarse fractions in the range of 5 to 20 microns dominate the X–ray diffraction intensity while the fine fractions can have low diffraction intensity. Thus the most reactive and sensitive part of the soil, most characteristic of the soil genesis, is the least reflected in a gross X–ray diffraction analysis of an unseparated soil.

The preparation for clay analysis of a clay species can be likened to the analysis for the element Ca. Calcium determination requires separation of it as CaO to weigh after ignition of CaC_2O_4, or "separation" of the element into ions in gaseous form in a flame emission spectrometer whereby it can give its characteristic emission lines. It is well known how many different elements interfere with the analytical separation and determination of Ca, so it must be "prepared" for analysis too. The ideal solution to the separation problem would be to get each clay mineral species as a separate fraction, to identify it, and to weigh it for the quantitative determination. In practice, only a limited degree of preconcentration of the species is possible.

In contrast to soil structure or fabric analyses, clay preparation for analysis aims at dispersion of the portion of the soil that can be dispersed into the fraction containing particles less than 2 microns in diameter without crystal chemical alteration of the species. The dispersed clay is then separated from the coarser parts of the soil.

A second question is, "What preparation is necessary before separation of the clay?" Normally the clay is aggregated and cemented into larger particles, and to get the characteristic portion of the soil separated from the larger primary particles requires removal of the cements and dispersion of the clay. The nature of the preparation depends upon the nature of the cements which aggregate the clay particles.

Requirements for dispersion

As outlined elsewhere (Jackson, 1956, chapter II), dispersion of soil or clay has specific requirements.

(1) Flocculating effects of soluble salts must be removed by extraction of the soluble material.

(2) The flocculating effects of divalent cations must be removed by substitution of a hydrated monovalent cation. Usually the ion used is Na, but sometimes Li is used.

(3) The cementation effects of organic matter are removed by oxidation with H_2O_2. This reagent, incidentally, removes pyrolusite (MnO_2) which can be determined as dissolved Mn. As a practical matter the free calcium carbonate must be removed to obtain efficient action of hydrogen peroxide. This is frequently accomplished by previously washing the soil with a buffer of pH 5 NaOAc. In special studies wherein the fraction of calcareous material is desired for study,

sodium hypobromite may be employed for an alkaline oxidation of the organic matter. It is rarely desirable to attempt an analysis of the mineral components of a surface soil clay fraction with the organic matter left in.

(4) The cementation action of free iron oxides is normally removed by a reduction–chelation system. The most widely used reductant is sodium dithionite ($Na_2S_2O_4$, sometimes known as sodium hydrosulfite), although H_2S and nascent H_2 have also been employed. To protect the octahedral iron of the layer silicate clay fraction from being removed by the acid conditions required for efficiency of the latter two reagents, the dithionite method can be employed in a neutral medium; in fact, this reagent has a better reduction effect when neutral than when acid (Aguilera and Jackson, 1953). It can be buffered at the neutral pH with a $NaHCO_3$ solution (Mehra and Jackson, 1960). The presence of a chelating agent assists in keeping the iron in solution and preventing the undesirable precipitation of FeS. Sodium citrate is an ideal chelating agent for this purpose. It efficiently chelates iron and aluminum ions, and in addition the citrate molecule is readily oxidized by heating with peroxide, thereby permitting its evaporation as volatile organic molecules rather than requiring a straightforward oxidation to CO_2 as required with many other chelating agents.

(5) The removal of the cementation action caused by colloidal SiO_2 and Al_2O_3 requires some attention. Since the late 1800's a brief boiling time in a dilute solution of Na_2CO_3 has been employed for dissolution of small amounts of colloidal silica and alumina in clays.

Other dispersion methods

Simple dispersion by shaking the soil in water, followed by sedimentation of the heavier particles may be employed for some purposes. This method works well for sediments involving little cementation of layer silicate clay particles. It is effective when minimum disturbance of the sample is essential. One such use is in electron microscopy of clay aggregates (Jackson, 1956, Chapter IX) for which simple sedimentation in water is preferred. However, much of the clay fraction may be sedimented away with the coarse portion of the sample when it is not completely dispersed. It is difficult to get orientation of clay particles by this method when the layer silicates are aggregated with random positioning. Many soils are so aggregated that some silicate clay species are missed entirely by methods which do not remove cements, such as 5 to 60 per cent or more of free iron oxides.

Soils can be dispersed by $NaPO_3$ (sodium metaphosphate or "Calgon") without the removal of $CaCO_3$ and organic matter. The $NaPO_3$ is an efficient dispersion reagent, complexing Ca and furnishing a Na saturated soil, and providing colloidal protective action. Unfortunately phosphate tends to react with clay to form aluminum phosphates (Kittrick and Jackson, 1954, 1955) and thus the method does not conform to the requisite that the mineral species not be altered by the dispersion.

Size separation by sedimentation

The dispersed clay fraction (particles less than 2 microns) can be separated by a 5–cm. sedimentation of coarser particles under gravity for 3.5 hours at 25°C. (Jackson, 1956, p. 114). The process can be hastened by use of a No. 2 International Centrifuge with No. 240 head, with which a 10–cm. sedimentation in a 100–ml. tube requires 2.9 minutes at 25°C. and 750 rpm (Jackson, 1956, p. 128).

Separations at 0.2 micron and 0.08 micron are useful in further segregating the clay species into more nearly monomineralic fractions of fine ($<$0.08 micron), medium (0.2–0.08 micron), and coarse (2–0.2 microns) clay. The narrower size limits permits the weaker X–ray diffraction intensity of the finer fractions to be given proper quantitative weighting, in comparison to the stronger diffraction of the coarser clay fractions.

Frequently, kaolinite and some iron oxide crystals exceed the 2 micron diameter. For this reason the fine silt (5–2 microns) is frequently X–rayed. Particles larger than 5 microns settle 5 cm. in 33 minutes at 25° C., or 10 cm. in 2.9 minutes at 25°C. and 300 rpm in 100–ml. tubes in a No. 2 International Centrifuge (Jackson, 1956, p. 128).

Cation exchange and solvation of clays for X-ray diffraction analysis

The main aim in the preparation of a clay specimen for X–ray diffraction analysis is to place the clay as much as possible in a condition for distinctive X–ray diffraction spacing by each of the clay mineral species. Long experience by many research workers has shown that the expansible clay minerals give characteristic spacings if the cation saturation and solvation are controlled in specific ways (Maegdefrau and Hofmann, 1938; Nagelschmidt, 1944; Favejee, 1939). Saturation with a large organic cation such as B–naphthylamine was suggested by Gieseking (1939) and Hendricks (1941). Clays of alkali soils showed (Kelley, *et al.,* 1940) greater spacings with Ca saturation than with the original ion saturations. Jackson and Hellman (1942) attributed the greater expansion found with calcium to "bridging" between the layers by the hydrated Ca ions which held the layers apart as the suspension medium evaporated. Drying from a nonpolar liquid such as benzene was found to be a distinct aid in the preparation of *random* powder samples, giving strong peaks. Use of a divalent metallic cation (calcium) and controlled solvation (water and benzene) was investigated (Jackson and Hellman, 1942; Hellman, Aldrich, and Jackson, 1943; Aldrich, Hellman, and Jackson, 1944) and found to improve greatly the X–ray diffractogram of clays. As pointed out by Jackson (1956, p. 180):

Solvation with glycerol (MacEwan, 1944; Bradley, 1945) or other polyhydroxy organic liquids increases the basal spacing of Mg or Ca saturated montmorillonite (the montmorillonite–beidellite–saponite–nontronite series) to 18 A and thus clearly differentiates it from the 14 A spacing of vermiculite and chlorite. To apply this 18 A diffraction spacing test to montmorillonite series minerals from soils (Jackson, *et al.,* 1954), the sample must (a) be prepared in the Mg or Ca saturated condition, (b) be dried *only* in the presence of (not prior to the addition of) glycerol in sufficient amount, and (c) be air–dried, at not greater than room temperature. Drying in the absence of sufficient glycerol, drying at temperatures in excess of 25° to 35°C., or drying with K or Na saturation all vitiate the test for montmorillonite series in soils because the spacing may contract to 10 to 14 A which would cause confusion with vermiculite or chlorite 14 A spacings. Control studies for a soil montmorillonite procedure are inadequate if based only on montmorillonite from bentonites.

The soil or other sample will have been segregated into size fractions previous to the cation saturation and mounting steps in X–ray diffraction analysis. The advantages gained by mineral segregation are (a) gain in analytical sensitivity; and (b) provision for chemical weathering interpretations according to the particle size function. As emphasized by Bray (1937) and reemphasized by this laboratory (Jackson, *et al.,* 1954) the occurrence in soils of much montmorillonite series minerals (including beidellite) may be entirely overlooked in the clay fraction (particles less than 2 microns diameter) unless the fine clay fraction of less than 0.08 micron is separated out and subjected to X–ray diffraction analysis by itself. Although montmorillonite may be detected in artificial mixtures in which it constitutes only 1 per cent (MacEwan, 1946), it is not detected in some soil clay samples when present in much larger amounts which are clearly shown by X–ray diffraction when separated out. Concentration of montmorillonite by segregation may involve stripping it from X–amorphous zones (Jackson, *et al.*, 1952). No report of the absence of montmorillonite should be accepted as valid unless the fine size fraction has been separated in the procedure. Finally, it should be pointed out that X–ray diffraction analysis is not diagnostic for montmorillonite or vermiculite series when the 18 and (or) 14 A spacings are interstratified in X–amorphous zones with too limited number of repetitions, in which case interlayer surface measurement and other methods of analysis must be employed for their determination.

Thermal as well as chemical treatments of the specimen are required in preparation of layer silicate clays for diffraction analysis (Brindley, 1955). Saturating different specimens with Mg and K, and different degrees of heating from room temperature to 500° or 600°C. are therefore employed. Data are needed from both parallel orientation and random specimens. Furthermore, factors of small crystals and poor crystallinity must be considered for layer silicate clays. The possible presence in a clay of amorphous materials such as oxides and allophane must be tested for by suitable techniques (detailed below). Such techniques for qualitative and semiquantitative detection of amorphous materials give the counterpart of the X–ray diffraction techniques for crystalline components of clays.

In the past decade, saturation of vermiculite and montmorillonite with Mg by suitable salt washings has been widely adopted. Solvation of the Mg clay with glycerol gives a 14.5 A spacing for vermiculite and a 17.7 or 18 A spacing for montmorillonite. A separate sample is saturated with K for testing collapsibility of expansible layer silicates.

It is important that no Mg salt be added to clay while the clay is in an alkaline condition, since precipitation of $Mg(OH)_2$ results in a change in the interlayer characteristics of the clay of the vermiculite or montmorillonite type. The following procedure is abstracted from Jackson (1956, chapter IV).

Procedure—An aliquot containing 50 mg. of each clay or fine silt fraction is suspended in 50 ml. of 1 *N* NaOAc–HOAc buffer of pH 5 and boiled gently for 5 minutes. Then 10 ml. of 1 *N* $MgCl_2$ (or KCl for the sample to be K saturated) is added. The suspension is thoroughly mixed and centrifuged. If the supernatant liquid is clear it is discarded; if not, 5 ml. of 10 *N* or a saturated solution of the appropriate salt is added to insure flocculation, and centrifugation is repeated. The clay is washed once with 1 *N* $Mg(OAc)_2$ (or KOAc) and twice with 1 *N* $MgCl_2$ (or KCl) to remove acetates which are difficult to wash out with alcohol. The clay is washed once with a small volume (10 ml.) of water and then once in 95 per cent ethanol. Washings with 99 per cent methanol and acetone are used as required to prevent dispersion of the clay. If acetone additions fail to produce a clear supernatant solution after centrifugation, 1 or 2 drops of 1 N chloride solution is added and washing continued.

To solvate the 50 mg. sample of clay, 10 per cent glycerol (by volume in water) is added as follows: 0.2 ml. for fine silt, 0.4 ml. for coarse and medium clay, and 0.9 ml. for fine clay. (Alternatively, Kittrick, 1961, suggests centrifuging the clay down from the 10 per cent glycerol solution, followed by decantation and draining of the tube for 0.5 hour. The imbibed solution controls the quantity of glycerol solution. Dr. C. I. Rich suggests use of 20 per cent glycerol for this technique.) Water is added to the tube to make a free–flowing suspension. A Vortex mixer is employed to obtain a smooth suspension. A pipette with rubber bulb is employed to remove about half the suspension for fine silt or coarse clay and about one third of it for medium or fine clay which is spread on a 2.6 x 4.6 cm. glass slide and allowed to dry. This is the parallel orientation powder specimen (clay particles with flakes oriented in parallel). It should appear moist with glycerol, but should not be wet or glistening. Excess glycerol can be removed (a) by warming the slide on a 110°C. steam plate or in a 110°C. oven, but the process must be monitored carefully to prevent excessive drying, or (b) by drying for 2 or 3 days in a 35°C. vacuum oven in the presence of a free glycerol surface.

Diffractograms of the Mg– and K–saturated specimens are made at room temperature. The K–saturated specimen is subsequently heated to 300°C. for 2 hours on an asbestos pad raised to the center of the furnace, cooled just sufficiently to be handled, and X–rayed; it is then similarly heated to 550°C. for 2 hours and cooled slowly in the furnace to 300°C. as a precaution against warping of the slide. Wax pencil markings on the *back of the slide* can be seen after heating. (Caution: no pencil marks should be placed on the front of the slide since many marking pencils contain crystalline components such as wax or kaolinite.)

Random powder specimens are also employed for X–ray diffraction analysis of soil materials. If iron oxides are present in quantity greater than about 5 per cent as found by analysis of the dithionite extract, they normally can best be determined by X–raying the entire undispersed soil to get at the nature of the iron oxide species. A small sample is powdered in an agate mortar and mounted in a wedge or capillary, the diffractogram being recorded on photographic film. The powder can also be spread on a flat surface for the diffractometer. The clay (7 to 10 mg.

per cm.^{2}) can be dried on 0.0003 inch thickness Al foil (Rich, 1957), mounted at 90° with respect to the X–ray beam, and X–rayed between 55° and 65° 2Θ (Cu radiation) to record the (060) diffraction peaks before and after 550°C. heating to destroy kaolinite–halloysite. The (060) reflection varies between 1.48 to 1.55 A in going from dioctahedral to trioctahedral layer silicates. The (110) peak at 4.45 A is a useful reflection of all layer silicates in a random powder specimen.

X-ray diffractogram interpretation

Identification of each crystalline mineral species or series present in the sample is the purpose of the qualitative interpretation of a diffraction pattern (Jackson, 1956, pp. 210-21). Since the diffraction pattern of each crystal species is a unique sequence of diffraction maxima, like a finger print, the pattern serves the purpose of identification of each separate species present. Ordinarily dependence is placed on the most intense one to three diffraction peaks for qualitative identification.

Several tables of diffraction spacings of crystalline substances, listed by chemical species and indexed according to diffraction intensity, are available (e.g., Brown, 1961). The basal diffraction spacings of the layer silicates in soils, especially of the expanding lattice type, vary within limits, with the nature of the interlayer cations and the solvation procedure employed. The principal diffraction spacings of Mg saturated, glycerol solvated specimens of some commonly occurring minerals in soils, often used as diagnostic peaks, are given in Table 1.

Montmorillonite gives a diagnostic peak at 17.7 to 18 A on Mg saturation and glycerol solvation, and has a fairly intense second order peak at 8.9–9.1 A. The spacing decreases on K–saturation and glycerol solvation, frequently giving a spacing of 14 A. The peak shifts to 10 A and is usually enhanced to give a sharp peak on heating to 300°C. A broad 10 A even after heating indicates (Sawhney and Jackson, 1958; Jackson, 1963b) that the mineral has hydroxy Al or sesquioxide interlayer material countering the layer charge and causing resistance of the mineral to thermal collapse. Such hydroxy Al or sesquioxide groups in montmorillonite and vermiculite provide the inorganic pH dependent cation exchange capacity of clays and soils (Jackson, 1963a; Schwertmann and Jackson, 1963, 1964).

Vermiculites give a diffraction spacing of 14.4 A on Mg saturation and glycerol solvation; the basal spacings may, however, vary slightly if

Table 1. Diagnostic diffraction spacings of layer silicates and other common minerals present in the soil. The basal spacings of layer silicates are for Mg-saturated glycerol-solvated specimens. The most diagnostic peaks are indicated by boldface type.

Mineral	Diffraction spacing (A)
Kaolinite	**7.15**, 3.57, 2.38
Halloysite	10.7–10.0, **7.6***, 3.40
Antigorite and related serpentine minerals	**7.3**, 3.63, 2.42
Mica, Illite	**10.1**, 4.98, 3.32
Attapulgite	**10.2–10.5**, 4.49, 2.62
Vermiculite	**14.4**, 7.18, 4.79, 3.60
Chlorite	**14.3**, **7.18**, **4.79**, 3.59, 2.87, 2.39
Montmorillonite	**17.7**, 8.85, 5.90, 4.33, 3.54
Quartz	3.34, **4.26**, 1.82
Dolomite	**2.88**, 2.19, 1.80
Calcite	**3.04**, 2.29, 2.10
Aragonite	**3.40**, 1.98, 3.27
Anatase	**3.51**, 1.89, 2.38
Rutile	**3.26**, 1.69, 2.49
Gypsum	**7.56**, 3.06, 4.27
Feldspars	**3.18–3.24**
Amphiboles	**8.40–8.48**
Gibbsite	**4.85**, 4.37, 2.39
Goethite	**4.18**, 2.45, 2.70
Hematite	**2.69**, **2.59**, 1.69
Ilmenite	**2.74**, 1.72, 2.54

* Partially dehydrated halloysite.

the saturating cations are different (Brown, 1961). Vermiculites give only a low second order peak at 7.0–7.1 A. True vermiculites give peaks of medium intensity at 4.79 A and 3.60 A. On K saturation and heating to 300°C., vermiculites tend to collapse to 10 A, though many specimens collapse on saturation with K or NH_4 even at room temperature. This divergence in behavior is related to the charge on the layer and the degree of development of hydroxy interlayers. A 14 A peak on Mg saturation and glycerol solvation and a 10 A peak of relatively high intensity on K saturation and heating to 300°C. are determinative criteria for the identification of vermiculite.

Chlorites give a basal diffraction spacing of 14 to 14.3 A. The second order peak at 7.0–7.1 A is usually strong, though the intensity varies with the nature of the interlayer cation coordinating hydroxyls. Specimens containing Fe in the interlayer give an intense second order peak and weak first order peak. Chlorites do not collapse on K saturation and heating to 550°C. On the other hand, the 14 A peak becomes sharper and more intense, while the 7 A peak weakens on heating to 550°C. Chlorites are noted for their heat stability. Chlorites, by the presence of a fairly strong 7 A peak, persistent on K saturation, and heating to 300°C., are differentiated from vermiculites.

Kaolinite has a basal spacing of 7 A coinciding with the second order peak of chlorite; however, kaolinite loses its crystallinity at 550°C. and gives no 14 A peak as does chlorite after heating. True chlorite can therefore be distinguished from kaolinite.

Halloysite of some soils gives a spacing of 10.1–10.7 A, but more often soil halloysite gives a spacing of about 7.6 A on Mg saturation and glycerol solvation. Heating to 400°C. decreases the spacing to 7.2 A (Brindley, 1955).

Intersalation of kaolinite and halloysite with KOAc gives a 14 A spacing (Wada, 1961), and this can be decreased to a diagnostic 11.6 A spacing on washing with 10 N NH_4NO_3 solution (Andrew, *et al.*, 1960). Confirmation and quantitative determination of kaolinite and halloysite are obtained by thermal decomposition–selective dissolution, the procedure for which is detailed in a following section.

Micas or illites give a diffraction peak at 10 A (Grim, *et al.*, 1937) persistent on Mg saturation and glycerol solvation, and are thus distinguished from montmorillonites, vermiculites, and other layer silicates which do not give this spacing when Mg saturated. In soil clays, the 10 A peak of room temperature specimens (and sometimes even after heating) is usually broad and is rarely sharp unless the content of mica is high. This is especially true in fine clay fractions. This is thought to result from a random stacking of mica layers with some expanded minerals. Introduction of expansible layers in the mica structure results in the asymmetry of the (001) peak toward the low angle side, broadening of the (002) peak, and asymmetry of the (003) peak toward the high angle side (Bradley, 1954).

There are reports of the presence of the fibrous clay mineral, attapulgite, in some soils (as reviewed elsewhere, Jackson, 1964b). Attapulgite gives a (110) spacing of 10.2–10.5 A, a (040) spacing of 4.49 A, and a (440) spacing of 2.62 A. Its presence in soils is confirmed by the presence of fibrous crystals by the electron microscope.

Recently another series of clay minerals has been recognized in soils (Brown, 1953; Rich and Obenshain, 1955) which is continuous from chlorite to vermiculite (Klages and White, 1957) and designated as intergradient 2:1–2:2 layer silicates or intergradient montmorillonite–vermiculite–chlorite (Dixon and Jackson, 1959, 1962; Jackson, 1963b). Precipitation of hydroxy Al, hydroxy sesquioxides, and possibly magnesium hydroxide as gibbsite–like (brucite–like) structures in the interlayer spaces of montmorillonite and vermiculite produces structures, the properties of which are intergradient between those of the expansible minerals and those of chlorite (Jackson, 1964b). Thus they give a 14 A spacing on Mg saturation and glycerol solvation, but the structures do not collapse to 14 A completely on K saturation and heating to 300°C. Instead they give broadened peaks of slightly higher diffraction spacing. When the interlayer islands of hydroxy Al or sesquioxides are extracted in citrate, fluoride, or NaOH solutions, the resulting mineral either gives a 14 A spacing (Rich, 1960; Sawhney, 1960) or an 18 A spacing (Tamura, 1957; Dixon and Jackson, 1959).

Another aspect in the identification of clay minerals in soils is the presence of interstratified or mixed–layer minerals in soils. There are two general types of interstratification possible: (a) a regular or ordered alternation of the minerals in a definite sequence, for which the resulting superlattice spacing is additive of the basal spacings of the minerals present and their different orders; and (b) a completely random interstratification in which the layers do not repeat themselves in any regular sequence but are randomly distributed in the complex. A regular interstratification has a definite periodicity and may thus be considered to be more of a well–defined mineral species than random types (MacEwan, Amil, and Brown, 1961). Random mixtures can be either binary, ternary, or quarternary mixtures involving two, three, or four minerals. Binary random mixture can be identified relatively simply as the diffraction spacings follow the Hendricks and Teller (1942) function of intermediate spacings (Brown and MacEwan, 1950, 1951) and diffraction intensities. Ternary and quarternary systems of randomly interstratified layers are difficult to identify; heating treatments usually resolve peaks of intermediate spacings characteristic of the resultant binary system of mixed layers having 10 and 14 A spacings.

Quartz usually gives two fairly strong peaks, at 3.34 and 4.26 A, the former being over twice as intense as the latter. Confusion between the quartz peak and the third order 3.33 A peak of mica is avoided by looking for the 4.26 A peak of quartz in such specimens. In general, more than 10 per cent quartz must be present to give a noticeable 4.26 A peak.

Feldspars give a peak between 3.18 and 3.24 A. Since feldspars in soils are usually mixtures of several species, doublets (two peaks very close to one another) are obtained in many specimens. Identification

of feldspars in soil clays is seldom a problem because of their infre-
quency. When present in abundance (Jackson, *et al.,* 1948; Hseung and
Jackson, 1952; Bydon and Patry, 1961) their diffraction peaks are noted.
Elemental allocation is employed for quantitative estimation.

Gypsum shows a characteristic peak at 7.56 A. As gypsum is fairly
soluble in water, the treatments and several washings involved in the
preparation of the clay for mineralogical analysis usually removes it
from the specimen unless its content is unusually high.

The carbonate minerals, calcite, dolomite, and aragonite, are easily
identified by their characteristic peaks at 3.04, 2.88, and 3.40 A, respectively. Their presence should, however, be checked in specimens
not treated with the acid buffer, as they are destroyed by this treatment.

Amphiboles give peaks in the region 8.40–8.48 A. There are several
reports of their presence in soils.

The accessory minerals, anatase and rutile, give peaks at 3.51 and
3.26 A, respectively. Rutile and anatase are commonly present in soil
clays and probably most of the titanium in soil clays is present in these
mineral forms. As their content in the soil clays is usually of the order
of 1 to 3 per cent, their presence is not easily detected; but treatment of
the soil clay with cold HF and HCl removes most of the silicate minerals
and the titanium mineral peaks become more prominent (Jackson,
1964a).

X–ray diffraction patterns can also be used for the identification of
the dioctahedral or trioctahedral nature of the mineral. The (060)
diffraction spacing of the layer silicates occurs in the range of 1.48 to
1.55 A. The spacing is diagnostic between the dioctahedral and trioctahedral 2:1 layer silicates. The 1:1 layer silicates tend to have a spacing
of about 1.49 A, while the 2:1 layer silicates generally have from 1.50 A
upward. The dioctahedral spacing is approximately 1.50 A and the
(002) spacing is strong; the trioctahedral forms have an (060) of 1.525
to 1.534 A, and the (002) is weak or absent. There are some excep-
tions, particularly glauconite. The chlorites (2:2 layer silicates) tend to
range from 1.53 to 1.56 A. Care, however, must be taken to avoid mis-
taken identification with the quartz line at 1.53 A.

Interlayering of expansible layer silicates in soils by chemical weathering

The following is an abstract of an invitation address given before
the 11th International Conference on Clays and Clay Minerals at

Ottawa, Ontario, August 15, 1962 (Jackson, 1963b) and reviewed for the National Science Foundation seminar. The material relates to the qualitative interpretation of X–ray diffraction patterns.

Mica cleavage along crystallographic cleavages and dislocation planes in the mica faces is seen as a special weathering source of both (a) frayed edge and (b) interstratification or mixed–layering in the equation

$$\text{mica} \rightleftharpoons \text{illite} \rightleftharpoons \text{vermiculite} \rightleftharpoons \text{montmorillonite}$$

of Jackson and others (1952). The tendency in weathered layer silicates for surface constancy (K unit cell surface plus sorption surface = constant) (Mehra and Jackson, 1959a) applies to both (a) and (b) and suggests that during weathering K occupies its full mica interlayer concentration until cleavage releases the K and simultaneously yields glycol adsorption surface. Cores of unweathered mica are seen as holding (hkl) orientation and juxtaposition of the K cavities in the frayed edge vermiculite and montmorillonite, thus accounting for exchangeable K ion preference (Schwertmann, 1962) by the species of these two minerals weathered from micas as compared to the species of these minerals derived by weathering of minerals other than layer silicates.

Intercalation of the expanded 2:1 layer silicates with hydroxy alumina interlayers appears to be a characteristic function of chemical weathering in soils, with the formation of 2:1–2:2 intergrades not only of 14 A spacing but also of swelling 18 A types that give broadened 10 A peaks and, if the interlayers are extensive, small 11–12, 14, 18 A and higher spacing peaks (along with the 10 A peak) at 550°C. Interlayer precipitates appear to be characteristic of soil clays, contrasting with "pure" minerals of deposits developed in less "open" environments than those of soils. The "2:2 lattice building" phenomenon in expansible 2:1 layer silicates relates to layer charge density and crystal size.

Intergradient 2:1–2:2 layer silicate minerals develop in soil clays by lattice building or precipitation of hydroxy aluminum attached on one interlayer surface of montmorillonite (18 A swelling intergrade) or on two interlayer surfaces of vermiculite (14 A intergrade). The 18 A intergrade appears to form more frequently in alkaline soils in which montmorillonite (about 3.5 M interlayer space) is more stable, while the 14 A intergrades appear most frequently in acid soils in which the reactions

$$\text{mica} \rightleftharpoons \text{vermiculite} \rightleftharpoons 14 \text{ A intergrade}$$

are favored by relatively rapid decomposition of any montmorillonite formed (higher specific surface of edges), with release of aluminum for interlayer "lattice building" in the more highly charged (about 10 M interlayer space) and larger vermiculite particles forming from mica. This disposition of aluminum tends to preclude free $Al(OH)_3$ formation in soils so long as there are actively weathering 2:1 layer silicates present in soils ("antigibbsite effect"). Accumulation of alumina (possibly with some iron, magnesium, and allophane) as interlayers in 2:1 minerals of soils is seen as a genetic stage in 2:2 → 1:1 weathering sequence through which kaolinite and halloysite develop in soils. Weathering proceeds by the reactions:

$$14 \text{ A intergrade} \rightleftharpoons \text{Al–chlorite} \rightleftharpoons \text{kaolin}$$

Free gibbsite can appear through weathering when leaching rates are rapid and the supply of silica is limited. The silicate layers of montmorillonite and vermiculite may serve sterically (Jackson, 1960) as a template for nucleating gibbsite–like crystal units during interlayer polymerization (Jackson, 1963a). The negative surfaces sorb the positive hydroxy ion units. The occurrence of gibbsite in a mixture with expansible layer silicates could tend to indicate geomorphic erosion and depositional mixing (Erhart, 1956) of materials weathered in different sites. Very rapid weathering of mica to kaolinite appears to be able to produce gibbsite concurrently from feldspar. Fluctuations of the pH of the soil solution system back and forth across the isoelectric pH 4.8 (Jackson, 1963a) of crystalline gibbsite should nucleate a separate crystalline gibbsite phase as follows: templated (+) aluminum hydroxide units sorbed on clay below pH 4.8 would become negative above pH 4.8 and thus be repelled and released, an "anti–antigibbsite effect." Intense pedogeochemical leaching of the sorbed (+) units would remove soluble anions and accelerate crystal growth of the released gibbsite phase.

The various weathering reactions and indexes are summarized (Jackson, 1963b, 1964b) in the equation

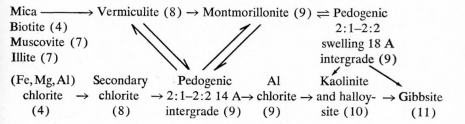

in which the numbers in parenthesis represent weathering indexes (Jackson, *et al.,* 1948).

Aluminum bonding in soils: a unifying principle of soil science

The following is an abstract of a lecture (Jackson, 1963a) on the above topic concerning the broader aspects of soil chemistry, presented before the general assembly of the Soil Science Society of America, Aug. 20, 1962, at Cornell University, Ithaca, N. Y., at the invitation of the President of the S.S.S.A., and reviewed for the N.S.F. seminar.

Clays are interrelated to a broad range of properties of soils. The high specific surface of clay mineral grains and the electrostatic charges of their surfaces permit the loose attachment of ions and this retards leaching. The ion adsorption property makes it probable that clays conditioned the evolutionary origin and development of life forms on earth and certainly clays were of key importance to the original biotic invasion of the land from the sea. Clays thus served *to introduce* the biotic factor of soil formation (Jackson, 1964b). The following is quoted from Jackson (1963a):

Aluminum bonding in soils has been briefly examined as related to acid strength of the inorganic cation exchangers of soils, to chemical weathering and colloid composition, to soil acidity and liming, to anion retention by soils, to soil aggregation, and to the major geomorphic cycle of the earth and other planets.

[*Aluminum bonding in relation to cation exchange of soil clays:*]

The aluminum ion bonds through oxygen to form a variety of functional groups underlying diverse properties of soils. One aluminum–bond functional group provides the cation exchange site of soil layer silicate clays. Pauling's m-rule of acid strength for oxy–acids, $(HO)_nO_mC$, applied to the 2:1 layer silicate clay formula of beidellite, considering all structural cations, yields $m = 1.6$, characteristic of a medium to strong acid strength (on an m–scale: $1 =$ weak; $2 =$ strong). The distance of 7 to 11 A apart (Jackson, 1960, 1963b) for the individual exchange valence charges may account for the "monovalent" character of the clay acid (Kelley, 1948, p. 46). The valence sites of these colloidal electrolytes are sufficiently well separated to act independently.

In the discussion, hydronium clay is used in preference to H clay; the latter has commonly been used, presumably because of the high mobility of $OH_3{}^+$ compared to that of the usual metallic cations the size of $OH_3{}^+$. The anomalously high conductance of hydronium and hydroxyl in aqueous solution is attributed to transfer of protons along the H bond by means of relatively fast quantum-mechanical tunneling under the activation energy maximum between two potential energy minima (reviewed by Pimentel and McClellan, 1960, pp. 31 and 253).

The predominance of aluminum saturation in electrodialyzed clays (Low, 1955; Aldrich and Buchanan, 1958) accounts for the earlier conclusion (Bradfield, 1923) that clay acids were weak acids, since the alumino-hexahydronium monomeric cation, $Al\ (-OH_2)_6{}^{3+}$, as discussed earlier (Jackson, 1960), is itself indeed a weak acid having a pk_1 value of 5, compared to HOAc of pk value 4.7, the acid to which Bradfield compared the soil acid.

The fact that monomeric aluminohexahydronium is simultaneously both an acid (dissociator of protons) and a cation capable of cation exchange reactions in soils (discussed in a later section) should not be allowed to confuse the issue. In older parlance, the ion was called a "hexahydrate" involving Werner "water" or "acquo groups," but is more properly viewed as substituted hydronium (an Al bond substituted for one H) in $OH_3{}^+$ (Jackson, 1960), because the pk_1 of H_2O is 14 while the pk_1 for the $(-OH_2)_6$ of aluminohexahydronium is 5.

According to Pauling's Rule 1 (1958, p. 453) the ratio of $pk_1:pk_2:pk_3$ of a polyfunctional acid such as H_3PO_4 is as 1:5:10. Thus the aluminohexahydronium cation of pk_1 value 5 should approximate $pk_2 = 10$. The solubility product of $Al(OH)_3$, k_1 of $Al(OH_2)_6{}^{3+}$, and the Pauling k_1/k_2 ratio of 10^5, applied to calculate concentrations of aluminohydronium monomeric cation species of valence of 3, 2, and 1, show the concentration of divalent, $Al(OH)(OH_2)_5{}^{2+}$, monovalent $Al(OH)_2(OH_2)_4{}^+$, monomers to be negligible compared to that of the trivalent monomer. The polymeric ions of the corresponding Al/OH ratios are polyvalent and strongly sorbed.

[*Aluminum in soil acidity:*]

It seems feasible to propose an aluminohydronium–hydroxyl edge pair $(-OH_2 \ldots OH)$ to balance the broken edge charges ($0.5-$ per edge hydroxyl and $0.5+$ per edge aluminohydronium) is not only silicate layers but also in gibbsite and interlayer aluminum. Dissociation of a proton from the edge hydronium $(Al-OH_2{}^{0.5+})$ functional group appears to be more feasible as a source of pH–dependent cation–exchange capacity (CEC) of soils than H dissociation from edge hydroxyl (Schofield, 1939). [The origin of pH dependent charge from hydroxy aluminum groups on surfaces of layer silicate clays has since been completely verified (Schwertmann and Jackson, 1963, 1964; Volk and Jackson, 1964)]. Soil acidity has been defined as a soil system's proton–yielding capacity in going from a given state to a reference state (Jackson, 1958). Soil acidity and its neutralization may be grouped according to the acid strength of its proton–retaining site: (I) exchangeable OH_3^+ (and free strong acids), (II) exchangeable $Al(-OH_2)_6^{3+}$, (III) polyaluminohydronium edge $OH_2^{0.5+}$ (and humus carboxyl), (IV) polyaluminohydronium edge pairs $OH_2^{0.5+}$ ... $OH^{0.5-}$ (and humus phenolic groups), and (V) hydroxyl hydrogen of gibbsite, silicic acid and humus.

Fundamentally, all five acidity groups depend on *proton dissociation,* that is "exchangeable H," but differ *only* in the acid strength of the functional group. The group I acidity is of minor importance in agricultural practice except in local problem areas involving pyrite and S oxidation. It is of theoretical interest in the laboratory (as explained in the opening section). Only groups II and III are of great concern in soil acidity and agricultural liming practice. Group IV is concerned in "supersaturation" of the CEC (Ca, Mg–humate) and in "hydrolytic acidity" (Na–soil + $H_2O \longrightarrow H$–soil + $NaOH$). The latter and a similar role of Group V has an important relationship to exchangeable Mg development in alkaline soils (Barshad, 1960). Acidity groups I and V provide the ultimate buffering of soils, providing the lower and upper pH limit through aluminosilicate mineral decomposition.

The aluminohexahydronium cation (Group II) is truly soluble (exchangeable) in KCl. This cation's dual role in both being a proton–exchanger (a pH–dependent site itself) and at the same time being exchangeable in KCl underlies the historical vascillation in nomenclature between "exchangeable H" and "exchangeable Al" of soil acidity ("the soil acidity merry–go–round" reviewed by Jenny, 1961).

The proton donors of still weaker acid (pH dependent) sources of exchangeable H (Group III) also receive attention in liming practice. The use of a salt of strong acid, a salt such as KCl, largely excludes the replacement of exchangeable hydrogen from the pH–dependent charge. For this reason, it was stated "salts of a strong acid cannot be used to displace exchangeable hydrogen [quantitatively] because they do not remove ('accept') the H from the solution" (Jackson, 1958, p. 73). Buffered solutions such as $Ba(OAc)_2$, Ba triethanolamine, NH_4OAc, and $Ca(OAc)_2$ have been widely employed. For example, Schachtschabel in Germany uses $Ca(OAc)_2$ (Schwertmann, 1961).

[*Aluminum in soil–plant relations:*]

The aluminum toxicity of soil acidity may involve aluminum bonding and solubility product relations at the soil–root interface and in solutions in soil and sap. Retention by soils of anions such as phosphate and sulfate is closely related to aluminum bonding of these anions (OH replacement). Some aspects of soil aggregate structure involve hydroxy aluminum bonding; loss of aggregates follows intensive cheluviation in the A_2 horizon. Aluminum bonding to oxygen and through oxygen to hydrogen in a real sense supplies a unifying principle for understanding many properties of the soil system, much as hydrogen bonding has served to unify understanding of many properties of water and of aqueous organic systems including living matter.

[*Aluminum bonding in time and space:*]

Intense scientific interest today is focused on *time* and *space,* and soil scientists share in this interest. Aluminum bonding in soils has been examined in the above discussion as it relates to several important properties of the *pedon* (U.S. Soil Survey Staff, 1960), the unit of soil in *space,* and as it influences *pedogeochemical weathering reactions* which occur as a function of *time* (Polynov, 1937; Jenny, 1941; Jackson, *et al.,* 1948; Jackson and Sherman, 1953).

Elements in outer space are similar to those on earth and presumably so are the compounds and *pedocosmochemical* reactions. The time that has elapsed since the last time the moon was heated to high (fusion) temperature by collisions appears from radiosotope dating of meteorites to be 4.5 aeons (billions of years), according to Urey (1960). The dark areas or mares of the moon are probably solidified lava and thus involve tetrahedral aluminum. The time so dated corresponds to the age of primordial earth and therefore the moon (may be) a reference point of zero time in the cycle of rock weathering and soil formation on earth in an atmosphere and hydrosphere containing water. Water (on earth) permitted hydrolysis of the primordial Al–O bond to form aluminohexahydronium (Jackson, 1960) which in turn was polymerized into layered hydroxide (Al-OH bonded) weathering products such as layer silicate clays and gibbsite. While our planet, earth, is believed to have a finite life of only a few tens of aeons, soil scientists may well participate with other space scientists in study of the problems of *pedocosmology.*

Specific surface measurement by glycerol sorption

The rate and degree of completion of many soil chemical reactions depend on the specific surface area of the reactants such as layer silicate clays and amorphous materials. Such important soil properties as water retention and cation exchange capacity have been shown to be highly correlated with the surface area exposed. Specific surface area is inversely proportional to particle size. Thus the surface area of soils differs with particle size distribution as well as with other properties such as type and amount of clay mineral and type and amount of organic matter.

Because of their fine particle size, clays have a greater amount of surface than the other size fractions of soils. The specific surface (square meters of surface area per gram) differs with type of clay mineral. Non–swelling clays such as kaolinite and mica have only an external surface, while swelling clays such as montmorillonite and vermiculite have an internal surface between the expanded layers. It appears that the interlayer surface property of expanding layer silicates should be used for their quantitative determination. Mineral surfaces adsorb polar molecules from the gaseous and liquid state. Clay–water complexes are examples of such phenomena. Polar organic molecules having hydroxyl groups have been shown to complex with minerals in a similar manner (Bradley, 1945; MacEwan, 1944, 1948). Montmorillonite adsorbs a duo–interlayer of glycerol between its expanded layers to give a c–spacing of 17.7 A, while vermiculite adsorbs only a mono–interlayer to give a c–spacing of 14 A. This difference between the montmorillonite–glycerol and the vermiculite–glycerol complexes is the basis for differentiation of the two minerals by X–ray diffraction.

However, X–ray diffraction gives only qualitative and semiquantitative data on clay minerals. Quantitative measurement of glycerol sorption to determine the interlayer surface of expanding minerals and hence the amount of such minerals has been employed to determine the contribution of expanding minerals in a mixture (Vanden Heuvel and Jackson, 1953; Diamond and Kinter, 1958; Mehra and Jackson, 1959a, 1959b; Milford and Jackson, 1962).

Other methods

Nitrogen gas adsorption was used for specific surface measurement by Brunauer, et al. (1938), who developed an equation to treat Van der Waals's gas adsorption by solids at low temperature. Emmett, et al. (1938), applied the method to specific surface measurement of soils and soil colloids. Specific surface values of 11 and 18 m^2 per gram for pure montmorillonite were obtained by Makower, et al. (1938), from whose low results Nelson and Hendricks (1943) concluded that the gas was adsorbed only on the external surfaces and suggested that the evacuation of the samples at low temperature caused the removal of interplanar water resulting in a collapse of the layers, thus preventing the ingress of nitrogen onto the interlayer surfaces. Use of molecules such as CO_2, O_2, Ar, and CH_4 also proved unsatisfactory for the measurement of interlayer surface of expanding layer silicates.

Harkins and Jura (1944) and Harkins (1952) described a method for determination of surface area of solids by measuring heat of immersion. The method involves the measurement of the energy change during immersional wetting of solids which are in equilibrium with the vapor of the liquid in which they are to be immersed. The free energy of the adsorbed film is equal to that of the liquid so that the energy lost on immersion is completely attributable to the loss of surface. This method works only for nonporous solids and is therefore not applicable to soils or soil colloids which contain minerals with interstices (zeolites, attapulgite) or interlayer spaces (montmorillonite, vermiculite).

The interlayer surface of montmorillonite has been determined by saturation with ethylene glycol and removal of the excess in vacuum (Dyal and Hendricks, 1950). Bower and Gschwend (1952) advocated removal of excess ethylene glycol by equilibration over $CaCl_2$. Walker (1950) found that ethylene glycol gave a limited penetration into Mg–vermiculite. The ethylene glycol method for specific surface determination is described by Mortland and Kemper (1964).

Glycerol sorption methods

Glycerol was shown to be adsorbed internally by expanding layer silicates when dried from aqueous solutions (MacEwan, 1944). Solvation of clay minerals from a ternary solution, followed by extraction of the glycerol with methanol and determination of the adsorbed glycerol by a periodate oxidation, was proposed as a method for surface area determination of soil minerals (Vanden Heuvel and Jackson, 1953). The accuracy and reproducibility of the method was poor because of adsorption of more than two layers of glycerol by montmorillonite. The results did, however, indicate that the sorption of glycerol quantitatively by soil minerals could be adapted to surface area determination.

Kinter and Diamond (1958) proposed a method in which glycerol was adsorbed from aqueous solution and heat was applied in a 110°C. opendraft oven with a free glycerol surface to remove excess glycerol. The samples were weighed at intervals until equilibrium was reached.

The method of Kinter and Diamond was modified by Mehra and Jackson (1959a), who used hydrogen saturated samples and allowed them to equilibrate while covered with a perforated aluminum cover in the oven. An equilibrium weight was obtained both with the cover on and off, because some montmorillonite and halloysite retained a duo–interlayer of glycerol in the covered dish. Montmorillonite and vermiculite retained a mono–interlayer of glycerol under these conditions. Mehra and Jackson (1959b) succeeded in forming a duo–interlayer of glycerol in montmorillonite by placing samples soaked in glycerol in a vacuum oven at 35°C. in the presence of a free glycerol surface until equilibrium was attained. Vermiculite adsorbs only a mono–interlayer under these conditions. Using both methods, the amounts of montmorillonite and vermiculite may be determined.

Milford and Jackson (1962) suggested modifications of the Mehra and Jackson (1959b) method. A 130°C. vacuum oven was employed to obtain a mono–interlayer in both vermiculite and montmorillonite. Magnesium saturation was used in preference to hydrogen saturation because hydrogen saturation liberates aluminum from the clay and causes polymerization of the glycerol molecule in montmorillonite interlayer spaces when a sample is heated to a high temperature in an evacuated atmosphere. Removal of amorphous and poorly crystalline material by the NaOH treatment of Hashimoto and Jackson (1960) was suggested for medium and fine clay fractions.

The lower than theoretical glycerol sorption by vermiculite in a vacuum oven at 110°C. was attributed to water of hydration of exchangeable Mg^{2+} in the sample of vermiculite dried at 110°C. (Milford and Jackson, in manuscript). Assuming that the cation exchange capacity of vermiculite is 150 meq. per 100 gm. and that each Mg^{2+} ion retains 3 molecules of water at 100°C., the amount of water held by the sample can be calculated and the error arising from retention of water and replacement of water by glycerol can be evaluated. When such corrections were applied to a number of standard samples the results obtained were found to be more compatible with the other mineralogical data.

Procedure

Vr mono–interlayer and Mt duo–interlayer—The following procedure is that of Mehra and Jackson (1959b) with the cation saturation modification of Milford and Jackson (1962).

A suspension containing approximately 100 mg. of mineral colloid which has been treated with H_2O_2 to remove organic matter, with dithionite–citrate–bicarbonate to remove iron oxides, and with NaOH to remove amorphous and poorly crystalline material, is placed in a 15–ml. centrifuge tube, boiled in NaOAc buffer of pH 5, and magnesium saturated by washing with $MgCl_2$ and MgOAc. It is washed free of salt and transferred to tared aluminum foil dishes which have been passivated by evaporation when half–filled with distilled water. The sample is dried to constant weight at 110°C. and the weight is recorded to 0.1 mg.

Five ml. of 2 per cent glycerol solution is added to the dish. The samples are covered and allowed to stand overnight to insure complete saturation of the clay. Excess water is removed by placing the samples on a steam plate until only a small amount of liquid remains.

The sample is then placed in a vacuum oven at 35°C. until equilibrium is attained. The equilibrium point is determined by obtaining constant weight to 0.1 mg. The weight of glycerol retained (X) by the sample is due to monolayer of glycerol on external surfaces, a mono–interlayer of glycerol in vermiculite and a duo–interlayer of glycerol in montmorillonite.

Mono–Interlayer for Vr and Mt—The samples are transferred to a 130°C. vacuum oven containing a glycerol condensation surface at 100°C. (Milford and Jackson, 1962) and heated to a constant weight, the weight being recorded to 0.1 mg. The loss in weight ($Z = X - Y$) is equal to the loss of one interlayer of glycerol from montmorillonite, and the weight of glycerol retained (Y) is attributable to a monolayer of glycerol on all external surfaces and a mono–interlayer in vermiculite and montmorillonite.

Calculation of results

The external surface of the particles is calculated assuming that the particles are plate shaped and have an average width 10 times their average thickness. The percentage glycerol necessary to give a monolayer coverage of external surface is calculated on the basis of a 4.15 A thick layer. These values are presented in Table 2.

Montmorillonite and vermiculite percentages are determined as follows:

$$
\begin{array}{ccccc}
\text{Per cent interlayer} & & \text{Per cent monolayer} & & \text{Per cent monolayer} \\
\text{glycerol} & = & \text{glycerol (Y)} & - & \text{external surface} \quad (1) \\
& & & & \text{glycerol}
\end{array}
$$

$$\frac{\text{Specific interlayer}}{\text{surface, m}^2/\text{gm.}} = \frac{\text{Per cent interlayer}}{\text{glycerol}} \times 38.2 \tag{2}$$

$$\frac{\text{Specific planar}}{\text{surface, m}^2/\text{gm.}} = \frac{\text{Specific interlayer}}{\text{surface}} + \frac{5}{6} \times \frac{\text{External}}{\text{surface}} \tag{3}$$

on the basis that platy particles $\frac{1}{10}$ as thick as broad have $\frac{1}{6}$ edge surface of the total external surface.

Aluminous montmorillonite and vermiculite have a unit cell weight of 720 and a planar surface of 808 m²/g. Soil clays frequently have 773 m² of planar surface per gram (Mehra and Jackson, 1959a).

$$\frac{\text{Per cent montmorillonite}}{+ \text{ vermiculite}} = \frac{\text{Planar surface, m}^2/\text{gm.} \times 100}{773} \tag{4}$$

$$\begin{array}{l}\text{Per cent glycerol sorbed} \\ \text{in second interlayer of} \\ \text{montmorillonite (Z)}\end{array} = \begin{array}{c}\text{Per cent glycerol} \\ \text{sorbed at 35°C.} \\ \text{(X)}\end{array} - \begin{array}{c}\text{Per cent glycerol} \\ \text{sorbed at 130°C.} \\ \text{(Y)}\end{array} \tag{5}$$

$$\begin{array}{l}\text{Planar surface attributable} \\ \text{to montmorillonite, m}^2/\text{gm.}\end{array} = 38.2 \times (Z) + \frac{5}{6} \times \begin{array}{c}\text{External} \\ \text{specific} \\ \text{surface}\end{array} \tag{6}$$

$$\begin{array}{l}\text{Per cent} \\ \text{montmorillonite}\end{array} = \frac{\text{Montmorillonite planar surface, m}^2/\text{gm.} \times 100}{773} \tag{7}$$

Table 2. Calculated specific surface values for various size fractions of expansible layer silicates (Jackson, 1956, p. 332).

| Equivalent spherical diameter, μ | Specific surface, m²/gm. | | | | Per cent glycerol for external surface monolayer |
	Total external	Edge	Total	Interlayer	
5 –2	1.14	0.19	808.2	807	0.06
2 –0.2	3.64	0.61	808.6	805	0.19
0.2–0.08	28.6	4.76	812.8	784	1.5
<0.08	80.2	13.36	821.4	741	4.4

Accuracy

The calculated external surface may introduce an error. Amorphous materials often have high external surface and their presence may result in spuriously high apparent contents of expanding minerals. Interlayer precipitates in expanding minerals may lower the interlayer surface, resulting in low values for expanding minerals. The density of a sorbed layer of glycerol may differ considerably from that of liquid glycerol.

Generally the method gives good results for expansible mineral fractions obtained by grinding large mineral grains.

The fact that vermiculite of clay size appears to adsorb less than a mono–interlayer of glycerol in the vacuum oven at 130°C. may be attributable to the possible retention of interlayer water at 110°C. which is expelled on glycerol solvation. This factor needs further evaluation.

When applied to soil mineral fractions the method gives results which comply with other mineralogical data for total expanding minerals (Equation 4). However, in medium and fine clay fractions the results obtained for montmorillonite are generally too high and are commonly greater than the value for expanding minerals. Capillary condensation may be a possible explanation for this anomaly.

Quartz, feldspar, and mica determinations by selective dissolution analysis

Quartz, feldspars, and mica are the dominant minerals in the earth's crust. Feldspars constitute almost 60 per cent of the minerals in igneous rocks, whereas quartz, because of its resistance to weathering, is the dominant mineral in sedimentary rocks. Mica, though less common than quartz and feldspar, often is a major component of acid igneous rocks and of sedimentary rocks.

The resistance of coarser particles of quartz to chemical weathering results in a high frequency distribution of quartz in soils. Feldspars, though they weather more readily than quartz, also are common soil minerals. The difference in weathering susceptibility between quartz and feldspar expressed as quartz/feldspar ratio is employed as an index of the degree of weathering of soils. Quartz and feldspars act as diluents for the more chemically active layer silicate minerals of soils. The major plant nutrient, potassium, occurs primarily in mica and feldspars in soils, and its availability to plants is determined by the mineral form in which it is present. Quartz is almost universally present in clay materials, and its determination must be considered (Brindley, 1961, p. 505). Feldspars are common in clay fractions and may be a major part of some samples (Brown, 1961, p. 470). Quantitative determinations of quartz, feldspars, and mica in soils and clays are therefore frequently required.

Other methods

Qualitative and semiquantitative determination of minerals by X–ray diffraction has long been employed (Clark and Reynolds, 1936). The method as usually employed involves comparing the intensity of characteristic reflections of a mineral with the intensity of the same reflections of samples of the mineral of known concentration. Limitations of the method include:

a) Particle size affects diffraction intensity (Jackson, 1956, p. 233) and should be approximately 1 micron for quartz, feldspar, and mica determination using CuKα radiation to obtain optimum results (Brindley, 1961).

b) Variations in crystallinity markedly alter the diffraction intensity of minerals (Pollack, *et al.,* 1954; Nagelschmidt, 1956). Pollack, *et al.* (1954), found that quartz from different sources gave intensities which differed by a factor of at least 2.

c) The presence of amorphous coatings on mineral grains greatly alters the diffraction intensity.

d) Variations in chemical composition cause variations in diffraction intensity.

e) The number of standard samples necessary in the case of multi–component mixtures is very great.

Sand and coarse silt fractions of quartz, feldspar, and mica may be determined by grain counts using the petrographic microscope. The method is tedious and cannot be applied to very small particles or to particles which, because of weathering or other chemical treatment, have severely etched surfaces. It therefore has a limited application in the case of soil mineral fractions.

Infrared absorption has been applied to mineral estimation (Lyon, *et al.,* 1959; Tuddenham and Lyon, 1960). The sample is placed in KBr discs at a concentration of ¼ per cent of sample and its absorption spectrum determined. The determined values varied from 70 to 140 per cent (Lyon, *et al.,* 1959) of the amounts present.

The inversion of quartz from alpha to beta form at 573°C. is accompanied by an energy change of 4.5 calories per gram. This energy change has been employed in quartz determination by the differential thermal method (Trombe, 1938; Grim, 1953; Grimshaw, 1953; Grimshaw and Robert, 1957; Sysoeva, 1958). Careful design of apparatus and control of technique is required and pyrometric equipment of high sensitivity is necessary (Grimshaw and Roberts, 1957) to record the small temperature change (about 3°C. per 1 gram quartz). Noncrystalline silica has been found to interfere with the determination (Berkelhamer, 1944).

Selective dissolution methods

Hot concentrated inorganic acids decompose many aluminosilicates. The amorphous silica released from aluminosilicates forms a gelatinous precipitate in the presence of the acid, which in the past was often separated from the nongelatinous material by its passage through a filter as a sol and solution. More recently the gelatinous silica is separated by dissolution in dilute alkali solution. Quartz remains relatively unattacked by such treatments and many methods for its determination are based on its relative insolubility in such acid–alkali treatments. The quartz is determined in the residue on the basis of (a) the weight of SiO_2 lost from the residue on volatilization by HF, or (b) the difference between the original total SiO_2 and the SiO_2 dissolved in NaOH. Feldspars constitute the most frequently occurring nonquartz mineral remaining in significant amounts in the residue.

The hot inorganic acids used for decomposition of aluminosilicates include a tri–acid mixture of concentrated hydrochloric, sulfuric, and nitric acids in the proportion 2:4:1 by volume (Hardy and Follett–Smith, 1931); phosphoric acid (Durkan, 1946; Talvitie, 1951; Jophcott and Wall, 1955); perchloric acid (Corey, 1952; Medicus, 1955; Jackson, 1956); 9 N H_2SO_4 (Shaw, 1934; Nagelschmidt, 1956); fluosilicic acid (Knopf, 1933); fluoboric acid (Line and Aradine, 1937); concentrated HCl followed by boiling in a solution of Na_2S and digestion in 6 N HCl–HNO₃ (Shchekaturina and Petrashen, 1958). The tri–acid mixture of HCl–HNO₃–H_2SO_4 has greater effectiveness than $HClO_4$ in decomposing layer silicates, particularly unheated kaolinite. Anorthoclase resists decomposition during digestion in either acid. Use of hot $HClO_4$ in the later stages of an acid digestion procedure has the advantage that the acid–released silica is quantitatively dehydrated; the metallic cations can be washed out with HCl, and the silicon from the aluminosilicates can be dissolved in dilute NaOH and determined quantitatively by the molybdosilicic acid method. Phosphoric acid interferes with molybdosilicate colorimetry. Talvitie (1951) found that the minerals albite, pyrophylite, sillimanite, kyanite, tourmaline, beryl, and topaz resist decomposition in H_3PO_4. Appreciable dissolution of quartz in H_3PO_4 was reported by Jophcott and Wall (1955). Both fluosilicic acid and fluoboric acid decompose, liberating HF which attacks quartz (Florentin and Heros, 1947).

A method for quantitative separation of potassium feldspars from potassium mica was proposed by Reynolds and Lessing (1962). It involves heating a sample at 825°C. for 2 hours, cooling, and boiling in concentrated HCl for 2 hours. The treatment removes most of the potassium from micas while the potassium content of feldspars remains unaffected. The method is applicable only to the fraction between 10 and 2 microns.

Pyrosulphate fusion has long been employed for the decomposition of aluminosilicate minerals (Smith, 1865). Smith suggested the use of sodium pyrosulphate in preference to potassium pyrosulphate which had previously been more commonly employed. Bisulphate is commonly used since it decomposes according to the reaction.

$$2KHSO_4 \rightarrow K_2S_2O_7 + H_2O$$

to form pyrosulphate. Water loss during the reaction causes considerable spattering. On further heating pyrosulphate decomposes in a quiet fusion liberating acid fumes thus:

$$K_2S_2O_7 \rightarrow K_2SO_4 + SO_3$$

The fusion serves as a high temperature acid treatment, dehydroxylating kaolinite and removing octahedral cations from 2:1 layer silicates.

Trostel and Wynne (1940) used this fusion for quartz determination in refractory clays. A sample was fused to bright red heat with potassium pyrosulphate, the melt was cooled, and the cake was dissolved in 150 to 200 ml. of hot water. Twelve gm. of sodium hydroxide was added and the suspension was digested for one half hour at 85° to 90°C. The undissolved quartz was filtered off and determined by difference after HF treatment. In an evaluation of quartz determination methods, Florentin and Heros (1947) found this method was the most satisfactory. The method was, however, applied only to rather coarse–textured refractory clays which contained little or no feldspars. Kiely and Jackson* using

* P. V. Kiely and M. L. Jackson, "Quantitative Determination of Quartz," Research Report No. 6, Feb. 22, 1962 and "Quartz Determination," Research Report No. 7, March 15, 1962, Department of Soil Science, University of Wisconsin.

the above method found that 11 per cent of the 2–0.2μ fraction of quartz was dissolved and that feldspars were only partly dissolved in the coarser fractions. Also filtration was found to be unsatisfactory in the case of fine fractions because of blocking of the filter and partially passing through the filter. Modifications were introduced to (1) reduce quartz dissolution, (2) minimize feldspar dissolution, and (3) overcome the filtration problem. The procedure adopted is given in the following.

Procedure

The sample should be a powder, not coarse aggregates. In preparation, a clay sample is washed successively with 0.05 N HCl, acetone, and benzene, by centrifugation. The clay is dried in a centrifuge tube, and then powdered with a spatula and a rubber–tipped rod. Silt or fine sand fractions may be used directly. Rock, gravel, or coarse sand samples are ground in an agate mortar, so that the powder passes a 60–mesh (per inch) sieve.

A 0.2-g. sample of powdered clay, silt, or sand fraction (dried at 105°C.) is weighed and transferred into a 50–ml. vitreous silica crucible. Approximately 15 gm. of $K_2S_2O_7$ powder is mixed with the sample by means of a glass rod. With the crucible in a fume hood, the $K_2S_2O_7$ is fused with a Meker burner, using a low flame at first until vigorous bubbling ceases, and thereafter using the full flame. With some samples it is advisable to cover the crucible to avoid loss by spattering. Much SO_3 will be evolved. The fusion is complete when some K_2SO_4 crystals float on the surface of the $K_2S_2O_7$ melt while in the full heat. It should *not* go to complete crystallization of the melt. The crucible is grasped with tongs, rotated so as to spread the melt on the crucible sides as the melt solidifies, and then allowed to cool.

A little 3 N HCl is added to the crucible, and the cake is carefully transferred to a 150–ml. beaker with the aid of a rubber–tipped rod. The fusion cake is then slaked in about 50 ml. of 3 N HCl, and the solutions heated just to boiling. When the fusion cake has disintegrated, the resulting suspension is transferred to a 70–ml. pointed centrifuge tube. The tube is centrifuged at 1800 rpm. for 4 minutes or longer if necessary to make the supernatant liquid clear. The supernatant solution is decanted and discarded. The crucible is washed again with 3 N HCl to complete the transfer of the residue (consisting of quartz, feldspars, and amorphous silica). The residue is then broken up in the tube with a glass rod. Centrifugation and decantation are repeated as before. The residue is given a third washing with 3 *N* HCl as before and transferred from the tube into a 500–ml. Ni or stainless steel beaker with the aid of a little 0.5 *N* NaOH. More 0.5 *N* NaOH is added to give a total volume of 100 ml. The suspension is brought rapidly to boiling over a Meker burner and boiled for exactly 2.5 minutes to dissolve amorphous silica (and a little alumina). The solution is cooled in a water bath. The solution is transferred to centrifuge tubes, the beaker scrubbed and washed with 0.5 *N* NaOH to insure complete transfer of the residue from beaker to tube, and the tubes are centrifuged to sediment the residue (usually mostly quartz and feldspars). The supernatant solution is discarded and the residue and tube are washed thoroughly 4 times with 3 *N* HCl to remove soluble Na and other soluble components. The residue in the tube is transferred into a tared platinum crucible (or Teflon beaker), dried at 105°C., and weighed in the crucible or beaker on an analytical balance.

To the weighed residue in the platinum crucible (or Teflon beaker), 2 drops of 60 per cent $HClO_4$, 1 drop of 18 *N* H_2SO_4, and 10 ml. of 48 per cent HF are added. This solution is evaporated to dryness on a sand bath in a fume hood at a temperature not greater than 225°C. The Teflon beaker should be buried in the sand to the lip to avoid condensation. The solution must not be boiled vigorously, or spattering and loss of sample will occur. When the HF is gone, the crucible or beaker is cooled and 5 ml. additional HF added. The solution is evaporated as before. The crucible or beaker is removed, cooled, and reweighed on an analytical balance.

Next, 6 ml. of 6 *N* HCl is added. The crucible or beaker is scrubbed with a rubber–tipped rod to obtain contact of HCl with the residue, and the solution warmed slightly. The rod is rinsed with 10 ml. of H_2O and the HCl solution is warmed nearly to boiling for 5 minutes to complete the dissolution of the perchlorates and sulfates in the residue. The solution is made to a volume of 100 ml. in a volumetric flask. The Na and K of this solution are determined *immediately* (to minimize contamination from glass) by means of a flame photometer. The Ca is determined on an aliquot of the 100 ml. of solution, with provision for elimination of Al interference if a flame photometer is used.

Calculation of results

The K, Na, and Ca content found in the residue is calculated as a percentage of the original sample employed. Then the percentages of equivalent feldspars left in the residue are given by:

Microcline content $\quad=$ per cent K $\times$ 7.1 (per cent $K_2O \times 5.9$) $\qquad$ (1)

Albite content $\qquad=$ per cent Na $\times$ 11.6 (per cent $Na_2O \times 8.5$) (2)

Anorthite–equiv-

$\quad$ alent content $\qquad=$ per cent Ca $\times$ 6.9 (per cent $CaO \times 4.95$) $\quad$ (3)

(in plagioclase)

based on 14.0 per cent K (16.9 per cent K_2O), 8.8 per cent Na (11.8 per cent Na_2O), and 14.4 per cent Ca (20.2 per cent CaO), which are contents of microcline (or orthoclase), albite, and anorthite, respectively. The latter two represent the equivalent endmembers of plagioclase.

The residue weight percentage of the original sample is calculated from the weighing before the HF treatment. This is "per cent residue." When only quartz and feldspar are present in the residue, as is substantially the case in soils from acid rocks and sedimentary rocks, the following relation holds:

$$\text{Per cent quartz} = \text{per cent residue} - \text{per cent feldspar} \qquad (4)$$

An alternative calculation is carried out when minerals other than quartz and feldspars (e.g., zircon) are present in appreciable quantities in the residue after the $K_2S_2O_7$–HCl–NaOH treatment, as indicated by X–ray diffraction analysis of a portion of the residue. For the alternative calculation, the SiO_2 content of the feldspars is obtained from 64.7 per cent SiO_2 in microcline, 68.7 per cent SiO_2 in albite, and 43.2 per cent SiO_2 in anorthite. Then:

$$\text{Per cent quartz} = (\text{per cent } SiO_2 \text{ lost by HF treatment}) - (\text{per cent } SiO_2 \text{ of feldspars}) \qquad (5)$$

Some exchange of K from potassium pyrosulphate for the Na of albite occurs during pyrosulphate fusion. To correct for this exchange the apparent albite content obtained from equation (2) is increased by the factor under the heading "Ab → Micr." in Table 3.

Table 3. Correction factors for quartz and feldspar determination

Size fraction in microns	Correction factors			
	Ab → Micr.	Quartz	Microcline	Albite
50–20	1.05	1.02	1.07	1.04
20– 5	1.08	1.03	1.15	1.07
5– 2	1.10	1.04	1.30	1.20
2– 0.2	—	1.05	—	—

The quantity by which the albite content is increased is deducted from the apparent microcline content since the loss apparent in albite content involves an equivalent apparent gain in microcline.

The correction factors under the headings "Quartz," "Microcline," and "Albite" in Table 3 are then applied to the results obtained from the above calculations to correct for solubility of minerals in the treatment. These corrections must *not* be made prior to the calculation in equation (4).

The mica content of the sample is obtained by subtracting the feldspar K_2O content from the total K_2O content and multiplying the resultant mica K_2O by 10, a factor for conversion to mica (Jackson, 1956, p. 543). The corrected microcline percentage is calculated to feldspar K_2O:

$$\text{Per cent Feldspar } K_2O = \frac{\text{per cent Microcline}}{5.9} \qquad (6)$$

$$\text{Mica } K_2O = \text{Total } K_2O - \text{Feldspar } K_2O \qquad (7)$$

$$\text{Per cent Mica} = \text{per cent Mica } K_2O \times 10 \qquad (8)$$

The details of development of this procedure and a corresponding $Na_2S_2O_7$ fusion procedure are to be published elsewhere (Jackson, 1964a; Kiely and Jackson, 1964a, 1964b).

Accuracy

The chief positive error for the quartz determination arises from the presence of nonquartz silicates other than feldspars (e.g., zircon, $ZrSiO_4$) which resist the $K_2S_2O_7$–HCl–NaOH treatments. The quantities of such minerals present in most soils are inappreciable, but the possibility of their being present must be considered for a given sample. Tremolite, generally rare in soils, goes mainly through with the quartz; its Ca analysis in the residue makes it appear mainly as "anorthite–equivalent." The residue may be examined with a microscope prior to the HF treatment (Trostel and Wynne, 1940). Examination by X–ray diffraction is highly useful; quartz and feldspar peaks are the only peaks present in most of the residues from soils. Shaw (1934) and Nagelschmidt (1956), using a 9 N H_2SO_4 digestion instead of $K_2S_2O_7$ fusion, took twice the residue weight after HF treatment (assuming 50 per cent SiO_2 was lost from the nonquartz minerals) as an approximation of the acid resistant nonquartz minerals.

The chief negative errors for quartz and feldspars arise (a) from their dissolution by the $K_2S_2O_7$–HCl–NaOH treatments and (b) from mechanical losses in transfers. The first approximation correction factors for these effects are given in the above table. For quartz in silt, the solubility error, based on SiO_2 dissolved, is 1 per cent; the correction factor of 1.03 also includes average losses in recovery of about 2 per cent. The residual error in the determination mainly reflects experimental variations from those represented in the correction factors and those of the emission spectrophotometric determinations. The overall error of the quartz determination is generally on the order of 2 to 3 per cent of the sample when only quartz and feldspars are present in the residue.

Amorphous material determination by selective dissolution analysis

Amorphous mineral colloids occur extensively in soils, as reviewed elsewhere (Jackson, 1956; Kanehiro and Whittig, 1961). Allophane is a general term for amorphous aluminosilicate gels of a wide range in composition (Ross and Kerr, 1934; White, 1953). The general Al_2O_3:SiO_2 mole ratio falls in the range of 0.5–1.3 (Jackson, 1964b). Other constituents include H_2O and OH; iron oxides are frequently combined in allophane (Aomine and Jackson, 1959; Jackson, 1964a). Sometimes up to 10 per cent P_2O_5 (White, 1953) may be present. The water is lost progressively with rise in temperature to over 400°C. Allophane occurring in surface soils as a product of weathering of volcanic ash characteristically is strongly associated with humus (Aomine and Yoshinaga, 1955), giving dark–colored soils known (Thorp and Smith, 1949) as the Ando great soil group (Ando in Japanese means *dark soil*), and also known as *Inceptisols* (Soil Survey Staff, 1960).

Allophane gives a stable porous structure to soils, predisposing them to high permeability, exhaustive leaching (Jackson, 1959), and hence, infertility. The porosity of freely–drained sandy soils subjects the limited amount of clay present to intensive leaching in humid climates, and can result in production of amorphous clay (Dyal, 1953; Whittig and Jackson, 1955; Jackson, 1959, 1964a), with cation exchange properties of allophane. The high specific surface and high aluminum activity of allophane are responsible for many important soil properties such as high lime requirement and high phosphate fixation (Wada, 1959). Analytically, the high specific surface results in the rapid dissolution of its Si and Al in alkaline solutions, a property utilized in the procedure to be given later in this discussion.

Other methods

Differential thermal analysis indicates allophane by a low temperature endotherm (160°C.), and surface soil allophane is indicated by a carbon–burning exotherm in the range of 450°-550°C. In relatively pure allophane deposits, the refractive index falls in the range of 1.480–1.483, varying with water content.

Markedly different values of cation–exchange capacity (CEC) have been reported for allophane and allophanic clays (Ross and Kerr, 1934; Birrell and Fieldes, 1952; Fieldes, Swindale, and Richardson, 1952; Aomine and Yoshinaga, 1955; Aomine and Kodama, 1956; Aomine and Jackson, 1959; Jackson, 1956, 1964a). Allophane is spectacular in the degree to which exchangeable cations hydrolyze from the exchange position during washing with aqueous alcohol (Birrell and Gradwell, 1956), and this is one reason for variability in CEC reported.

Another reason for variability of the measured CEC of allophane arises from its property of having its surface composition and net negative charge altered by changes in the pH of the solution in which it has been equilibrated prior to the determination of the CEC. It was noticed (Aomine and Jackson, 1959) that the CEC of allophanic clay separates varies a great deal according to the pH of the dispersion reagents employed for separation. The clay fraction originally separated in an alkaline medium (about pH 10.7) showed a high (150 meq per 100 gm.) exchange capacity, as determined at pH 7 with KOAc, while the clay fraction from the same soil originally separated with an acid dispersion medium (about pH 3.5) had an exchange capacity (similarly measured) of only about $\frac{1}{3}$ of that of the sample receiving alkaline dispersion. The CEC of the acid–dispersed sample was increased to equal that of the former on treatment with a mildly alkaline buffer. The increase in net negative exchange charge, created by the Na_2CO_3 buffer treatment, which is measurable as CEC at pH 7 possibly results from an increase in the tetrahedral coordination (Jackson, 1963a, Fig. 4) of Al at surfaces. The reciprocal reaction in dilute HOAc buffer (pH 3.5) restores the proton to the allophane surface structure and eliminates the corresponding amount of net negative charge at pH 7, possibly by increase of octahedral coordination (Jackson, 1963a, Fig. 4) of Al at surfaces.

This characteristic increase in CEC, exhibited by a number of allophanic soils, developed on rapidly weathered volcanic ash and also by two standard allophanes of Ross and Kerr (1934), and designated the "CEC delta value," has been applied for quantitative determination of allophane content in soils (Jackson, 1956, p. 856-57; Aomine and Jackson, 1959; Jackson, 1964a). The CEC delta value was measured (Aomine and Jackson, 1959, p. 212) as 18 for halloysite, 0 for kaolinite, 10 for Wyoming montmorillonite, 0.5 for gibbsite, and 0 for quartz. The method provides a rather specific criterion for allophane, supplementing the selective dissolution of various types of amorphous aluminosilicates along with free SiO_2 and Al_2O_3. This phenomenon involves a relatively newly associated property of allophane, but has since been observed with a rather wide variety of soils in a number of laboratories. It recalls the earlier observations of "build–up and break–down of soil zeolites" (Burgess, 1929) and CEC of undried amorphous hydrous oxides (Fieldes, *et al.*, 1952).

Selective dissolution of amorphous materials

The commonly used method of characterizing amorphous materials of soils is to determine their relative resistance to dissolution in various alkaline solutions. Alumina and silica, and amorphous (high specific surface) aluminosilicates form soluble sodium silicates and sodium aluminates in NaOH solutions. Historically, both NaOH and Na_2CO_3 solutions have been employed for dissolving silica and alumina cements, for cleaning mineral grains, and for dispersing clays. A 2 per cent Na_2CO_3 solution has a pH value of about 10.7, which is about the same as that of 0.0003 N NaOH (Jackson, 1956, p. 72); it is buffered at this pH by hydrolysis. A 2 per cent solution of Na_2CO_3, though dissolving only small amounts of silica, has a remarkably favorable dispersion effect on soils and clays (Jackson, Whittig, and Pennington, 1950) when used after the removal of exchangeable Ca and Mg (Jackson, 1956). It has a moderate solvent effect for free amorphous silica when not too much alumina is to be dissolved (Hillebrand and Lundell, 1929). It is ineffective in simultaneously dissolving appreciable amounts of both free silica and alumina from soils (Hashimoto and Jackson, 1960) and the amorphous aluminosilicates of dehydroxylated kaolinite (Hislop, 1944). Alumina tends to precipitate when the amount of silica dissolved from soil increases (Jackson, 1964a).

Sodium hydroxide solutions have long been used for selective dissolution of various constituents of soils. A boiling solution of 0.5 N NaOH was used for the dissolution of amorphous silica from soils (Hardy and Follett–Smith, 1931). This solution was used for a 4–hour digestion at 100°C. to dissolve free silica and (or) alumina in montmorillonitic samples (Foster, 1953) and in soils (Dyal, 1953; Whittig, *et al.,* 1957). Treatment with 0.5 N NaOH dissolved 2 to 15 times as much "free Al_2O_3" as "free SiO_2" from one soil fraction (less than 0.3μ) high in both aluminum phosphate and amorphous silicate (Dyal, 1953). Gibbsite was dissolved from soil samples high in goethite and halloysite by digestion of the samples in 1.25 N NaOH on a steambath for 20 minutes (Muñoz Taboadela, 1953; Mackenzie and Robertson, 1961). Rapid dissolution of crystalline layer silicates such as kaolinite and montmorillonite in a dilute suspension in boiling 0.5 N NaOH has been demonstrated (Hashimoto and Jackson, 1960).

Use of a high ratio of 0.5 N NaOH volume to sample weight (Hashimoto and Jackson, 1960), so as to avoid saturation of the solution with respect to silica and alumina, brings about an entirely different selective dissolution result with this reagent as compared to results with higher sample to solution ratios often employed. Boiling a soil or clay for only 2.5 minutes in a large excess of 0.5 N NaOH causes dissolution of free amorphous silica, free alumina, and large percentages of amorphous combined aluminosilicates including allophane. A similar treatment with a small volume of NaOH solution may dissolve all of the free amorphous silica or free alumina, but not both; amorphous aluminosilicates are dissolved only to a limited extent in concentrated suspensions. Clay fractions of soils may contain as much as 30 per cent (Tamura, *et al.,* 1953) to nearly 100 per cent (Aomine and Yoshinaga, 1955; Aomine and Jackson, 1959) of amorphous materials, and therefore a large capacity factor in a selective dissolution analysis method is important (Jackson, 1964a).

Selective dissolution of hydrous silica and alumina and of amorphous aluminosilicates depends upon the fact that these materials have a higher specific surface (giving a higher dissolution rate) than crystalline clays. Careful limitation of treatment time is essential because the crystalline clays are appreciably soluble during an hour or so of treatment of dilute suspensions in NaOH (Hashimoto and Jackson, 1960). Crystalline quartz is not extensively dissolved in the brief extraction time (150 seconds of boiling) given in the procedure and thus can be determined otherwise (as given in a previous section).

Heating the sample to 400°C. followed by extraction with 0.5 N NaOH dissolves some interlayer alumina (Dixon and Jackson, 1959, 1962; Jackson, 1963a, 1963b), which frequently occurs in expanded layer silicates of soils. An increment of alumina, silica, and iron oxide often becomes soluble as a result of heating to 400°C., suggesting that an allophane–like interlayer precipitate may be characteristic of expanded layer silicates of some soils (Dixon and Jackson, 1962). The extraction of the additional amounts of Al_2O_3, SiO_2, and Fe_2O_3 after the 400°C. heating treatment (in excess of amounts extracted before the heating treatment) causes the expanded layer silicates of many soils to have different properties from those of clays not subjected to thermal plus NaOH treatment. The treated clays undergo more complete thermal collapse at 300°C., have an increase in the measurable interlayer specific surface, and have an increase in cation exchange capacity. Scarcely recognizable 18 A montmorillonite diffraction peaks of Tama soil clay, for example, became clearly resolved after 0.5 N NaOH extraction of quickly soluble constituents from the clay (Glenn, *et al.,* 1960). Free alumina, including gibbsite, should be extracted from samples by 0.5 N NaOH treatment prior to heating to 400°C., since dehydroxylated alumina is not quickly soluble in NaOH (Hashimoto and Jackson, 1960).

Procedure

Removal of free iron oxides—This treatment (Aguilera and Jackson, 1953; Jackson, 1956; Mehra and Jackson, 1960; Jackson, 1964a) is ordinarily given in the dispersion of the soil and, if so, need not be repeated for a separated clay — rather the NaOH extraction (below) is given directly.

A 40 ml. portion of 0.3 M Na citrate solution and 5 ml. of 1 M NaHCO$_3$ solution are added to a 1 to 5 gm. soil or clay sample in a centrifuge tube. (A smaller sample is used with clay or with soil containing over 10 per cent of free iron oxides.) The tube is shaken to mix the contents, and then the tube is heated in a water bath at 80°C. for several minutes, the contents of the tube being stirred with a thermometer. When the suspension temperature reaches 80°C. (no higher), 1 gm. of $Na_2S_2O_4$ powder is added, measured with a calibrated spoon, and the suspension is immediately stirred vigorously for 1 minute. The tube is heated for 15 minutes with intermittent stirring and addition of 1 gm. or more of $Na_2S_2O_4$ at the end of 5 and 10 minutes. To obtain flocculation, 10 ml. of saturated NaCl is mixed into the suspension, and the tube promptly centrifuged. (Occasionally, addition of 10 ml. of acetone may be necessary to obtain complete flocculation as indicated by a clear supernatant solution after centrifugation.) The iron in the clear supernatant solution is determined by KSCN (Jackson, 1956, 1958) or by orthophenanthroline.

Ordinarily, the single $Na_2S_2O_4$ treatment given above suffices to remove the free oxides from soils containing a few per cent of not too crystalline iron oxides (the usual situation). For soils high in free iron oxides (5 to 60 per cent), particularly if crystalline goethite or coarsely crystalline hematite is present, 2 or 3 of the above treatments may be required, as judged by persistence of brown or red colors.

Removal of amorphous aluminosilicates—The following NaOH–heating procedure* is that of Hashimoto and Jackson (1960); it is also given in Jackson (1964a). A volume of clay suspension (Hanna and Jackson, in manuscript) containing 100 mg. of Na saturated sample (the weight is based on drying a separate aliquot), from which free iron oxides have been removed, is transferred into a 500–ml. nickel or stainless steel beaker. (Alternatively, the aggregates of dried clay, silt, soil, or deposit sample are crushed in a small mortar; a sample, dried from a nonpolar solvent such as benzene, is rubbed and mixed with a spatula. Then a 0.100 g. sample is weighed and transferred to a nickel or stainless steel beaker.) A 100 ml. volume of 0.5 N NaOH is added, lumps are rubbed with a rubber–tipped rod to provide good dispersion, and the solution is immediately heated to boiling and boiled for 2.5 minutes (the total heating time is approximately 5 minutes). The beaker and contents are promptly cooled to room temperature in a water bath, and the supernatant liquid is removed by centrifugation. The dissolved Si is immediately determined colorimetrically as molybdosilicate (Jack-

* Presented in 1958 at the 7th Clay Conference in Washington, D. C.

son, 1958) and the dissolved Al determined colorimetrically as the salt of aurin tricarboxylic acid (Jackson, 1958).

The iron oxide released (now giving a brown stain to the residue) is extracted by the $Na_2S_2O_4$–citrate–bicarbonate method as given above. The undissolved residue is examined by means of X–ray diffraction, since the removal of amorphous materials frequently discloses interesting crystalline components in the residue, such as mica, montmorillonite, or chlorite, which were not clearly revealed in the diffractogram of the material before the above treatments were given.

Removal of amorphous interlayer material—The following procedure is that of Dixon and Jackson (1959, 1960, 1962). To determine amorphous interlayer material, a second 100 mg. sample is H saturated (by washing it with 0.05 N HCl, acetone, and benzene). The sample is dried, heated at 400°C. for 4 hours, and allowed to cool. The sample is then powdered by a rubber–tipped rod. A weighed portion is then extracted by the same procedures as given above for amorphous aluminosilicates including both the NaOH and dithionite procedures.

Calculation of results

The percentages of SiO_2, Al_2O_3 and Fe_2O_3 dissolved in the extractions are calculated. If the cation exchange capacity indicates the presence of allophane, 21 per cent of H_2O is added to the total percentage of allophane–derived SiO_2 plus Al_2O_3 plus Fe_2O_3 extracted, to give the percentage of allophane dissolved (100°C. basis). If other evidence indicates the presence of gibbsite, 35 per cent of H_2O is added to the percentage of gibbsite–derived Al_2O_3 extracted, to give the percentage of gibbsite dissolved. Free amorphous alumina and (or) silica (uncombined) in the sample are also represented in the dissolved constituents.

The difference in per cent Al_2O_3 extracted before and after heating at 400°C. is multiplied by 4.40 to obtain the theoretical chlorite equivalent of the interlayer alumina extracted.

Accuracy

An aluminosilicate precipitate may form in the NaOH solution if the solution after the extraction is allowed to stand for an appreciable time prior to the Si and Al determination. Also serious contamination with these elements occurs if the NaOH solution stands in contact with glass before or after the extraction.

Selective dissolution in 0.5 N NaOH of amorphous aluminosilicates, silica, and alumina does not give a complete differentiation of the crystalline from the amorphous state because of the transitional nature of the boundary. For example, poorly crystalline halloysite minerals, closely related genetically with allophane (Sudo, 1954), are appreciably attacked by 0.5 N NaOH, and this must be taken into consideration. The separation of amorphous from truly crystalline materials is accurate to within about 5 per cent of the amount present.

Highly crystalline gibbsite may require two or more successive NaOH treatments for its complete dissolution (Hashimoto and Jackson, 1960). Magnesium hydroxide is, of course, not dissolved by NaOH. Magnesium–silicate minerals apparently are protected by $Mg(OH)_2$ formation at surfaces during treatment with NaOH, for they are relatively stable to the NaOH treatment. Such protection may account in part for the remarkable resistance of chlorite to dissolution (Hashimoto and Jackson, 1960).

Kaolinite plus halloysite determination by selective dissolution analysis

When kaolinite and halloysite are heated to 525°-550°C., the crystals are converted to amorphous material through dehydroxylation. The silica and alumina of such amorphous material can be dissolved (Hashimoto and Jackson, 1960) in the flash NaOH treatment outlined above for allophane and other amorphous alumina and silica.

It is desirable to remove gibbsite and the original amorphous material from the sample prior to heating for this determination. In the absence of gibbsite, the amorphous material of the original sample can be determined on a separate unheated sample and the amounts subtracted from those obtained after heating a second sample.

A certain amount of material dissolves from the interlayer positions of intergradient clays after heating the clay to 400°C. (Dixon and Jackson, 1959, 1960, 1962). For greatest precision the sample should be treated for removal of interlayer materials before the kaolinite plus halloysite determination.

Procedure

Removal of interlayer material—The following procedure is that of Dixon and Jackson (1959). The sample is H–saturated, heated at 400°C. for 4 hours, and powdered with a spatula and rubber–tipped rod. A 100 mg. subsample is extracted as in the paragraph titled "kaolinite plus halloysite" which follows.

Alternatively this procedure can be carried out on a separate sample and the percentages of materials dissolved after 400°C. preheating are subtracted from those obtained from the kaolinite dissolution treatment.

Kaolinite plus halloysite—The following procedure* is that of Hashimoto and Jackson (1960). Dr. C. I. Rich suggested using 550°C. instead of 525°C. The sample in which kaolinite plus halloysite is to be determined is first freed of gibbsite along with amorphous and inter-layer materials by the procedures given previously. The sample is then H–saturated and oven–dried. Kaolinite and halloysite are then con-verted to amorphous aluminosilicates by being heated to 525° to 550°C. for 4 hours.

The sample is crushed by spatula and rubber–tipped rod and a 100 mg. subsample is placed in a Ni or stainless steel beaker. Then 100 ml. of 0.5 N NaOH is added, and the sample is dispersed by trituration with a rubber–tipped rod. The suspension is heated rapidly to boiling and boiled 2.5 minutes (The total heating time is approximately 5 min-utes). The beaker content is immediately cooled in a water bath to room temperature and the supernatant liquid is removed by centrifugation. The dissolved Si and Al are immediately determined colorimetrically (Jackson, 1958, pp. 296-300). On standing, aluminosilicate may precipitate. The iron oxide released (still remaining in the residue) is dissolved by $Na_2S_2O_4$–citrate–bicarbonate as given in the section on removal of amorphous materials.

Calculation of results

The percentages of Al_2O_3, SiO_2, and Fe_2O_3 dissolved are calculated on an oven–dry basis for the samples heated at 400°C. and 525°-550°C. If the treatments are given to separate samples (in parallel instead of

* Presented in 1958 at the 7th Clay Conference in Washington, D. C.

successive), the difference is calculated in SiO_2, Al_2O_3, and Fe_2O_3 recovered after the 2 heating treatments. The molar ratio of SiO_2/Al_2O_3 is calculated for the material released as a result of 525°-550°C. heating as compared to 400°C. heating. If this ratio is near 2, kaolinite plus halloysite dissolution is indicated. The content of kaolinite plus halloysite is calculated from the 39.5 per cent Al_2O_3 in kaolinite. This result may be checked by taking the difference between amorphous silica dissolved from samples preheated at the two temperatures, based on 46.5 per cent SiO_2 in kaolinite.

Accuracy

Good checks (agreement to 1 or 2 per cent of the sample) are generally found (Dixon and Jackson, 1962) between the Al_2O_3 basis and the SiO_2 basis for samples containing kaolinite and halloysite, even when considerable intergradient vermiculite–chlorite is present. Kaolinite plus halloysite can be sharply differentiated from chlorite minerals (which give also a 7 A diffraction peak) because the chlorite is remarkably insoluble (under 1 per cent) in the NaOH treatment.

If the percentage of Fe_2O_3 recovered is appreciably greater after 525°-550°C. than after 400°C. heating (the case for fine clays of some soils) the presence of nontronite or ferruginous vermiculite is indicated and the method for deducing kaolinite plus halloysite becomes more difficult (Hashimoto and Jackson, 1960).

The percentage of NaOH–dissolved amorphous product which results from kaolinite plus halloysite decomposition between 525° and 400°C. checks well (Andrew, *et al.,* 1960) with the lattice–expansion method for these minerals, a fact that further supports the NaOH–dissolution method for kaolinite plus halloysite.

References

Aguilera, N. H., and Jackson, M. L. (1953) Iron oxide removal from soils and clays: *Soil Sci. Soc. Am. Proc.,* v. 17, pp. 359-64; v. 18, pp. 223 and 350.

Aldrich, D. G., Hellman, N. N., and Jackson, M. L. (1944) Hydration control of montmorillonite as required for its identification and estimation by X-ray diffraction methods: *Soil Sci.,* v. 57, pp. 215-31.

Aldrich, D. G., and Buchanan, J. R. (1958) Anomalies in techniques for preparing H-bentonites: *Soil Sci. Soc. Am. Proc.,* v. 22, pp. 281-85.

Andrew, R. W., Jackson, M. L., and Wada, K. (1960) Intersalation as a technique for differentiation of kaolinite from chloritic minerals by X-ray diffraction: *Soil Sci. Soc. Am. Proc.*, v. 24, pp. 422-24.

Aomine, S., and Yoshinaga, N. (1955) Clay mineralogy of some well-drained volcanic ash soils in Japan: *Soil Sci.*, v. 79, pp. 349-58.

Aomine, S., and Kodama, I. (1956) Clay minerals of some arable soils in Miyazaki Prefecture: *J. Fac. Agr. Kyushu Univ.*, v. 10, pp. 325-44.

Aomine, S., and Jackson, M. L. (1959) Allophane determination in Ando soils by cation-exchange capacity delta value: *Soil Sci. Soc. Am. Proc.*, v. 23, pp. 210-14.

Barshad, I. (1960) Significance of the presence of exchangeable magnesium ions in acidified clays: *Science*, v. 131, pp. 988-90.

Berkelhamer, L. H. (1944) D.T.A. of quartz: *Rep. Invest. U.S. Bur. Mines*, No. 3763.

Birrell, K. S., and Fieldes, M. (1952) Allophane in volcanic ash soils: *J. Soil Sci.*, v. 3, pp. 156-66.

Birrell, K. S., and Gradwell, M. (1956) Ion-exchange phenomena in some soils containing amorphous mineral constituents: *J. Soil Sci.*, v. 7, pp. 130-47.

Bower, C. A., and Gschwend, F. B. (1952) Ethylene glycol retention by soils as a measure of surface area and interlayer swelling: *Soil Sci. Soc. Am. Proc.*, v. 16, pp. 342-45.

Bradfield, R. (1923) The nature of the acidity of the colloidal clay of acid soils: *J. Am. Chem. Soc.*, v. 45, pp. 2669-78.

Bradley, W. F. (1945) Molecular association between montmorillonite and some polyfunctional organic liquids: *J. Am. Chem. Soc.*, v. 67, pp. 975-81.

Bradley, W. F. (1954) X-ray diffraction criteria of chloritic material: *Clays and Clay Minerals*, Nat. Acad. Sci.—Nat. Res. Council Pub. 327, Washington, D.C., pp. 324-34.

Bray, R. H. (1937) Chemical and physical changes in soil colloids with advancing development in Illinois soils: *Soil Sci.*, v. 43, pp. 1-14.

Brindley, G. W. (1955) Structural mineralogy of clays: *Clays and Clay Technology*, California Division of Mines, Bulletin 169, San Francisco, pp. 33-43.

Brindley, G. W. (1961) Quantitative analysis of clay mixture: *The X-ray Identification and Crystal Structures of Clay Minerals*, ed. G. Brown, Mineralogical Society, London, pp. 489-516.

Brown, G., and MacEwan, D. M. C. (1950) The interpretation of X-ray diagrams of soil clays II: Structures with random interstratification: *J. Soil Sci.*, v. 1, pp. 239-53.

Brown, G., and MacEwan, D. M. C. (1951) X-ray diffraction by structures with random interstratification. *The X-ray Identification and Crystal Structures of Clay Minerals*, ed. G. W. Brindley, Mineralogical Society, London, pp. 266-84.

Brown, G. (1953) The dioctahedral analogue of vermiculite: *Clay Min. Bull.*, v. 2, pp. 64-69.

Brown, G. (editor) (1961) *The X-ray Identification and Crystal Structures of Clay Minerals,* Mineralogical Society, London.

Brunauer, S., Emmett, P. H., and Teller, E. (1938) Adsorption of gases in multimolecular layers: *J. Am. Chem. Soc.,* v. 60, pp. 309-19.

Brydon, J. E., and Patry, L. M. (1961) Mineralogy of Champlain Sea sediments and a Rideau clay soil profile: *Canadian J. Soil Sci.,* v. 40, pp. 169-91.

Burgess, P. S. (1929) The so-called "build-up" and "break-down" of soil zeolites as influenced by reaction: *Arizona Agr. Exp. Sta. Tech. Bull.,* no. 28, pp. 101-35.

Clark, G. L., and Reynolds, D. H. (1936) Quantitative analysis of mine dusts, an X-ray diffraction method: *Ind. Eng. Chem., A. E.,* v. 8, pp. 36-40.

Corey, R. B. (1952) Allocation of elemental constituents to mineral species in polycomponent colloids of soils: Ph.D. Thesis, University of Wisconsin, Madison.

Diamond, S., and Kinter, E. B. (1958) Surface area of clay minerals derived from measurements of glycerol retention: *Clays and Clay Minerals,* Nat. Acad. Sci.—Nat. Res. Council Pub. 566, Washington, D.C., pp. 334-47.

Dixon, J. B., and Jackson, M. L. (1959) Dissolution of interlayers from intergradient soil clays after preheating at 400°C: *Science,* v. 129, pp. 1616-17.

Dixon, J. B., and Jackson, M. L. (1960) Mineralogical analysis of soil clays involving vermiculite-chlorite-kaolinite differentiation: *Clays and Clay Minerals,* 8th Conf., Pergamon Press, London, pp. 274-86.

Dixon, J. B., and Jackson, M. L. (1962) Properties of intergradient chlorite-expansible layer silicates of soils: *Soil Sci. Soc. Am. Proc.,* v. 26, pp. 358-62.

Durkan, T. M. (1946) Determination of free silica in industrial dust: *J. Industr. Hyg.,* v. 28, pp. 217-28.

Dyal, R. S., and Hendricks, S. B. (1950) Total surface in polar liquids as a characteristic index: *Soil Sci.,* v. 69, pp. 421-32.

Dyal, R. S. (1953) Mica leptyls and wavellite content of clay fraction from Gainesville loamy fine sand of Florida: *Soil Sci. Soc. Am. Proc.,* v. 17, pp. 55-58.

Emmett, P. H., Brunauer, S., and Love, K. S. (1938) The measurement of surface area of soils and soil colloids by the use of low temperature Van der Waals adsorption isotherms: *Soil Sci.,* v. 45, pp. 57-65.

Erhart, H. (1956) *La Genèse des Sols en tant que Phénomène Géologique,* Masson et Cie, Paris.

Favejee, J. Ch. L. (1939) Zur Methodik der Rontgenographischen Bodenforshung: *Ztschr. Krist.,* v. 100, pp. 425-36.

Fieldes, M., Swindale, L. D., and Richardson, J. P. (1952) Relation of colloidal hydrous oxides to the high cation-exchange capacity of some tropical soils of the Cook Islands: *Soil Sci.,* v. 74, pp. 197-205.

Florentin, M. D., and Heros, M. (1947) Dosage de la silice libre (quartz) dans les silicates: *Bul. Soc. Chim. France,* 1947M, pp. 213-15.

Foster, M. D. (1953) Geochemical studies of clay minerals. III. The determination of free silica and free alumina in montmorillonite: *Geochem. Cosmochim. Acta.,* v. 3, pp. 143-54.

Gieseking, J. E. (1939) Mechanism of cation exchanges in the montmorillonite-bentonite-nontronite type of clay minerals: *Soil Sci.,* v. 47, pp. 1-13.

Glenn, R. C., Jackson, M. L., Hole, F. D., and Lee, G. B. (1960) Chemical weathering of layer silicate clays in loess-derived Tama silt loam of southwestern Wisconsin: *Clays and Clay Minerals,* 8th Conf., Pergamon Press, London, pp. 63-83.

Grim, R. E., Bray, R. H., and Bradley, W. F. (1937) Mica in argillaceous sediments: *Am. Min.,* v. 22, pp. 813-29.

Grim, R. E. (1953) *Clay Mineralogy,* McGraw-Hill Book Co., New York.

Grimshaw, R. W. (1953) Quantitative estimation of silica minerals: *Clay Min. Bull.,* v. 2, pp. 2-7.

Grimshaw, R. W., and Roberts, A. L. (1957) The silica minerals: *The Differential Thermal Investigation of Clays,* The Mineralogical Society, London, pp. 275-98.

Hardy, F., and Follett-Smith, R. R. (1931) Studies in tropical soils. II. Some characteristic igneous rock soil profiles in British Guiana, South America: *J. Agr. Sci.,* v. 21, pp. 739-61.

Harkins, W. D., and Jura, G. (1944) Surface of solids: XIII: *J. Am. Chem. Soc.,* v. 66, pp. 1366-73.

Harkins, W. D. (1952) *The Physical Chemistry of Surface Films,* Reinhold Publishing Corp., New York.

Hashimoto, I., and Jackson, M. L. (1960) Rapid dissolution of allophane and kaolinite-halloysite after dehydration: *Clays and Clay Minerals,* 7th Conf., Pergamon Press, London, pp. 102-13.

Hellman, N. N., Aldrich, D. G., and Jackson, M. L. (1943) Further note on X-ray diffraction procedure for the positive differentiation of montmorillonite from hydrous mica: *Soil Sci. Soc. Am. Proc.,* v. 7, pp. 194-200.

Hendricks, S. B. (1941) Base exchange of the clay mineral montmorillonite for organic cations and its dependence upon adsorption due to Van der Waals forces: *J. Phys. Chem.,* v. 45, pp. 65-81.

Hendricks, S. B., and Teller, E. (1942) X-ray interference in partially ordered layer silicates: *J. Chem. Phys.,* v. 10, pp. 147-67.

Hillebrand, W. F., and Lundell, G. E. F. (1929) *Applied Inorganic Analysis,* 10th printing, John Wiley and Sons, New York, pp. 705 and 715.

Hislop, J. F. (1944) The decomposition of clay by heat: *Trans. Brit. Ceram. Soc.,* v. 43, pp. 49-51.

Hseung, Y., and Jackson, M. L. (1952) Mineral composition of the clay fraction: III. of some main soil groups of China: *Soil Sci. Soc. Am. Proc.,* v. 16, pp. 294-97.

Jackson, M. L., and Hellman, N. N. (1942) X-ray diffraction procedure for positive differentiation of montmorillonite from hydrous mica: *Soil Sci. Soc. Am. Proc.,* v. 6, pp. 133-45.

Jackson, M. L., Tyler, S. A., Willis, A. L., Bourbeau, G. A., and Pennington,

R. P. (1948) Weathering sequence of clay-size minerals in soils and sediments: *J. Phys. Colloid Chem.,* v. 52, pp. 1237-60.

Jackson, M. L., Whittig, L. D., and Pennington, R. P. (1950) Segregation procedure for the mineralogical analysis of soils: *Soil Sci. Soc. Am. Proc.,* v. 14, pp. 77-81.

Jackson, M. L., Hseung, Y., Corey, R. B., Evans, E. J., and Vanden Heuvel, R. C. (1952) Weathering sequence of clay-size minerals in soils and sediments: II. chemical weathering of layer silicates: *Soil Sci. Soc. Am. Proc.,* v. 16, pp. 3-6.

Jackson, M. L., and Sherman, G. D. (1953) Chemical weathering of minerals in soils: *Advances in Agron.,* v. 5, Academic Press, Inc., New York, pp. 219-318.

Jackson, M. L., Whittig, L. D., Vanden Heuvel, R. C., Kaufman, A., and Brown, B. E. (1954) Some analyses of soil montmorin, vermiculite, mica, chlorite, and interstratified layer silicates: *Clays and Clay Minerals,* Nat. Acad. Sci.—Nat. Res. Council Pub. 327, Washington, D.C., pp. 218-40.

Jackson, M. L. (1956) *Soil Chemical Analysis—Advanced Course,* published by the author, Dept. of Soil Science, Univ. of Wisconsin, Madison.

Jackson, M. L. (1958) *Soil Chemical Analysis,* Prentice-Hall, Inc., Englewood Cliffs, New Jersey.

Jackson, M. L. (1959) Frequency distribution of clay minerals in major great soil groups as related to the factors of soil formation: *Clays and Clay Minerals,* 6th Conf., Pergamon Press, London, pp. 133-43.

Jackson, M. L. (1960) Structural role of hydronium in layer silicates during soil genesis: *Trans. Intern. Congr. Soil Sci.,* v. 2, 7th Congr., Madison, Wisconsin, pp. 445-55.

Jackson, M. L. (1963a) Aluminum bonding in soils: a unifying principle in soil science: *Soil Sci. Soc. Am. Proc.,* v. 27, pp. 1-10.

Jackson, M. L. (1963b) Interlayering of expansible layer silicates in soils by chemical weathering: *Clays and Clay Minerals,* 11th Conf., Pergamon Press, London, pp. 29-46.

Jackson, M. L. (1964a) Free oxides, hydroxides, and amorphous aluminosilicates: *Methods of Soil Analysis,* Agronomy Monograph, No. 9, American Society of Agronomy, Madison, Wis.

Jackson, M. L. (1964b) Chemical composition of soils. Ch. II in *Chemistry of the Soil,* 2nd edition, F. E. Bear editor. Reinhold Publishing Co., New York.

Jenny, H. (1941) *Factors of Soil Formation,* McGraw-Hill Book Co., New York.

Jenny, H. (1961) Reflections on the soil acidity merry-go-round: *Soil Sci. Soc. Am. Proc.,* v. 25, pp. 428-32.

Jophcott, C. M., and Wall, H. F. V. (1955) Determination of quartz of various particle sizes in quartz-silicate mixture: *Arch. Indust. Hlth.,* v. 11, pp. 425-30.

Kanehiro, Y., and Whittig, L. D. (1961) Amorphous mineral colloids of soils of the Pacific region and adjacent areas: *Pacific Science,* v. 40, pp. 477-82.

Kelley, W. P., Dore, W. H., and Page, J. B. (1940) The colloidal constituents of American alkali soils: *Soil Sci.,* v. 51, pp. 101-23.

Kelley, W. P. (1948) *Cation Exchange in Soils,* Reinhold Publishing Corp., New York.

Kiely, P. V., and Jackson, M. L. (1964a) Selective dissolution of micas from potassium feldspars by sodium pyrosulfate fusion of soils and sediments: *Am. Mineralogist* (in press).

Kiely, P. V., and Jackson, M. L. (1964b) Quartz, feldspar, and mica determinations by sodium pyrosulfate fusion: In manuscript.

Kittrick, J. A., and Jackson, M. L. (1954) Electron microscope observations of the formation of aluminum phosphate crystals with kaolinite as the source of aluminum: *Science,* v. 120, pp. 508-9.

Kittrick, J. A., and Jackson, M. L. (1955) Rate of phosphate reaction with soil minerals and electron microscope observations on the reaction mechanism: *Soil Sci. Soc. Am. Proc.,* v. 19, pp. 292-95.

Kittrick, J. A. (1961) A comparison of the moving liquid and glass-slide methods for the preparation of oriented X-ray diffraction specimens: *Soil Sci.,* v. 92, pp. 155-60.

Klages, M. G., and White, J. L. (1957) A chlorite-like mineral in Indiana soils: *Soil Sci. Soc. Am. Proc.,* v. 21, pp. 16-20.

Knopf, A. (1933) The quantitative determination of quartz in dust: *U.S. Pub. Health Repts.,* v. 48, pp. 183-90.

Line, W. R., and Aradine, P. W. (1937) Determination of quartz in the presence of silicates: *Ind. Eng. Chem., A. E.,* v. 9, pp. 60-63.

Low, P. F. (1955) The role of aluminum in the titration of bentonite: *Soil Sci. Soc. Am. Proc.,* v. 19, pp. 135-39.

Lyon, R. J. P., Tuddenham, W. M., and Thompson, C. S. (1959) Quantitative mineralogy in 30 minutes: *Econ. Geol.,* v. 54, pp. 1047-55.

MacEwan, D. M. C. (1944) Identification of the montmorillonite group of minerals by X-rays: *Nature,* v. 154, pp. 577-78.

MacEwan, D. M. C. (1946) Identification of montmorillonite: *J. Soc. Chem. Ind.,* v. 65, pp. 298-305.

MacEwan, D. M. C. (1948) Complexes of clays with organic compounds: I. Complex formation between montmorillonite and halloysite and certain organic liquids: *Trans. Faraday Soc.,* v. 44, pp. 349-67.

MacEwan, D. M. C., Amil, R. A., and Brown, G. (1961) Interstratified clay minerals: *The X-ray Identification and Crystal Structures of Clay Minerals,* ed. G. Brown, Mineralogical Society, London, pp. 393-445.

Mackenzie, R. C., and Robertson, R. H. S. (1961) The quantitative determination of halloysite, goethite, and gibbsite: *Acta Universtatis Carolinae — Geologica Supplementum,* v. 1, pp. 139-49.

Maegdefrau, E., and Hofmann, U. (1938) Die Kristallstruktur des Montmorillonits: *Z. Krist,* v. 98, pp. 299-323.

Makower, B., Shaw, J. M., and Alexander, L. T. (1938) The specific surface and density of soils and their colloids: *Soil Sci. Soc. Am. Proc.,* v. 2, pp. 101-8.

Medicus, K. (1955) Schnellbestimmung der Kieselsäure im Bauxit nach der Perchlorsäure Method: *Zeit. anal. Chemie.,* v. 145, pp. 337-38.

Mehra, O. P., and Jackson, M. L. (1959a) Constancy of the sum of mica unit cell potassium surface and interlayer sorption surface in vermiculite-illite clays: *Soil Sci. Soc. Am. Proc.,* v. 23, pp. 101-5.

Mehra, O. P., and Jackson, M. L. (1959b) Specific surface determination by duo-interlayer and mono-interlayer glycerol sorption for vermiculite and montmorillonite analysis: *Soil Sci. Soc. Am. Proc.,* v. 23, pp. 351-54.

Mehra, O. P., and Jackson, M. L. (1960) Iron oxide removal from soils and clays by a dithionite citrate system buffered with sodium bicarbonate: *Clays and Clay Minerals,* 7th Conf., Pergamon Press, London, pp. 317-27.

Milford, M. H., and Jackson, M. L. (1962) Illite content and size distribution in relation to potassium availability in some soils of North Central United States: *Agron. Abstracts,* American Society of Agronomy, Madison, Wisconsin, p. 21.

Mortland, M. M., and Kemper, W. D. (1964) Specific surface: *Methods of Soil Analysis,* Agronomy Monograph, No. 9, American Society of Agronomy, Madison, Wis.

Muñož Taboadela, M. (1953) The clay mineralogy of some soils from Spain and from Rio Muni (West Africa): *J. Soil Sci.,* v. 4, pp. 48-55.

Nagelschmidt, G. (1944) The mineralogy of soil colloids: *Imp. Bur. Soil Sci., Tech. Com. No. 42,* pp. 1-33.

Nagelschmidt, G. (1956) Inter-laboratory trials on the determination of quartz in dusts of respirable size: *Analyst,* v. 81, pp. 210-19.

Nelson, L. A., and Hendricks, S. B. (1943) Specific surface of some clay minerals, soils and soil colloids: *Soil Sci.,* v. 56, pp. 285-96.

Pauling, L. (1958) *General Chemistry,* W. H. Freeman Co., San Francisco, Calif.

Pimentel, G. C., and McClellan, A. L. (1960) *The Hydrogen Bond,* W. H. Freeman Co., San Francisco, Calif.

Pollack, S. S., Whiteside, E. P., and Varowe, D. E. Van (1954) X-ray diffraction of common silica minerals and possible applications to studies of soil genesis: *Soil Sci. Soc. Am. Proc.,* v. 18, pp. 268-72.

Polynov, B. B. (1937) *Cycle of Weathering,* Trans. by A. Muir, Thomas Murby and Co., London.

Reynolds, R. C., and Lessing, P. (1962) The determination of dioctahedral mica and potassium feldspars in submicroscopic grain sizes: *Am. Min.,* v. 47, pp. 979-82.

Rich, C. I., and Obenshain, S. S. (1955) Chemical and clay mineral properties of a Red-Yellow Podzolic soil derived from muscovite schist: *Soil Sci. Soc. Am. Proc.,* v. 19, pp. 334-39.

Rich, C. I. (1957) Determination of (060) reflections of clay minerals by means of counter type X-ray diffraction instruments: *Am. Min.,* v. 42, pp. 569-70.

Rich, C. I. (1960) Aluminum in interlayers of vermiculite: *Soil Sci. Soc. Am. Proc.,* v. 24, 26-32.

Ross, C. S., and Kerr, P. F. (1934) Halloysite and allophane: *U.S. Geol. Survey, Prof. Paper,* 185 G., pp. 135-48.

Sawhney, B. L., and Jackson, M. L. (1958) Soil montmorillonite formulas: *Soil Sci. Soc. Am. Proc.,* v. 22, pp. 115-18.

Sawhney, B. L. (1960) Weathering and aluminum interlayers in a soil catena: Hollis-Charlton-Sutton-Leicester: *Soil Sci. Soc. Am. Proc.,* v. 24, pp. 221-26.

Schofield, R. K. (1939) The electrical charges on clay particles: *Soils and Fertilizers,* v. 2, pp. 1-5.

Schwertmann, U. (1961) Über das Vorkommen und die Entstehung von Jarosit in Marschböden (Maibolt): *Die Naturwissenschaften,* v. 6, pp. 159-60.

Schwertmann, U. (1962) Die selektive Kationensorption der Tonfraktion einiger Böden aus Sedimenten: *Z. Pflanzenernähr. Düng., Bodenk.,* v. 97, pp. 9-25.

Schwertmann, U., and Jackson, M. L. (1963) Hydrogen-aluminum clays: a third buffer range appearing in potentiometric titration: *Science,* v. 139, pp. 1052-54.

Schwertmann, U., and Jackson, M. L. (1964) Influence of hydroxy aluminum ions on pH titration curves of hydronium-aluminum clays: *Soil Sci. Soc. Am. Proc.,* v. 28, pp. 179-83.

Shaw, A. (1934) The determination of free silica in coal-measure rocks: *Analyst,* v. 59, pp. 446-61.

Shchekaturina, L. G., and Petrashen, V. I. (1958) Determination of free silica in coal dust: *Opredelenie Svobodnoi Dvuokisi Kremniya v Gorn. Porodakh i Rudn. Pyli,* Akad. Nauk S.S.S.R., Inst. Gorn. Dela, Sbornik Statei., pp. 54-57.

Smith, J. L. (1865) On the use of the bisulphate of soda as a substitute for the bisulphate of potash in the decomposition of minerals, especially the aluminous minerals: *Am. J. Sci. and Arts,* v. 40, pp. 248-49.

Soil Survey Staff. (1960) *Soil Classification — A Comprehensive System. 7th Approximation,* Soil Conservation Service, U.S.D.A., Washington, D. C.

Sudo, T. (1954) Clay mineralogical aspects of the alteration of volcanic glass in Japan: *Clay Min. Bull.,* v. 2, pp. 96-106.

Sysoeva, R. S. (1958) Test of parallel determination of the free silica in the dust of a crushing mill by chemical, petrographic, X-ray spectral and thermal methods: *Opredelenie Svobodnoi Dvuokisi Kremniya v Gorn. Porodakh i Rudn. Pyli,* Akad. Nauk S.S.S.R., Inst. Gorn. Dela, Sbornik Statei., pp. 103-10.

Talvitie, N. A. (1951) Determination of quartz in presence of silicate using phosphoric acid: *Anal. Chem.,* v. 23, pp. 623-26.

Tamura, T., Jackson, M. L., and Sherman, G. D. (1953) Mineral content of low humic, humic and hydrol humic latosols of Hawaii: *Soil Sci. Soc. Am. Proc.,* v. 17, pp. 343-46.

Tamura, T. (1957) Identification of the 14 A clay mineral component: *Am. Min.,* v. 42, pp. 107-10.

Thorp, J., and Smith, G. D. (1949) Higher categories of soil classification: order, suborder and great soil group: *Soil Sci.,* v. 67, pp. 117-26.

Trombe, F. (1947) *Comptes rendus, Ac. Sc.,* v. 207, p. 1110 (Cited by Florentin and Heros).

Trostel, L. J., and Wynne, D. J. (1940) Determination of quartz (free silica) in refractory clays: *J. Am. Ceram. Soc.,* v. 23, pp. 18-22.

Tuddenham, W. M., and Lyon, R. S. P. (1960) Infrared techniques in the identification and measurement of minerals: *Anal. Chem.,* v. 32, pp. 1630-34.

Urey, H. C. (1960) The origin and nature of the moon: *Endeavour 19,* v. 74, pp. 87-99.

Vanden Heuvel, R. C., and Jackson, M. L. (1953) Surface determination of mineral colloids by glycerol sorption and its application to interstratified layer silicates: *Agron. Abstracts,* American Society of Agronomy, Madison, Wisconsin.

Volk, V. V., and Jackson, M. L. (1964) Characterization of the inorganic pH dependent cation exchange charge of soils: *Clays and Clay Minerals,* 12th Conf., Pergamon Press, London, pp. 281-95.

Wada, K. (1959) Reaction of phosphate with allophane and halloysite: *Soil Sci.,* v. 87, pp. 325-30.

Wada, K. (1961) Lattice expansion of kaolin minerals by KCH_3COO treatment: *Am. Min.,* v. 46, pp. 78-91.

Walker, G. F. (1950) Vermiculite-organic complexes: *Nature,* v. 166, pp. 695-96.

White, W. A. (1953) Allophanes from Lawrence County, Indiana: *Am. Min.,* v. 38, pp. 634-42.

Whittig, L. D., and Jackson, M. L. (1955) Interstratified layer silicates in some soils of northern Wisconsin: *Clays and Clay Minerals,* Nat. Acad. Sci.—Nat. Res. Council Pub. 395, Washington, D.C., pp. 322-36.

Whittig, L. D., Kilmer, V. J., Roberts, R. C., and Cady, J. G. (1957) Characteristics and genesis of Cascade and Powell soils of northwestern Oregon: *Soil Sci. Soc. Am. Proc.,* v. 21, pp. 226-32.

IX ... X-ray Spectrographic Analysis of Soils

A. H. Beavers and Robert L. Jones

Introduction

Rapidity and ease of handling are two of the most sought after characteristics of an analytical technique or instrument. In addition to these characteristics the X–ray spectrograph provides high levels of precision and accuracy when applied to routine soil analysis of materials. Rarely has such an instrument or tool been placed in the hands of the investigator with which he can rapidly and accurately characterize the status of soil weathering and chemical *milieu* of the soil.

When used in conjunction with other techniques for characterizing the mineral suite, data from X–ray spectrographic analyses provide a broad and encompassing "picture" of soil development.

Origin and properties of X rays

X rays are produced when high–energy electrons or X rays impinge upon matter. The energy yielded in this process follows the well established relationship:

$$\Delta E = h\upsilon \qquad (1)$$

where h is Planck's constant and υ is frequency. In X–ray spectrographic analysis the energy exchange occurs between photons and electrons near the nucleus, wherein electrons in the K, L, or M shells are knocked from their usual position. Radiation is produced when electrons fall from higher energy levels to fill these vacancies. For example, electrons falling from levels in the L shell into the K shell produce Kα radiation, and electrons falling from the M and N shells produce Kβ radiation. Similarly, electrons falling from O, N, and M shells into lower levels produce L and M series radiation lines. Characteristic Kα $_1$ and Lα $_1$ lines for important elements in soils research are given in Table 1. From equa-

Table 1. Absorption edges, K and L series lines for principal elements of analytical interest in soil genesis investigations.

Z	Element	K α $_1$	L α $_1$	K edge	
		A	A	A	Kv
12	Mg	9.889	—	9.5117	1.303
13	Al	8.337	—	7.9511	1.559
14	Si	7.125	—	6.7446	1.837
15	P	6.155	—	5.7866	2.142
19	K	3.741	—	3.4365	3.606
20	Ca	3.358	—	3.0702	4.037
22	Ti	2.748	—	2.4973	4.963
25	Mn	2.102	—	1.8964	6.535
26	Fe	1.936	17.602	1.7433	7.109
29	Cu	1.541	13.357	1.3804	8.978
40	Zr	0.786	6.070	0.6888	17.993

tion (1) it is apparent that Kα radiation will be of a longer wave length than Kβ radiation for any element. Similar relationships occur throughout the series of lines. The intensity of radiation or number of quanta of radiation produced is statistically greater for Kα radiation than other lines among elements with atomic number less than 57 when 50 kv. exciting energy is used. This radiation, therefore, is of greatest analytical interest for most soil and clay mineral investigations. Among elements of higher atomic number the analysis of L lines becomes important or 75 to 100 kv. exciting sources must be used to obtain Kα lines.

The other principal type of radiation from the tube is that produced by the deceleration of electrons in the target; it is called white radiation.

About half of the background radiation encountered in X–ray spectrographic analysis arises from scattering of primary radiation produced at the target. Some of the background is attributable to coherently scattered radiation which is produced by elastic collisions of photons and atoms of Z > 11. More background radiation is produced by inelastic collisions between photons and low atomic number elements (Z > 11). The loss of energy of these latter photons follows the relationship

$$d\lambda = 0.24\ (1-\cos \Phi) \tag{2}$$

where Φ is the angle between incident and scattered radiation. This scattered or Compton radiation manifests itself as broad peaks on the long wave–length side of primary radiation lines. The background radiation which is not attributable to either incoherently or coherently scattered radiation is caused by scattering of secondary radiation by the analyzing crystal.

The minimum wave length of radiation obtainable from any target is given by the equation

$$\lambda\ min = 12,393/V \tag{3}$$

where V is the exciting potential across the tube. The minimum voltages for operation of common targets used in X–ray spectrographic analysis are given in Table 2. Generally the tube is operated at 3 to 5 times the minimum voltage to obtain maximum efficiency.

Table 2. Potential minima and wave length for common targets. Note: Tubes are generally operated 3 to 5 times V_{min}.

Target	$V_{min.}$	Line	λ
	kv		A
Gold	14.4	L	1.28
Platinum	13.9	L	1.31
Tungsten	12.1	L	1.48
Molybdenum	20.0	K	.71
Copper	9.0	K	1.54
Iron	7.1	K	1.94
Chromium	6.0	K	2.29

Implicit in the discussion of X–ray excitation is the characteristic of absorption of X–ray photons. Each element possesses unique absorptive properties for different wave lengths of radiation (Table 1). An example of the absorption characteristics of iron, cobalt, and nickel is given in Fig. 1. At frequencies corresponding to ionization of K and L electrons and subsequent emission of respective series lines, there are abrupt decreases in mass absorption coefficients called absorption edges (Fig. 1). Irradiation at energies just shorter than the wave lengths

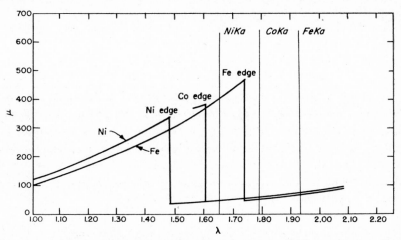

Figure 1. Mass absorption characteristics and Kα emission lines for iron, cobalt, and nickel.

corresponding to these frequencies causes emission of the complete series of lines within a shell. There is one absorption edge for the K, three for the L, and five for the M series. Thus, for low atomic number elements (Z = < 50) 50 kv primary radiation is of sufficient energy to excite all of the series of lines commonly analyzed in soils research. For heavier elements either higher energy radiation is necessary in order to obtain K series lines, or L series lines must be utilized in analysis.

From Fig. 1 it is apparent that the absorptive properties of a material are of great analytical interest. Obviously, radiation of certain wave lengths is strongly absorbed and other wave lengths are readily transmitted by the material being irradiated.

Instrumentation

The past decade has brought rapid change to X–ray spectrograph instrumentation. From the field of electronics new schemes for stabilization, development of better amplification, and improved design and development of counters and target tubes have made possible improved precision, accuracy, and extension of the limit of detectability. With the advent of the transistor the trend to miniaturization in the unit can be expected as well as decreased "warm up" time.

In the following paragraph aspects of instrumentation important to the analyst are outlined. They are covered in the sequence which the radiation follows from target tube to detector.

Target Tubes

A variety of target elements are currently available to the analyst. Choice of a specific target depends on the relationships among the elements to be analyzed. Ideally, the target should be composed of the element having a Kα wave length of just slightly shorter than the absorption edge of the element to be analyzed. Consequently, the target element would be two atomic numbers greater than the element in question. Practically this cannot be realized under all circumstances. Therefore, choice of tube involves some compromise. High atomic number tubes like tungsten, platinum, and gold utilize the L series for excitation at 50 kv. Tubes currently in use and the elements for which they are most efficient are given in Table 3. The data in Table 3 point

Table 3. X-ray target tubes and elements analyzed.

Target element*	Line series	Elements
Cr	K	12–22
Mo	K	≥ 12**
W	L	≥ 12**
Pt	L	≥ 12**
Au	L	≥ 12**

 * 50 KVP
 ** More efficient with heavier elements.

out that for excitation by primary radiation the white portion of the spectrum becomes especially important in generation of secondary radiation or fluorescence. If an analyst were confronted with the choice of one tube he would probably choose either a tungsten or a platinum tube. A chromium tube would be complementary to either of these tubes because of its efficiency for elements less than Z equal 22. Five–fold greater intensity for low atomic number elements is obtained with the chromium tube as compared with the tungsten tube.

Collimators

Secondary radiation eminating from the sample undergoes collimation at least one time. In some instruments a collimator is placed between sample and analyzing crystal in order to reduce the intensity of scattered radiation reaching the crystal. In all instruments employing dispersive optics, a collimator is placed in the path between the crystal and detector. This collimator essentially provides a line source of radiation to the detector and, therefore, can be considered to be a monochromator that satisfies the Bragg equation.

Collimators constructed of bundles of parallel plates are called Soller slits. They range in spacing of the plates from 5 to 20 mils. The small or 5 mil slits are used in high resolution work for separation of closely spaced analytical lines and at low angles. Use of this size of slit decreases intensity. Slits of 20 mil spacing and larger are used for low resolution where no analytical lines interfere and in cases where high intensities are important.

For most analytical purposes X rays must be reflected. Bragg (1912) recognized that planes of regularly spaced atoms acted as gratings from which X rays were specularly reflected. To Bragg we are indebted for the law

$$n\lambda = 2d \sin \Theta \tag{4}$$

where n is an integral number, d is the interplanar distance, and Θ is the angle of incident rays with the plane. From this law it is possible to determine either λ or d. In spectrographic analysis 2d is known rather accurately; therefore, the derivation of λ depends on the use of some detection means used in conjunction with a goniometer to measure the angle between the X–ray source (specimen) and the reflecting medium (crystal). The reader interested in derivation of the Bragg equation is referred to Klug and Alexander (1954).

Analyzing Crystals

In order to analyze the polychromatic secondary radiation emerging from the sample in dispersive instruments it is necessary to place a diffracting medium between the sample and detector. Usually this is accomplished by using flat or curved crystals. In this account we will confine our discussion to flat crystals. Selection of a crystal of high quality is important, because of the properties of resolution and reflective intensities sought in it. Line broadening is a characteristic of all crystals but is minimized, paradoxically, with imperfect crystals. According to the Bragg equation a crystal should reflect all wave lengths shorter than its 2d spacing. Most efficient diffraction is obtained by choosing the crystal with the smallest 2d spacing that will diffract the required wave length. This derives from $d\Theta/d\lambda$, or dispersion, which increases with decreasing 2d. If the reflection from a crystal is monochromatic within the limits established by the collimator, it is generally satisfactory for chemical analysis (Birks, 1959, pp. 19-25). The suitability of common crystals for different elements is given in Table 4.

Table 4. Analyzing crystals.

Crystal	2d spacing	Application Z	Element
	A		
$CaSO_4 \cdot 2H_2O$	15.21	12*	Mg
ADP	10.64	12	Mg
EDT	8.80	13–19	Al–K
Pentaerythritol	8.76	13–19	Al–K
SiO_2 (1011)	6.69	15–19	P–K
NaCl	5.64	16–56	S–Ba
LiF	4.03	19–79	K–Au
Topaz	2.71	≥ 23	$\geq$ V

* Most efficiently reflected. The $CaSO_4 \cdot 2H_2O$ crystal is capable of analyzing Na (11) with special instrumentation.

The high efficiency and 2d spacing of the LiF crystal makes it a good choice when only one crystal is obtainable, but analysis is limited to elements of atomic number greater than 18.

Detectors

We shall concern ourselves in this account with gas–filled and scintillation detectors which are the most common devices now used for measurement of X–ray quanta in analytical work. Also, this account is necessarily brief and the reader is referred to the fine reviews of Liebhafsky, *et al.* (1960, pp. 42-67), and Birks (1959, pp. 40-57) for more complete treatments.

In construction, the gas–filled detectors (Geiger and proportion counters) are essentially the same. They consist of a tube envelope made negative to ground and a central wire made positive. Either at the end or side of the tube is a window generally constructed of beryllium. By minor alterations in design and changing the voltage impressed across the tube it becomes either a Geiger or proportional counter. In the Geiger tube, the tube gas is usually argon at 0.5 to 0.7 atmosphere pressure with less than 1 per cent chlorine or bromine. The voltage at which the tube is operated is below that at which the tube would go into continuous discharge or corona. When an X–ray quantum enters the tube through the window it ionizes a number of argon molecules proportional to its energy (or wave length). Because of the high voltage across the tube the electrons produced in the ionization process migrate rapidly toward the positive wire eventually gaining enough energy to produce more ion pairs (electrons and argon ions) upon collision with argon molecules. This ionization event, which is called the Townsend avalanche, is eventually stopped by a sheath of positive ions moving radially from the wire, the effect of which is to reduce the field strength near the wire. The positive ions are eventually "quenched" by bromine or chlorine molecules thus mitigating more ionizations if the ions strike the tube sheet or wall. The electrons reaching the wire lower its potential, causing a voltage pulse of several millivolts across a capacitor. With amplification the pulse is ready for scaling or integrating circuits. The energy of the quantum initiating ionization of the Geiger tube is not important because the Townsend phenomenon described above and the size of the pulses are not proportional to the energy of the radiation. The Geiger tube is characterized by low counting rates attributed to inability (coincidence loss) of the counter to register quanta received during the so–called dead time (about one–half millisecond) at which time the positive ion sheath leaves the wire.

Proportional counters are similar to Geiger tubes but are operated at lower voltages. As their name suggests these counters yield pulses that are on the order of microvolts that are proportional to the energies of incident X–ray quanta. In addition to the desirable property of proportionality, the proportional tube is capable of much higher counter rates (approaching 1,000,000 cps) because "dead time" is approximately 0.2 microseconds. As with Geiger tubes choice of counter gas (Fig. 2) enables the analyst to limit the sensitivity of the detector for different energy levels. Quantum efficiencies of several proportional counters are reproduced in Fig. 2.

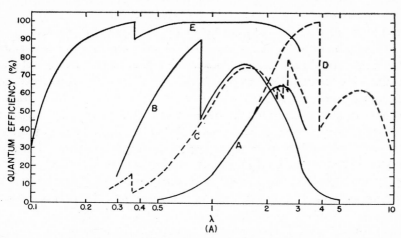

Figure 2. Quantum efficiency of detectors (after Bertin and Longobucco, 1962b). (A) Ar—filled Geiger counter, Be window, (B) Kr—filled proportional counter, Be window, (C) Xe—filled proportional counter, Be window, (D) Ar—methane proportional counter, and (E) scintillation counter, NaI phosphor.

Flow–proportional counters, useful in detection of low energy quanta, are modifications of proportional counters where the window is made very thin to reduce absorption and a gas mixture of argon and methane is streamed into the counter under a slight positive pressure. When used in conjunction with a vacuum or helium path between sample and detector, the flow–proportional counter is necessary for routine investigation of elements between sodium and titanium.

Among commonly used counters the scintillation counter has, by far, the greatest range of application. The scintillation counter consists of a phosphor such as a sodium (thallium) iodide crystal and a photomultiplier. Scintillations, the number of which is proportional to quanta energy, are detected in the photomultiplier. Generally the scintillation counter is used as an integrating detector which uses the photomultiplier to trap all the light. Dead times are very short; therefore, counting rates approach those of proportional counters. The efficiency of the scintillation counter for a wide range of energies is evident from Fig. 2. Because of the high efficiency of scintillation counters for short wave length radiation, these counters are characterized by high backgrounds.

Pulse height selection

Using appropriate circuitry it is possible when proportional and scintillation detectors are employed to discriminate, or "filter out," all pulses which do not have the energy of the analytical line. Pulse height selection is particularly valuable in separating analytical lines from rational orders of other lines which are reflected at the wave length of the analytical line at hand. Fundamentally, the circuit consists of a base—line or voltage below which all pulses are sorted out and a window above which pulses having higher amplitudes are sorted out. As a result of these two sorting schemes there exists an amplitude or pulse height (voltage) span that is selected; thus, we have pulse height selection.

Statistical consideration

The distribution of X–ray quanta received at the detector and eventually recorded as intensity measurements follows the Gaussian distribution. Therefore, standard deviation of a count is $N^{\frac{1}{2}}$, and the coefficient of variation is

$$\sigma \text{ per cent} = 100(N)^{\frac{1}{2}} / N \tag{5}$$

where N is total counts; more meaningful expressions of precision are obtained by introducing the background term. Thus, using

$$100 \, U_p = \frac{67.5(N_t + N_b)^{\frac{1}{2}}}{N_t - N_b} \tag{6}$$

where N_t is peak height and N_b is background, which is the deviation expected 50 per cent of the time, we arrive at the probable error (U_p). This equation is solved for several peak to background ratios and reproduced in Fig. 3. For practical purposes a 100,000 total count is sufficient for most soils work and puts the counting error well within 1 per cent more than 90 per cent of the time for elements in moderate abundance.

The limit of detectability is closely associated with background. Birks (1959, pp. 54-55) considers a minimum peak height of three standard deviations above background as the limit. For example, with a 100 count background ($\sigma = 10$ counts) the background remains be-

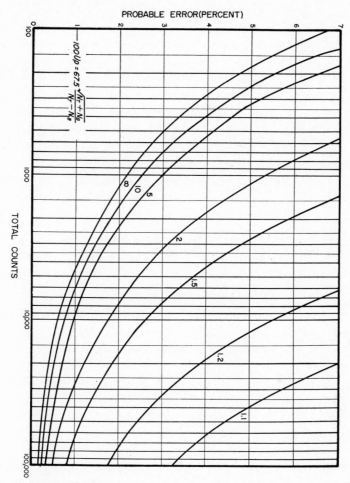

PROBABLE ERROR(PERCENT)

Figure 3. The probable error associated with several peak to background ratios.

tween 70 and 130 counts 99 per cent of the time and the probable error is 67.5 $(130 + 100)^{\frac{1}{2}}/30$ or 34 per cent. If the 30 count peak represents a lower detectable limit of 100 ppm. the count would give 66 to 134 ppm. 50 per cent of the time or 50 to 150 ppm. 68 per cent of time. The latter is obtained by removing 67.5 from equation (6). The use of three standard deviations is advantageous because it gives a 50 per cent coefficient of variation over a wide range of counts.

Sample preparation

Powders

Analysis with the X–ray spectrograph offers a variety of sample forms (e.g., solid, powder, or liquids). In this account we will confine our discussion of sample preparation techniques to those which we generally use, and which are applicable for soil and clay analyses. For a survey report of sample preparation techniques for a variety of materials the reader should refer to Bertin and Longobucco (1962a). The techniques used for preparing soil materials depends upon the required accuracy of data, but of equal importance is the intended use of data. Often, without any special pre–treatment, a rapid survey of elemental composition can be made. This survey may provide valuable information for further investigations. However, for detailed soil genesis studies, analysis of total sample, regardless of accuracy, is likely to provide information of only a general nature. We have found that detailed elemental analysis of component size fractions provides valuable information for evaluating soil development. The physical–chemical basis for separating the soil into fractions is twofold. First the sample matrix is considerably simplified and, second, minerals tend to concentrate in fractions that enables one to rationalize elemental data with mineral composition. For example, the potassium content of the clay fraction can be allocated to illite, and in the silts, zirconium and titanium can be allocated to zircon and rutile, respectively. After pre–treatment with H_2O_2 to remove organic matter and subsequent dispersion, the soil is fractionated into sand, silt, and clay separates.

If sand represents a considerable portion of the soil, separation into different size fractions by sieving is advised, with subsequent grinding to about 20μ in diameter for each separate. In our studies we have generally fractionated (Beavers and Jones, 1962) the silt into 20–50μ and 2–20μ size fractions. The coarse–silt separate (20–50μ) is then ground. Grinding can be carried out using one of several mechanical mortars and mixers (e.g., Wig–L–Bug, Fisher mechanical mortar, or that supplied by Spex Industries). For laboratories dealing with samples having a common suite of minerals, e.g., loessial soils in north central United States, fractionation and grinding of coarse–silt and sand separates for most studies is all the pre–treatment necessary. For support and ease of handling, duplicate samples from each size separate, including the clays, are pressed at 4000 psi. into metal cups (Beavers, 1960).

For laboratories dealing with a variety of samples having different suites of minerals, fusion of sample provides a more homogenous matrix and therefore a more accurate and precise analysis. Fusion of sample also provides an easy means of adding internal standards and high absorbing elements, e.g., La_2O_3 (Rose, *et al.,* 1963), in addition to simplifying the preparation of standards by addition techniques.

Our method of fusion is quite similar to that described by Classie (1957), who used 100 mg. of sample and 10 grams of borax fused to form a glass disc. We have found that a ratio of one part of sample can be fused with one part of lithium tetraborate. Lithium carbonate can be substituted for up to 50 per cent of the lithium tetraborate to reduce viscosity and enhance melt properties. For analysis of elements present in small amounts, the high sample–to–flux ratio is desired. After the melt is poured and the glass disc cooled, one side, the side to be irradiated, is ground and polished on a lap–wheel. Alternatively, the glass may be ground, pressed, and treated as a powder. Fusions are carried out in either platinum or graphite crucibles, the latter being desirable because the melt does not adhere to the crucible.

Solutions

Solution extracts and solutions containing solutes of dissolved minerals are readily analyzed either in solution form or as the residue. The solution is analyzed in cells having a mylar top or bottom, depending on the equipment being used. Solution analysis lends itself particularly to analysis of heavy elements and to lighter elements in moderate concentration. Solutions, of course, also lend themselves to efficient preparation of standards and control of concentration. In solution analyses, background is high because of scattering from light elements (hydrogen and oxygen). Also, the 0.25 mil Mylar cell covering reduces the radiation intensity of low atomic number elements such as potassium and calcium by one–third.

Dried residues

Drying of 0.1 to 0.2 ml. of solution on a planchet offers advantages over solution analysis, particularly for low atomic number elements present in low concentration. For example, a solution containing 1 m.e. of potassium per liter (39 µg per ml.) will yield a net intensity of only a few counts per second. However, by drying 0.1 ml. of the solution on an aluminum planchet (3.9 µg of K) a net intensity increase of tenfold or more can be expected. Results of the same order are found for calcium. Dried residues, therefore, make possible the analysis of solutions, such as soil extracts at the 1.0 ppm. range.

Solution residues of K and Ca are prepared by the following method. Aluminum discs are used as planchets. The area of irradiation by the primary X–ray beam is scribed on a planchet. After the aluminum planchet is oxidized by passing it through a flame several times to insure wetting, the scribed outline of the beam area is traced with either a resin (like Permount) or a graphite pencil to contain the solution within the irradiated area.

Depending upon equipment used, 0.1 to 0.2 ml. of solution is transferred to the planchet with a micro–pipette and rapidly dried at low temperature. The residue should be uniform in thickness over the entire irradiated area. High intensities obtained from microgram amounts (microsamples) of the dried residues are attributable to negligible self–absorption by the sample wherein each atom emits X rays independently of others. Linearity of intensity is generally achieved with up to 10 micrograms of the element. This type of analysis is analogous to what is often referred to as "infinitely thin sample analysis," and is applicable to determination of cation exchange capacity, exchangeable cations, extractable iron, etc.

Standards

It is of utmost importance that the matrix of the standard approximate that of the unknown (Bertin and Longobucco, 1962b). For most analytical work the authors have utilized standards analyzed by other methods which give straight line relationships between intensity and concentration. Certain of the National Bureau of Standards' analyzed samples are particularly useful and give very good intensity–concentration relationships (Beavers, 1960). To ascertain the similarity of matrices of several samples it is informative to make step–wise additions of the element to be analyzed for and determine the fluorescence yield. For Illinois soils and parent materials sampled over wide geographic areas the authors have noted no great differences in fluorescence yield attributable to matrix effects among samples of the same size fraction. Standards have also been prepared using the addition technique over

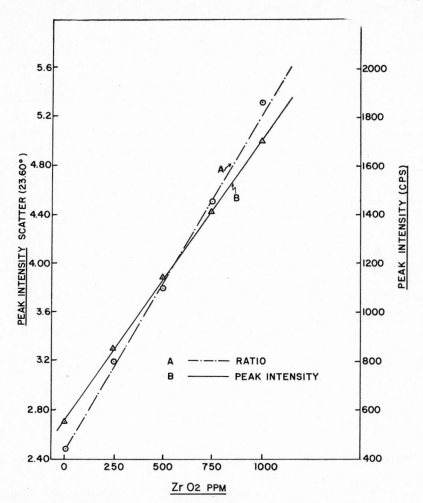

Figure 4. Relationship between zirconium as net counts and peak to background ratio to added ZrO₂.

concentration ranges of several per cent which were compatible with content ranges of unknown elements in the samples. The addition of zirconium to a total soil (Cisne silt loam) is graphically presented in Fig. 4. Note that a peak to background ratio is presented for zirconium. Use of the ratio for elements in low amounts having high and variable backgrounds contributed by instrumental variations gives more consistent results.

Application

Clay mineral analyses

Clay minerals lend themselves to analysis by pressed sample, fused and microsample techniques. Clay minerals from Illinois soils analyzed using wet chemical methods give a straight line regression using pressed samples in spectrographic analysis over the concentration range 1.4–5.3 per cent K_2O. The same clays were analyzed by X–ray diffraction and gave a straight–line relationship between illite and K_2O contents, which enables one to estimate illite content of unknown samples from K_2O analyses. Dilute clay suspensions can be analyzed after drying following the procedure for dried residues.

Recently, unpublished data obtained by the authors and a report by Weed and Leonard (1963) indicate that spectrographic determination of adsorbed strontium is a valid means for cation exchange capacity determination of soil clay minerals. Hinckley and Bates (1960) indirectly measured cation exchange capacity when they determined the amount of montmorillonite in kaolinite using analyses for absorbed strontium as a measure of the montmorillonite present. Molloy and Kerr (1960) used the analyses of the API reference clay minerals for preparation of standard curves.

Weathering ratios and chemical characterization

Difficulty arises in quantitative characterization of pedogenic processes by petrographic methods because of the difficulty and time required to determine the number of mineral species that are sensitive to soil forming processes and still maintain appropriate levels of statistical significance. Also, wet chemical methods of analysis are often time consuming and difficult (e.g., the determination of zirconium). That the X–ray spectrograph is an accurate and precise tool with which weathering can be simply and rapidly obtained has been demonstrated.

For example, Beavers, *et al.* (1963), showed that the calcium content of silt–size minerals in a chronosequence of Illinois soils is a sensitive measure of weathering (Fig. 5). By introducing zirconium analysis, it is possible to erect a $CaO–ZrO_2$ molar ratio weathering index which provides a measure of the weathering of relatively easily weathered calcium minerals to stable zircon. The ratio has the added value that it can be manipulated mathematically. The development of many other meaningful ratios is evident.

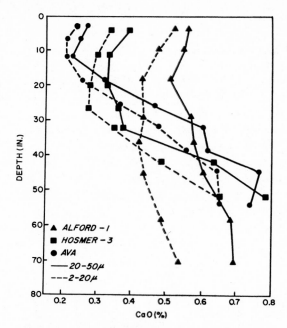

Figure 5. Distribution of calcium in the fine (2-20μ) and coarse (20-50μ) silt fractions from a chronosequence of loessial soils in southern Illinois (after Beavers et al., 1963).

Using spectrographic data from a developmental sequence of youthful soils in Illinois, Jones and Beavers (1964) demonstrated differences in Peorian loess that might otherwise be attributed to genetic processes. Alexander, *et al.* (1962), used spectrographic analyses of zirconium to characterize differences between till and loess in northern Illinois.

Analysis of a specific element, like potassium in illite, offers a fruitful means for characterizing the course of soil weathering. In conclusion, it may be said that the application of X–ray spectrographic analysis to soils research is in its infancy.

References

Alexander, J. D., Beavers, A. H., and Johnson, P. R. (1962) Zirconium content of coarse silt in loess and till of Wisconsin age in northern Illinois: *Soil Sci. Soc. Am. Proc.*, v. 26, pp. 189-91.

Beavers, A. H. (1960) Use of X-ray spectrographic analysis for the study of soil genesis: *7th. Int. Cong. Soil Sci.,* Madison, Wis., v. 2, pp. 1-9.

Beavers, A. H., Fehrenbacher, J. B., Johnson, P. R., and Jones, R. L. (1963) CaO-ZrO$_2$ molar ratios as an index of weathering: *Soil Sci. Soc. Am. Proc.,* v. 27, pp. 408-12.

Bertin, E. P., and Longobucco, R. J. (1962a) Sample preparation methods for X-ray fluorescence emission spectrometry: *Norelco Reporter,* v. 9, pp. 31-43.

Bertin, E. P., and Longobucco, R. J. (1962b) Spectral line interference in X-ray fluorescence spectrometry: *Norelco Reporter,* v. 9, pp. 64-72.

Birks, L. S. (1959) *X-ray spectrochemical analysis:* Interscience Publishers, Inc., New York, 137 pages.

Classie, F. (1957) Accurate X-ray fluorescence analysis without internal standard: *Norelco Reporter,* v. 4, pp. 3-7, 17, 19, 20.

Hinckley, D. N., and Bates, T. F. (1960) An X-ray fluorescence method for the quantitative determination of small amounts of montmorillonite in kaolin clays: *Am. Min.,* v. 45, pp. 239-45.

Jones, R. L., and Beavers, A. H. (1964) Some mineralogical and chemical properties of Seaton, Fayette and Clinton soils in Illinois: *Ill. Agr. Exp. Sta. Bull.* 701, 27 pp.

Klug, H. P., and Alexander, L. E. (1954) *X-ray diffraction procedures:* John Wiley and Sons, New York, 617 pages.

Liebhafsky, H. A., Pfeiffer, H. G., Winslow, E. H., and Zemany, P. D. (1960) *X-ray absorption and emission in analytical chemistry:* John Wiley and Sons, Inc., New York, 357 pages.

Molloy, M. W., and Kerr, P. F. (1960) X-ray spectrochemical analysis: An application to certain light elements in clay minerals and volcanic glass: *Am. Min.,* v. 45, pp. 911-36.

Rose, H. J., Jr., Adler, I., and Flanagan, F. J. (1963) X-ray fluorescence analysis of the light elements in rocks and minerals: *App. Spect.,* v. 17, pp. 81-85.

Weed, S. B., and Leonard, R. A. (1963) Determination of adsorbed strontium by X-ray emission in cation-exchange capacity determinations of clays: *Soil Sci. Soc. Am. Proc.,* v. 27, pp. 474-75.

X . . . Chemical Analysis in the Quantitative Mineralogical Examination of Clays

M. L. Jackson and R. C. Mackenzie

Although the approach to obtaining the ultimate quantitative analysis of clays in mineralogical examination has been rather different in Madison and in Aberdeen, nevertheless it is interesting that there are so many points of fundamental agreement. In the two decades 1930–1950 analysis for the chemical elements was increasingly neglected. This was consequent upon the application of X–ray powder diffraction techniques to clays (Hadding, 1923; Rinne, 1924; Hendricks and Fry, 1930; Pauling, 1930; Kelley, Dore, and Brown, 1931; Hofmann, Endell, and Wilm, 1933) and the appreciation that clays were only infrequently monomineralic. The balance has now, however, been redressed, and the authors consider that chemical analyses do, in fact, when properly interpreted, add considerably to quantitative knowledge of any clay system.

As a general starting point, it is recommended that the soil be separated into different size fractions, since a total chemical analysis of any soil is of value solely in assessing a geochemical balance sheet. The only exception to the above rule is in the case of some laterites, and perhaps some latosols, in which the soil itself consists entirely or almost entirely of layer silicates and oxide minerals formed by surficial weathering. In the latter soils, size fractionation would often be largely meaningless, since the sand fractions contain large quantities of cemented aggregates of clay minerals and do not reflect the primary minerals from which the soil was derived. In other types of soils the sand fractions and coarse silt fractions reflect the primary minerals of the soil parent material, whereas the clay fraction is usually comprised predominantly of secondary minerals. Such secondary minerals are formed by pedochemical weathering or are inherited from sedimentary rocks. The minerals in the clay fraction of soils are of special importance to soil properties, and since the quantitative analysis of clay is enormously simplified by the removal of coarser–grained primary minerals, it is advisable in general to analyze the different size fractions separately.

Since the coarser fractions can be readily examined by many techniques, the following discussion will be concerned entirely with the clay fraction, for which the mineralogical composition has generally to be assessed by deduction rather than by direct observation.

Techniques

Prior to any chemical analysis the clay fraction should be examined by all available structural analysis techniques such as X–ray diffraction, differential thermal analysis, infrared absorption spectroscopy, electron microscopy, and electron diffraction. For such an examination, taking into account the effect of exchangeable ion, solvation with different liquids, and thermal treatment, it is generally possible to determine certain minerals quantitatively and others semiquantitatively.

Selective dissolution analysis can also be applied in a quantitative manner not only to determine free oxides but also certain other minerals as outlined in previous lectures. For free iron oxide determination sodium dithionite is very effective, although details of the technique employed in Madison and Aberdeen differ (Aguilera and Jackson, 1953; Mehra and Jackson, 1960; Mitchell and Mackenzie, 1954). Techniques for determining amorphous alumina and silica (allophane) also differ in that in Madison a 2.5 minute extraction with 0.5 N NaOH (Hashimoto and Jackson, 1960; Glenn, et al., 1960) and a method based on cation–exchange capacity measurement (Aomine and Jackson, 1959) are employed, whereas in Aberdeen successive extraction with a 5 per cent sodium carbonate solution is preferred (Mitchell and Farmer, 1962). In either event, the results have to be interpreted with caution since it is known that extremely fine and poorly crystalline clay particles dissolve along with truly amorphous material; nevertheless, the figures obtained are significant. At both localities, chemical analyses of the extracts from the selective dissolution techniques are carried out according to fairly standard methods. It is considered that prior to the total chemical analysis of the clay, the sample should be saturated with a known cation and for this Ca^{2+} can be recommended. Such a saturation can readily be performed by the centrifuge method described elsewhere (Mackenzie and Bishui, 1958; Jackson, 1958). The techniques employed in Madison and Aberdeen for the determination of the constituent elements of clays differ slightly and a comparison of these is given in Table 1.

Table 1: Determination of constituents of clay elements.

	MADISON[1]	ABERDEEN
SiO_2	Molybdosilicate yellow	Gravimetric or molybdosilicate blue[2]
Al_2O_3	Aluminum	Aluminum[3]
Fe_2O_3	Tiron	E.D.T.A. or salicylate[4]
TiO_2	Tiron	Colorimetric peroxide
CaO	Flame emission	E.D.T.A. using murexide[2]
MgO	Flame emission	E.D.T.A. using eriochrome black[2]
K_2O	} HF–$HClO_4$ dissolution followed by	Lawrence–Smith fusion followed by
Na_2O	} flame emission spectrography	flame photometry
H_2O	Loss on ignition at 100°C., 350°C., 540°C., and 900°C.	Loss on ignition at 110°C., 300°C., and 1000°C.
FeO	HF + H_2SO_4 treatment followed by $KMnO_4$ titration	HF + H_2SO_4 treatment followed by $KMnO_4$ titration
MnO	Periodate	Periodate

[1] Jackson (1958).
[2] Shapiro and Brannock (1956).
[3] Robertson (1950).
[4] Scott (1941).

Interpretation of results

One use of chemical analysis is for assessment of the accurate ionic formulas of colloidal minerals, such as members of the montmorillonite group (Sawhney and Jackson, 1958; Mackenzie, 1960), through proper allocation of the appropriate elements to the indicated impurities. With suitable allowance for impurities it is possible to determine with a considerable degree of accuracy the actual ionic composition of the principal mineral.

The more general application of allocation of the amounts of chemical elements to the clay mineral species indicated by the structural analysis techniques employed serves to improve the quantitative analysis of polymineralic samples. The proper allocation of the qualities of elements found by the chemical analysis permits a derivation of quantities of different mineral species unique to the proportions of the elements present.

Examples of these types of allocation will be given. The end–member compositions of several minerals likely to occur as components or contaminants in soil clays are given in Table 2. Many of these are

Table 2. *Composition of various minerals for allocation of analyses (in percentages), with abbreviations employed in succeeding tables.*

Mineral	SiO_2	TiO_2	Al_2O_3	Fe_2O_3	FeO	CaO	MgO	K_2O	Na_2O	H_2O
Quartz (Qtz)	100	—	—	—	—	—	—	—	—	—
Opaline silica	100*	—	—	—	—	—	—	—	—	—
Albite (Ab)	68.7	—	19.5	—	—	—	—	—	11.8	—
Anorthite (An)	43.2	—	36.7	—	—	20.1	—	—	—	—
Orthoclase (Or)	64.7	—	18.4	—	—	—	—	16.9	—	—
Illite	51.0	—	28.0	4.0	—	—	3.0	6.5	—	7.5
Kaolinite	46.5	—	39.6	—	—	—	—	—	—	13.9
Antigorite	43.5	—	—	—	—	—	43.5	—	—	13.0
Sphene (Sph)	30.6	40.8	—	—	—	28.6	—	—	—	—
Mg chlorite (*)	30.2	—	22.0	—	—	—	34.8	—	—	13.0
Fe chlorite (*)	23.8	—	17.3	(54.1)**	48.7	—	—	—	—	10.2
Ilmenite	—	52.6	—	(52.6)**	47.4	—	—	—	—	—
Anatase	—	100	—	—	—	—	—	—	—	—
Gibbsite	—	—	65.4	—	—	—	—	—	—	34.6
Boehmite ⎫	—	—	85.0	—	—	—	—	—	—	15.0
Diaspore ⎬										
Goethite ⎫	—	—	—	89.9	—	—	—	—	—	10.1
Lepidocrocite ⎬										
Hematite	—	—	—	100	—	—	—	—	—	—

* In calculation of smectite ionic formulas by the method of Mackenzie (1957) the H_2O+ figure need not be corrected.

(*) After Brough and Robertson (1958).

** For use where FeO has not been determined separately.

invariable and can be applied without alteration. On the other hand some compositions, particularly those for illite and chlorites, are highly variable and may need to be varied as other analyses of these minerals are published. In view of compositional uncertainties correction for illite or chlorite should not be made on the basis of Table 2 if the amounts present exceed 10 per cent; correction for higher amounts might well lead to considerable error — as is clear from one example given below. The composition given for illite is the mean of a number of published analyses and is representative of hydrous micas in which some potassium is replaced by other cations (hydronium, hydrogen, or hydroxy–hydrates of metallic cations) or water (concurrent with lowered charge) as reviewed elsewhere (Jackson, 1963, 1964). Mica of full potassium content can be evaluated for various particle sizes from end–member compositions (Table 3), with an average value of 10 per cent K_2O being used at Madison for dioctahedral micas common in clays (9 per cent for ferruginous micas), illustrated in one of the examples given.

Table 3. Potassium content calculated for mica of varying particle size and number of crystal layers, from Jackson (1956, p. 544).

Number of 10 A mica layers in particle	Number of K inter-layers in particle	Per cent K non-exchange-able	**Particle size**		**Per cent K_2O in mica sample**	
			Thickness, microns	Width, microns*	Of biotite composition	Of muscovite composition
Very large	Very large	—	—	—	10.5	11.8
50	49	98	0.051	0.51	10.3	11.6
20	19	95	0.021	0.21	10.0	11.2
17	16	94	0.018	0.18	9.9	11.1
15	14	93	0.015	0.15	9.8	11.0
10	9	90	0.010	0.10	9.4	10.6
8	7	88	0.008	0.08	9.2	10.3

* Assumed to be 10x thickness.

Formula of principal mineral

To exemplify the derivation of the formula of a major mineral constituent, one may cite the application to a series of smectites (Mackenzie, 1960); one example will be taken as illustrative, the chemical analysis and *modus operandi* being demonstrated in Table 4. From structural and selective dissolution techniques it was shown that this particular sample of smectite contains 2 to 4 per cent quartz, 15 to 30 per cent feldspar, which was mainly plagioclase with Na > Ca, and 1.11 per cent free Fe_2O_3. In such an instance it would not introduce any great error if the quartz percentage were taken as 3.0 for calculation purposes, and consequently the percentage of SiO_2 corresponding to quartz and Fe_2O_3 corresponding to free iron oxide can be deducted from the total chemical analysis. The feldspar is somewhat uncertain, but it is known that

Table 4. Grey Fuller's Earth, Dunning, Perthshire, Scotland.

Analysis		Corrections								Corrected analysis
		Qtz	Fe_2O_3	Ab	An	Or	Sph	H_2O-	Σ	
SiO_2	55.10	3.00		11.19	2.99	5.67	0.22		23.07	32.03
TiO_2	0.30						0.30		0.30	—
Al_2O_3	21.36			3.18	2.54	1.61			7.33	14.03
Fe_2O_3	3.18		1.11						1.11	2.07
FeO	0.20								—	0.20
CaO	2.90				1.39		0.21		1.60	1.30
MgO	2.51								—	2.51
MnO	0.00								—	—
Na_2O	1.92			1.92					1.92	—
K_2O	1.48					1.48			1.48	—
H_2O+	4.90							2.37*	2.37	2.53
H_2O-	6.82							6.82	6.82	—
Σ	100.67	3.00	1.11	16.29	6.92	8.76	0.73	9.19	46.00	54.67

Ionic formula from corrected analysis: Analyst—J. B. Craig
$0.62M+ (Si_{7.30} Al_{0.70}) (Al_{3.07} Fe^{3+}_{0.36} Fe^{2+}_{0.04} Mg_{0.86}) O_{20} (OH)_4$
* Excess hygroscopic moisture calculated by the method of Mackenzie (1957).

the Na_2O and K_2O are nonexchangeable (since the sample was subjected to prior saturation with Ca^{2+}), and it is therefore highly probable that both these components are in the feldspar since no other contaminant containing them (such as mica) was shown to be present. The Na_2O can then be deducted along with corresponding amounts of Al_2O_3 and SiO_2 as albite, and the K_2O also along with Al_2O_3 and SiO_2 as orthoclase. CaO content must now be split up between exchangeable cation and anorthite, and possibly also sphene, $CaTiO_3$, since this is a common constituent of English fuller's earths (Brammall and Leech, 1940). Since the amount of TiO_2 is small it matters little in this instance whether it is attributed to anatase or sphene, but sphene has been chosen. In these calculations it is quite valid to assess the feldspar from the three end members, as this will correspond to the composition, irrespective of which actual feldspars are present. These are all the contaminants known to be present in this particular sample, and consequently allowance for the composition of these leaves us with the analytical figures corresponding to the pure smectite. This corrected analysis is given in the last column and works out to give a very reasonable ionic formula. The technique of calculating this ionic formula has been described in full by Mackenzie (1960); it also enables assessment of the amount of excess H_2O — i.e., that amount of hygroscopic moisture which was trapped in the mineral even at 300°C. This admittedly can be assessed only on the basis of $O_{20}(OH)_4$ per formula cell, and if these proportions of O and OH should vary then the amount of excess H_2O- will also be affected. However, since in normal practice it is impossible to calculate the absolute O:OH ratio, it seems reasonable to assume (until it is proved to the contrary) that these proportions are adhered to in the smectite lattice, or at least that deviation from them is very small. O_{24} is demanded by the ideal structure and the variant is thus H.

Therefore, from the chemical analysis and the above considerations, it is possible to deduce that the composition of this sample is, within close limits: 3 per cent quartz, 1 per cent free Fe_2O_3, 32 per cent feldspar (23.2 per cent plagioclase with Na > Ca and 8.8 per cent orthoclase), 1 per cent sphene, 9 per cent hygroscopic moisture, and 54 per cent smectite. Thus, not only has it been possible to determine the ionic formula of the smectite but simultaneously to refine the mineralogical analysis. A further refinement may be made in the structural formula by application of the method of Osthaus (1954) to determine the amount of tetrahedral Fe. This technique, however, requires further investigation, since it did not appear to apply to all samples investigated (Mackenzie, 1960).

Allocation of elements for quantitative mineralogical analysis

The quantitative mineralogical analysis of a sample based on X–ray diffraction, integral thermal analysis, differential thermal analysis, specific surface determination, intersalation of kaolinite, infrared adsorption, selective dissolution analysis, and cation–exchange capacity values may be refined considerably by applying the semiquantitative results obtained to the elemental composition of the sample and making the necessary adjustment to correct for any discrepancies which may occur. The process is subject to some uncertainty as some minerals, particularly layer silicates, have considerable isomorphous substitution. This quantitative assignment of elemental oxides (including OH and H_2O) to specific minerals present in a sample is generally termed "chemical allocation."

The process of chemical allocation of elements to their minerals may best be explained by reference to a specific sample. Analytical data obtained for a 2–0.2μ fraction of the A_1 horizon of Moorepark soil will be employed. The analytical data (by P. V. Kiely) follow:

X–ray diffraction analysis:

Mica   **** — 10 A peak at room temperature with Mg saturation and glycerol solvation.

Kaolinite   *** — 7 A peak which disappears on heating to 500°C.; intersalation with NH_4NO_3 gives 11.6 A kaolinite peak.

Quartz   ** — 4.26 and 3.34 A peaks, fairly strong.

Chlorite   * — 14 A reinforcement after heating to 600°C.

Vermiculite   * — 14 A peak at room temperature which is reduced in intensity by K saturation and heating to 300°C.

Montmorillonite   * — Very slight 18 A peak.

Partial chemical analysis (all values in per cent):

SiO_2	58.4			
Al_2O_3	15.7	H_2O loss in the temperature range:		
Fe_2O_3	4.01	110°–350°C.	2.40	
TiO_2	1.37	350°–540°C.	4.21	
K_2O	6.01	540°–900°C.	0.70	
MgO	1.96			

	SiO_2	Al_2O_3
Dissolved by 0.5 N NaOH after heating to 110°C.	2.02	0.81
Dissolved by 0.5 N NaOH after heating to 525°C.	6.01	4.06

Kaolinite was allocated on the basis of selective dissolution analysis, expansible minerals on the basis of mono–interlayer specific surface determination, amorphous minerals on the basis of their solubility in 0.5 N NaOH, chlorite on X–ray diffraction analysis and allocation of Al_2O_3, and rutile on the basis of TiO_2 determination and the rutile diffractogram of an HF residue. The quartz content was determined by deducting the SiO_2 allocated to other minerals from the total SiO_2 content and allocation of the remaining SiO_2 to quartz as follows:

---

* Number of asterisks indicate relative quantities.

Allocated percentage of SiO_2

	Illite basis	Mica basis
Illite, Mica (See Table 5)	47.4	27.8
Kaolinite	3.72	3.72
Amorphous	2.02	2.02
Vermiculite and montmorillonite	3.2	3.2
Chlorite	0.33	0.33
Total (allocated)	56.67	37.07
Total SiO_2 (determined)	58.4	58.4
Quartz (difference)	1.7	21.3

Illite allocated on the basis of 6.5 per cent K_2O gave too low quartz and 116 per cent total mineral (Table 5), a figure that is obviously too high.

Table 5. Composition of Moorepark soil clay

Constituents and basis		Percentages indicated	
		A	B
Mica	Allocation of K_2O	93*	60**
Kaolinite	Selective dissolution analysis	9	9
Expansible***	Mono–interlayer specific surface	5	5
Amorphous	Solubility in 0.5 N NaOH	4	4
Chlorite	14 A reinforcement and Al_2O_3 allocation	2	2
Quartz	(Total SiO_2)—(Allocated SiO_2)	2	21****
Rutile	TiO_2 analysis	1	1
Total		116	102

    * Illite based on 6.5 per cent K_2O in Fithian illite (Table 2).
    ** Based on 10 per cent K_2O in fine grained mica (Table 3).
    *** Four per cent montmorillonite and 1 per cent vermiculite.
    **** The quartz percentage by fusion (Jackson, Chapter VIII, this volume) was 16 per cent; the feldspars 1 per cent; total 98 per cent.

A full allocation of the Al_2O_3, MgO, and Fe_2O_3 required shows an insufficiency of these to use nearly all of the SiO_2 as layer silicates. Mica allocated on the basis of 10 per cent K_2O (Table 3) gave a rational content of quartz and other minerals, with a total nearly 100 per cent, and the other calculated oxide percentages in agreement with experiment. It is interesting to note that Brough and Robertson (1958) also found that it was necessary to employ the muscovite composition in assessing the mica content of Scottish fire–clays. The present sample, however, with its high K_2O content, is illustrative of a clay which contains around 60 per cent mica and for which the assumption of 6.5 per cent K_2O in mica gives irrationally high overestimation of results. Underestimation of the mica content of clays is more common. Thus, an occurrence of 0.5 to 2 per cent or more K_2O is common in hydrous clays consisting dominantly of montmorillonite, vermiculite, and chlorite (Schmehl and Jackson, 1957; Sawhney and Jackson, 1958; Mehra and Jackson, 1959). For such clays 5 to 20 per cent or more of micas is reported on the basis of 10 per cent K_2O in mica for samples in which the mica would otherwise be overlooked altogether.

The above sample of allocation based initially on K_2O and SiO_2 is illustrative of the procedure. Allocations based initially on Al_2O_3 and H_2O lost in various temperature ranges frequently are useful for lateritic type of clays (Tamura, *et al.,* 1953, 1955). The allocation progresses by successive approximation (Jackson, 1956, p. 538) until the percentage of minerals uniquely fits the elemental content determined.

The refinement of data leading to assessment of the validity of a mineral species is further illustrated by an investigation on halloysitic clays (Mackenzie and Robertson, 1961). Here again one example will suffice as an application of the technique. In this particular example the minerals halloysite, kaolinite, gibbsite, and goethite were deduced to be present and estimated quantitatively from differential thermal curves using selective dissolution techniques to distinguish between gibbsite and goethite (Muñoz Taboadela, 1953). The other minerals shown in Table 6 were found to be present by other investigational methods. It is interesting to note here that the sodium dithionite treatment did not remove all the Fe_2O_3 from the clay and it was first assumed that the amount left was present in the halloysite lattice. Applying the same calculation techniques as described above for smectites, taking the halloysite formula as $(Al,Fe)_4Si_4O_{10}(OH)_8$, and adding this to the total composition of impurities, it was found that the calculated analysis deviated somewhat from the observed one. If, however, the Fe_2O_3 were not in the halloysite lattice, but were present as free Fe_2O_3 which, possibly for some steric reason, was not removed by dithionite, then the calculated analysis and the observed analysis agreed exactly so that the actual composition of the clay deviated slightly from that

Table 6. Composition of Guma Clay

Mineral	Original estimation (Per cent)	Final estimation* (Per cent)
Moist partially–hydrated halloysite (including 7.1 per cent water)	57.4	53.9
Kaolinite	10.0	10.0
Quartz	2.0	2.0
Gibbsite	12.5	12.5
Hematite	3.9	7.4
Goethite	7.0	7.0
Anatase	0.3	0.3
Sphene	1.3	1.3
Magnetite	1.4	1.4
Muscovite	4.2	4.2
Total	100.0	100.0

* On basis of chemical analysis.

which was originally assessed and is that given in the final column of Table 6. The same argument was applied to several halloysitic clays and it was shown that in no instance would calculated and observed analyses agree if the iron were considered to be in the halloysite lattice. It seems therefore a reasonable conclusion from this study that the mineral ferrihalloysite did not exist in these materials which are in fact mixtures of halloysite with free iron oxide.

Conclusions

From the above discussion it is clear that the chemical analysis of a clay, even if it be polymineralic, can serve several useful functions. Quite apart from the information given by selective dissolution techniques and the geochemical and perhaps ceramic value of a total analysis, allocation of the elements quantitatively to the minerals known to be present not only enables one to determine the ionic constitution of one component, but also permits a quantitative mineralogical analysis from semiquantitative data or final refinement of quantitative data. During such processes other facts also emerge — e.g., the K_2O content of the mica present or the validity of the evidence for a specific mineral. Consequently, any mineralogical analysis of a clay must be incomplete without proper use of the evidence of chemical analysis.

References

Aguilera, N. H., and Jackson, M. L. (1953) Iron oxide removal from soils and clays: *Soil Sci. Soc. Am. Proc.,* v. 17, pp. 359-64; v. 118, p. 223 and p. 350.

Aomine, S., and Jackson, M. L. (1959) Allophane determination in Ando soils by cation-exchange capacity delta value: *Soil Sci. Soc. Am. Proc.,* v. 23, pp. 210-14.

Brammall, A., and Leech, J. G. C. (1940) Montmorillonite in fuller's earth, Nutfield, Surrey: *Geol. Mag.,* v. 77, pp. 102-12.

Brindley, G. W., and Youell, R. F. (1951) A chemical determination of "tetrahedral" and "octahedral" aluminum ions in a silicate: *Acta. Cryst.,* v. 4, pp. 495-96.

Brough, J., and Robertson, R. H. S. (1958) A chlorite convention for the appraisal of Scottish fireclays: *Clay Min. Bull.,* v. 3, pp. 221-31.

Glenn, R. C., Jackson, M. L., Hole, F. D., and Lee, G. B. (1960) Chemical weathering of layer silicate clays in loess-derived Tama silt loam of southwestern Wisconsin: *Clays and Clay Minerals,* 8th Conf., Pergamon Press, London, pp. 63-83.

Hadding, A. (1923) Eine röntgenographishe Methode kristalline und kryptokristalline Substanzen zu identifizieren: *Ztsch. Krist.,* v. 58, pp. 108-11.

Hashimoto, I., and Jackson, M. L. (1960) Rapid dissolution of allophane and kaolinite-halloysite after dehydration: *Clays and Clay Minerals,* 7th Conf., Pergamon Press, London, pp. 102-13.

Hendricks, S. B., and Fry, W. H. (1930) The results of X-ray and microscopical examinations of soil colloids: *Soil Sci.,* v. 29, pp. 457-78.

Hofmann, C., Endell, K., and Wilm, D. (1933) Crystal structure and properties of montmorillonite: *Ztsch. Krist.,* v. 86, pp. 340-48.

Jackson, M. L. (1956) *Soil Chemical Analysis — Advanced Course,* published by the author, Dept. of Soil Science, Univ. of Wisconsin, Madison.

Jackson, M. L. (1958) *Soil Chemical Analysis,* Prentice-Hall, Inc., Englewood Cliffs, New Jersey.

Jackson, M. L. (1963) Interlayering of expansible layer silicates in soils by chemical weathering: *Clays and Clay Minerals,* 11th Conf., Pergamon Press, London, pp. 29-46.

Jackson, M. L. (1964) Chemical composition of soils: Ch. II in *Chemistry of the Soil,* 2nd edition, ed. F. E. Bear, Reinhold Publishing Corp., New York.

Kelley, W. P., Dore, W. H., and Brown, S. M. (1931) The nature of base exchange material of bentonite, soils, and zeolites, as revealed by chemical investigation and X-ray analysis: *Soil Sci.,* v. 31, pp. 25-55.

Mackenzie, R. C. (1957) Saponite from Allt Ribhein, Fiskavaig Bay, Skye: *Miner. Mag.,* v. 31, pp. 672-80.

Mackenzie, R. C., and Bishui, B. M. (1958) The montmorillonite differential thermal curve. II. Effect of exchangeable cations on the dehydroxylation of normal montmorillonite: *Clay Min. Bull.,* v. 3, pp. 276-86.

Mackenzie, R. C. (1960) The evaluation of clay mineral competition with particular reference to smectites: *Silicates Industr.,* v. 25, pp. 12-18, 71-75.

Mackenzie, R. C., and Robertson, R. H. S. (1961) The quantitative determination of halloysite, goethite and gibbsite: *Acta Univ. Carol., Geol.,* Suppl. 1, pp. 139-49.

Mehra, O. P., and Jackson, M. L. (1960) Iron oxide removal from soils and clays by a dithionite citrate system buffered with sodium bicarbonate: *Clays and Clay Minerals,* 7th Conf., Pergamon Press, London, pp. 317-27.

Mehra, O. P., and Jackson, M. L. (1959) Constancy of the sum of mica unit cell potassium surface and interlayer sorption surface of vermiculite-illite clays: *Soil Sci. Soc. Am. Proc.,* v. 23, pp. 101-5.

Mitchell, B. D., and Mackenzie, R. C. (1954) Removal of free-iron oxide from clays: *Soil Sci.,* v. 77, pp. 173-84.

Mitchell, B. D., and Farmer, V. C. (1962) Amorphous clay minerals in some Scottish soil profiles: *Clay Min. Bull.,* v. 5, pp. 128-44.

Muñoz Taboadela, M. (1953) The clay mineralogy of some soils from Spain and from Rio Muni (West Africa): *J. Soil Sci.,* v. 4, pp. 48-55.

Osthaus, B. B. (1954) Chemical determination of tetrahedral ions in nontronite and montmorillonite: *Clays and Clay Minerals,* 2nd Conf., Natl. Acad. Sci.-Natl. Res. Council Pub. 327, Washington, D. C., pp. 404-17.

Pauling, L. (1930) The structure of mica and related minerals: *Proc. Nat. Acad. Sci.,* v. 16, pp. 123-29.

Rinne, F. (1924) Röntgenographische Untersuchungen an einigen feinzerteilten Mineralien, Kunstprodukte und dichten Gesteinen: *Ztsch. Krist.,* v. 60, pp. 55-69.

Robertson, G. (1950) The colorimetric determination of aluminum in silicate materials: *J. Sci. Food Agri.,* No. 2, pp. 59-63.

Sawhney, B. L., and Jackson, M. L. (1958) Soil montmorillonite formulas: *Soil Sci. Soc. Am. Proc.,* v. 22, pp. 115-18.

Schmehl, W. R., and Jackson, M. L. (1957) Mineralogical analyses of soil clays from Colorado surface soils: *Soil Sci. Soc. Am. Proc.,* v. 21, pp. 373-80.

Scott, R. O. (1941) The colorimetric estimation of iron with sodium salicylate: *Analyst,* v. 66, pp. 142-48.

Shapiro, L., and Brannock, W. W. (1956) Rapid analysis of silicate rocks: *U.S. Geol. Surv.,* Bull. 1036 C, pp. 19-55.

Tamura, T., Jackson, M. L., and Sherman, G. D. (1953) Mineral content of Low Humic, Humic and Hydrol Humic Latosols of Hawaii: *Soil Sci. Soc. Am. Proc.,* v. 17, pp. 343-46.

Tamura, T., Jackson, M. L., and Sherman, G. D. (1955) Mineral content of a Latosolic Brown Forest soil and a Humic Ferruginous Latosol of Hawaii: *Soil Sci. Soc. Am. Proc.,* v. 19, pp. 435-39.

Subject Index